Miller & Levine

Biology

Laboratory Manual A

PEARSON

Boston, Massachusetts   Chandler, Arizona   Glenview, Illinois   Upper Saddle River, New Jersey

Brief Contents

To the Teacher T3

Guidelines for Lab Safety T4

Organisms in the Biology Lab T9

Master Materials List T16

Lab Skills Labs 1

Chapter Labs 17

Additional Labs 213

Selected Quick Labs 289

Appendixes 307

ISBN-13: 978-0-13-368716-3

ISBN-10: 0-13-368716-3

7 8 9 10 V011 13

To the Teacher

The *Miller & Levine Biology* lab program provides a variety of opportunities for inquiry. In the student textbook, there are quick labs and data analysis activities. There is also a pre-lab page at the end of each chapter that previews the corresponding chapter lab in the lab manual.

The program includes two lab manuals, each of which is provided as a consumable student version and an annotated Teacher's Edition. The worksheets in the student version are also available as editable worksheets. The annotations offer extensive point-of-use teaching support, including time required, expected results, answers, advance preparation instructions, and teaching tips related to the procedure.

The format of the investigations is consistent within a manual, but the type of lab varies among Design Your Own, Real-World, Forensics, and Skills labs. Most labs have guided inquiry and some offer open-ended inquiry.

Laboratory Manual A

This manual is aimed at the average or above-average student, who can benefit from a greater degree of inquiry. *Laboratory Manual A* includes

- 3 introductory labs that address lab safety and equipment, scientific method, and use of a microscope

- 35 chapter labs

- 15 additional labs

- 5 appendixes that address making a hypothesis, presenting data, making measurements, laboratory techniques, and evaluating technology

Laboratory Manual B

This manual is aimed at students who require more support, including those who will be using the *Miller & Levine Biology, Foundation Edition*. The introductory labs and chapter labs from *Laboratory Manual A* have been modified to reflect a lower reading level and shorter attention span. *Laboratory Manual B* also includes

- 43 data analysis activities, the majority based on activities in the on-level textbook

- 24 additional hands-on activities

- the 5 appendixes from *Laboratory Manual A*

Guidelines for Lab Safety

A concern for safety should be an integral part of the planning, preparation, and implementation of a laboratory program. When this goal is met, the time your students spend in the lab should be enjoyable and instructive. Maintaining a safe environment in the lab requires a partnership between you and your students. Once students realize that safe laboratory practices are a required part of a biology course, they will be more likely to adopt a serious approach to lab work. See the safety rules for students on pages vi–ix and the Safety Contract on page xi.

You may need to expand or modify the guidelines presented here to meet local and state government regulations and policies, as well as school regulations and policies. Check with your school administration for specific information on local safety requirements.

Organizing the Work Space

Students should do their experiments on a flat surface. Do not use desks with slanted tops for wet labs. Set up several locations around the laboratory where students can obtain supplies.

Arrange the furniture and equipment in the laboratory to minimize accidents. The space between lab benches or tables should be wide enough for students to gather equipment and supplies without colliding with other students.

Assign each student or group of students a laboratory station. Stress the need to keep work areas clean and uncluttered. Provide a designated area for personal property away from the work areas. Make sure students do not use the floor and lab benches as storage areas. Have students remove all unnecessary papers, books, and equipment from their work areas.

Interactions With Students

What you do before, during, and after students have completed a lab will affect lab safety.

Pre-Lab

Emphasize safety precautions and demonstrate the proper use of equipment. Also demonstrate any potentially risky procedures. Model good lab practice by wearing any required protective equipment during the demonstrations. Make sure any visitors to the laboratory also wear safety equipment.

Discuss any unusual cleanup procedures, such as marked containers for waste materials or for glassware that needs to be sterilized. Point out the locations of these containers.

During Lab

Students should have prior approval for any experiments they do. Students should never work in the laboratory without adult supervision.

Make sure students understand both the short-term and long-term consequences of engaging in inappropriate behavior, such as practical jokes. Take swift action if you observe such behavior while you move about the room.

End of Lab

Remind students to follow the guidelines you discussed for waste disposal. If necessary, have students unplug microscopes, turn off heat sources, and return all equipment to its proper place. Make sure students wash glassware and wipe up spills. Remind students to wash their hands thoroughly with soap and warm water.

Stress that other classes will be using the laboratory and that the work areas need to be left in a clean, safe condition. You may wish to institute a policy of not dismissing the class until you are satisfied with the cleanup.

Safety Equipment

Any room where labs are done should have a fire extinguisher, a fire blanket, and a first-aid kit. If exposure to hazardous chemicals is a risk, an eye-wash station and a safety shower should be within a 20-second walk. You also need access to a fire alarm and a phone or an intercom connection to the office. If any of these items are missing or not working, you may need to modify your lab program until the situation is remedied.

Make sure students know the location and correct use of all safety equipment. Where appropriate and practical, have students operate the equipment. Make sure all safety equipment is in good working order. All malfunctions should be promptly reported to the proper school or district administrator.

Fire Equipment At the beginning of the school year, show students how to operate the fire extinguisher. (The sound and action of a carbon-dioxide extinguisher can be startling for someone who has never used one or observed one being used.) Also show students how to smother flames with a fire blanket. Remind students that hot plates and gas burners should be turned off when not in use.

Eye-Wash Station Use the eye-wash station if corrosive or irritating chemicals splash onto a student's face or into a student's eyes. The exposed area should be kept in the running water for 15 minutes.

Safety Shower A stream of water from a tap may be sufficient to remove small amounts of many chemicals that splash on a student's skin or clothing. For more hazardous chemicals or for larger amounts of a chemical, have the student stand under the safety shower for a minimum of 15 minutes. Because the student will need to remove contaminated clothing, keep a robe or other type of replacement clothing handy.

Spill Kits Consider setting up one or two spill kits. The contents of a spill kit are used to neutralize acids and bases so that they can be cleaned up more easily. Baking soda can be used to neutralize acids. Vinegar can be used to neutralize bases. Science supply houses sell spill kits for acids, bases, and other chemicals.

Consult Materials Safety Data Sheets (MSDS) for instructions about first aid and proper disposal of chemicals.

Fume Hood Your room should be well ventilated when students work with chemicals. You may need a fume hood for some volatile chemicals. Check the Materials Safety Data Sheets (MSDS) for data on chemicals you use. Warn students about chemicals that are flammable, corrosive, toxic, or possibly irritating.

Safety Goggles Ideally, at the beginning of the school year, students should be assigned a pair of safety goggles for their exclusive use throughout the year. Unless the safety goggles are brand new, they should be disinfected with an alcohol wipe. If it is necessary for students to share their safety goggles with other students during the year, the goggles must be disinfected every time they are used.

First-Aid Kit A typical first-aid kit contains antiseptics, bandages, gauze pads, and scissors. Most kits also contain instructions for simple first-aid procedures. Do not dispense any medication, including aspirin.

Storage of Reagents

Keep all reagents in a locked storage area that is accessible only to you or individuals under your direct supervision. Label all reagents clearly. Check local and state regulations for the maximum permissible amounts of reagents allowed in school. Take frequent inventories of reagents and keep up-to-date records of use.

Store large containers near floor level. Make sure that shelves have a raised lip at the front to keep containers from sliding forward. Store chemicals that are incompatible in separate areas of the stockroom.

Flammable Liquids The National Fire Protection Association recommends that you store flammable liquids in vented, flame-resistant cabinets. Also check local and state regulations for storage of flammable liquids.

Explosive Materials Do not store explosive reagents in school. If you find such materials, have them removed by trained fire or police bomb squads or by other qualified officials.

Refrigerators Never store flammable liquids in a refrigerator unless the refrigerator is explosion-proof. Clean refrigerators frequently and safely discard old material. Do not store food where microbial cultures are stored.

Carcinogens For information on carcinogens, see the most recent U.S. Department of Health and Human Services Report on Carcinogens or the recommendations from the American Chemical Society's Committee on Chemical Safety. If you have doubts about the hazards of any reagent, contact a local health agency.

Formaldehyde is a carcinogen and mutagen. Contact a qualified health authority or a licensed commercial company to remove any specimens preserved with formaldehyde. You should be able to purchase specimens that are not preserved with formaldehyde. None of the labs in this manual require preserved specimens.

Avoiding Injuries

The most common injuries in a biology lab are cuts and burns. If you teach students to follow a few simple rules, you should be able to minimize the risk of cuts and burns.

Avoiding Cuts From Broken Glass

To reduce the risk of cuts, discard glassware that has a crack or chip. Have students check for cracks or chips before they use glassware. Use only borosilicate glassware.

Provide a brush, a dustpan, and a separate container for broken glass. Remind students never to pick up broken glass with their hands.

Wrap glass tubing in several layers of toweling and use a lubricant when you insert glass tubing into a stopper.

Immerse minor cuts in cool running water. For cuts that are bleeding heavily, apply pressure with folded toweling or gauze. Call a health professional immediately.

Avoiding Cuts From Sharp Instruments

Make sure specimens are firmly secured on a dissection tray or cutting board. Students should never dissect a hand-held specimen. Make sure that scalpels and scissors are sharp and adequate for the job. Store dissecting instruments in a locked cabinet. Inventory materials before students leave the room.

If students use razor blades to cut tissues for slide mounts, use only single-edged non-injectable blades.

Avoiding Burns

Remind students that hot glassware generally does not "look" hot. Let heated glassware cool for several minutes before touching it or use heat-resistant gloves. Remind students never to hand hot glassware to another person.

One of the most dangerous chemicals in a lab is boiling water. Water baths should be set up away from the edge of a lab table or bench.

Immerse minor burns in cool running water. Call a health professional if a student sustains a more serious burn.

Avoiding Illnesses

Reminding students to wash their hands at the end of every lab period is one of the best ways to reduce the risk of illness. Plus, hand washing is a good habit to establish.

Microbial Cultures

Never culture known pathogens. Handle all bacterial cultures as if they were pathogenic. Plates in which bacteria are growing should be firmly sealed with clear tape. Remind students not to remove the tape when they make their observations. Use a high-temperature gas flame to sterilize loops.

Cultures should be killed before disposal. Autoclave cultures and contaminated glassware at 15 pounds pressure per square inch (103.4 kPa) for 20 minutes. Incinerate disposable plates.

To avoid unwanted cultures, clean glassware frequently with laboratory detergent. Most deposits can be removed with dilute hydrochloric acid or sodium hydroxide solution. Do not permit students to eat or drink from laboratory glassware.

Shared Equipment

As previously noted, it is important to disinfect safety goggles between uses if the goggles are used by more than one student. Use a soft cloth dipped in isopropyl alcohol to clean the eyepiece of each microscope between viewers.

Human Samples

The National Association of Biology Teachers recommends that you avoid using human body fluids and tissues. You can buy materials that mimic the properties of human samples.

If you want students to work with human tissues, follow the Universal Precautions for Handling Human Body Samples outlined by the Centers for Disease Control and Prevention.

The minimum precautions that you should take are as follows:

- Students should handle only their own personal samples.
- Students must wear protective goggles, gloves, and aprons.
- You must strictly supervise the handling and disposal of samples.

Field Studies

Before taking the students on a field study, examine the area for possible safety hazards. Look for terrain or water hazards and poisonous plants and animals. Obtain the necessary written permission from parents and school authorities.

Instruct students on proper dress and behavior. If students are to work in small groups, decide in advance when and where they will reassemble. Do not allow any student to travel alone.

Identify any students who have health problems, especially allergies. Alert these students to potential hazards. Be sure they are adequately prepared to deal with emergencies.

Take a first-aid kit on all field trips. Add items such as a bee-sting kit, meat tenderizer for insect bites, tweezers, and calamine lotion.

Working With Solutions

General guidelines for preparing solutions and media include the following:

- Clearly label each solution with its name, concentration, date of preparation, and any appropriate warnings such as "flammable."

- Before preparing a solution, rinse clean glassware thoroughly in distilled water.

- Pour concentrated acids and bases into water, stirring constantly. Never pour water into concentrated acids or bases.

- Store stains in dropper bottles.

Percentage Solutions: Volume/Volume

To prepare a solution of a given percentage, dissolve the number of milliliters of solute equal to the percentage in enough solvent to make 100 mL of solution. For example, to make a 10% solution of hydrochloric acid (HCl), add 10 mL of concentrated HCl to enough distilled water to bring the volume to 100 mL.

Percentage Solutions: Mass/Volume

To prepare a solution of a given percentage, dissolve the number of grams of solute equal to the percentage in enough solvent to make 100 mL of solution. For example, to make a 3% solution of sodium chloride, add 3 g of NaCl to a graduated cylinder. Add enough distilled water to bring the volume to 100 mL.

Reducing the Concentration of a Solution

Place the number of milliliters of the existing solution that is equal to the percentage of the new concentration into a graduated cylinder. Add distilled water to bring the volume to an amount equal to the original percentage. For example, to reduce an 80% glucose solution to 20%, use 20 mL of 80% glucose. Add enough distilled water to bring the volume to 80 mL.

Indicator Substitutions

You can often replace the pH indicators that are suggested for use with others that are equally effective. Use this table of common indicators to make your substitutions.

Indicator	pH Range	Color Change
Thymol blue	1.2–2.5	Red to yellow
Bromphenol blue	3.0–4.5	Yellow to blue
Congo red	3.0–5.0	Blue to red
Methyl orange	3.0–4.5	Orange-red to yellow
Litmus	4.5–8.5	Red to blue
Alizarin red	5.0–7.0	Yellow to red
Bromcresol purple	5.5–7.0	Yellow to purple
Bromthymol blue	6.0–7.5	Yellow to blue
Phenol red	6.5–8.0	Yellow to red
Neutral red	7.0–8.0	Red to yellow
Cresol red	7.0–9.0	Yellow to red
Thymol blue (alkaline)	8.0–10.0	Yellow to blue
Phenolpthalein	8.0–10.0	Colorless to red
Alizarin yellow	10.0–12.0	Colorless to yellow

Organisms in the Biology Lab

A biology curriculum in which students had no opportunity to observe and experiment with organisms would be incomplete and dull. The decisions you make about the use of organisms, especially animals, should reflect your personal views and your assessment of your students' needs, interest, maturity, and ability to behave responsibly. Your decisions should also reflect accepted practices.

This section presents an overview of the guidelines for working with animals. It is followed by the NABT guidelines for working with animals, which are more detailed. At the end of the section, you will find instructions on caring for species that are used in the labs in this lab manual.

The Use of Animals

Although there are many advantages to providing students with opportunities to study animals, it is important to be aware of and sensitive to ethical and practical concerns. The concerns vary depending on whether you are observing animals in the classroom or doing experiments with animals.

Observing Animals in the Classroom

1. Check state and local codes on animal welfare, as well as school regulations.

2. Animals need to be nonpoisonous.

3. Purchase animals only from reputable dealers. Mammals that have not been recently purchased from a reliable source should be vaccinated for rabies. Quarantine an animal to make sure that it is disease-free before bringing it into the classroom.

4. Determine whether a proper habitat can be maintained in the classroom situation.

5. An animal's living quarters should be clean and appropriately spacious.

6. Use small luggage padlocks on cages to prevent the accidental release of animals.

7. Remove wastes from living quarters daily. Thoroughly clean the quarters periodically to ensure that they are odor-free.

8. Provide a daily supply of fresh water and fulfill other needs specific to a species.

9. Provide for the care of the animals during weekends and school vacations. Inform the custodial staff of the presence of animals. Discuss issues that could affect the welfare of animals, such as the use of insecticides.

10. Stress that animals should be handled *only* when necessary for their care. Don't allow students to tap on enclosures or otherwise disturb the animals.

11. Caution students on the possible risks of improper handling of species, including cuts, bites, and stings.

12. Make sure students thoroughly wash their hands with soap and warm water after handling animals or their containers.

13. Return animals to their natural habitats after an observation period of not longer than 14 days. Do not release nonnative species or laboratory-bred animals into the environment.

Using Animals in Experiments

1. An experiment that involves live animals needs a clearly defined objective relating to the explication of a scientific principle.

2. Before performing the experiment, check local and state regulations. In some states, certification is required before a teacher is permitted to experiment with animals.

3. Whenever possible, substitute plants or invertebrates for vertebrates.

4. Do not do any procedures that will cause pain, discomfort, or harm to vertebrates.

Handling Ethical Issues With Students

There is much controversy regarding the use of animals in scientific research. This controversy extends to the use of both live and preserved animals in the biology laboratory.

A discussion about what uses of animals are appropriate in a biology classroom can be frustrating and emotionally charged. However, it can provide an opportunity for students to closely examine a current issue. Consider having students read print and online articles about this issue. Students could also contact groups or individuals with varying points of view on the topic.

Stress that it is important to make a rational, informed decision before taking a stand on any issue. Point out that it is vital to know and understand the arguments on both sides of an issue. Help students analyze the sources they find in terms of slant, bias, and the reliability and objectivity of the author(s). Teach them to learn to distinguish between fact and opinion. Encourage them to question what they read and hear. Challenge them to discover the hidden assumptions and implications of different points of view.

Although none of the labs in this manual use preserved specimens, there are a few labs in which students dissect an animal, in this case a squid, or handle animal parts, such as chicken wings. It is also likely that you will use labs from other sources that do require students to work with preserved specimens.

If dissections are a part of your curriculum, make sure that students maintain a serious, respectful attitude toward the specimens. If a student chooses to avoid a dissection because of ethical or religious concerns, you should respect that student's opinion. If possible provide the student with an alternative, such as a video or simulation.

National Association of Biology Teachers

The labs in this manual meet the National Association of Biology Teachers (NABT) guidelines for the use of animals in the classroom. Not all of the guidelines are applicable to the labs in this manual, but they may be applicable to other labs that you do.

> The national Association of Biology Teachers (NABT) has developed the following set of guidelines to be used when working with live animals.

Living things are the subject of biology, and their direct study is an appropriate and necessary part of biology teaching. Textbook instruction alone cannot provide students with a basic understanding of life and life processes. We further recognize the importance of research to understanding life processes and providing information on health, disease, medical care, and agriculture.

The abuse of any living organism for experimentation or any other purpose is intolerable in any segment of society. Because biology deals specifically with living things, professional biological educators must be especially cognizant of their responsibility to prevent inhumane treatment to living organisms in the name of science and research. This responsibility should extend beyond the confines of the teacher's classroom to the rest of the school and community.

The National Association of Biology Teachers, in speaking to the dilemma of providing a sound biological education, while addressing the problem of humane experimentation, presents the following guidelines on the use of live animals.

A. Biological experimentation should lead to and be consistent with respect for life and all living things. Humane treatment and care of animals should be an integral part of any lesson that includes living animals.

B. All aspects of exercises and/or experiments dealing with living things must be within the comprehension and capabilities of the students involved. It is recognized that these parameters are necessarily vague, but it is expected that competent teachers of biology can recognize these limitations.

C. Lower orders of life such as bacteria, fungi, protozoans, and invertebrates can reveal much basic biological information and are preferable as subjects for invasive studies whenever possible.

D. Vertebrate animals may be used as experimental organisms in the following situations:

  1. Observations of normal living patterns of wild animals in the free-living state or in zoological parks, gardens, or aquatica.

  2. Observations of normal living patterns of pets, fish, or domestic animals.

  3. Observations of biological phenomena, i.e., including ovulation in frogs through hormone injections that do not cause discomfort or adverse effects to the animals.

E. Animals should be properly cared for as described in the following guidelines:

  1. Appropriate quarters for the animals being used should be provided in a place free from undue stresses. If housed in the classroom itself, animals should not be constantly subjected to disturbances that might be caused by students in the classroom or other upsetting activities.

  2. All animals used in teaching or research programs must receive proper care. Quarters should provide for sanitation, protection from the elements, and have sufficient space for normal behavioral and postural requirements of the species. Quarters shall be easily cleaned, ventilated and lighted. Proper temperature regulation shall be provided.

  3. Proper food and clean drinking water for those animals requiring water shall be available at all times in suitable containers.

  4. Animals' care shall be supervised by a science teacher experienced in proper animal care.

  5. If euthanasia is necessary, animals shall be sacrificed in an approved, humane manner by an adult experienced in the use of such procedures. Laboratory animals should not be released in the environment if they were not originally a part of the native fauna. The introduction of nonnative species which may become feral must be avoided.

  6. The procurement and use of wild or domestic animals must comply with existing local, state, or federal rules regarding the same.

F. Animal studies should be carried out under the provisions of the following guidelines:

  1. All animal studies should be carried out under the direct supervision of a competent science teacher. It is the responsibility of that teacher to ensure that the student has the necessary comprehension of the study being done.

  2. Students should not be allowed to take animals home to carry out experimental studies. These studies should be done in a suitable area in the school.

3. Students doing projects with vertebrate animals should adhere to the following:

   a. No experimental procedures should be attempted that would subject vertebrate animals to pain or distinct discomfort, or interfere with their health in any way. Pithing of live frogs should be carried out by a teacher experienced in such procedures and should not be part of the general class activity.

   b. Students should not perform surgery on living vertebrate animals except under the direct supervision of a qualified biomedical scientist.

4. Experimental procedures should not involve the use of microorganisms pathogenic to humans or other animals, ionizing radiation, carcinogens, drugs, or chemicals at toxic levels, drugs known to produce adverse or teratogenic effects, pain causing drugs, alcohol in any form, electric shock, exercise until exhaustion, or other distressing stimuli.

5. Behavioral studies should use only positive reinforcement in training studies.

6. Egg embryos subjected to experimental manipulation must be destroyed humanely at least two days prior to hatching. Normal egg embryos allowed to hatch must be treated humanely within these guidelines.

7. The administration of anesthetics should be carried out by a qualified science teacher competent in such procedures. (The legal ramifications of student use of anesthetics are complex and such use should be avoided.)

G. The use of living animals for science fair projects and displays shall be in accordance with these guidelines. In addition, no living vertebrate animals shall be used in displays for science fair exhibitions.

H. It is recognized that an exceptionally talented student may wish to conduct original research in the biological or medical sciences. In those cases where the research value of a specific project is obvious by its potential contribution to science, but its execution would be otherwise prohibited by the guidelines governing the selection of an appropriate animal or procedure, exceptions can be obtained if:

1. the project is approved by and carried out under the direct supervision of a qualified biomedical scientist or a designated adult supervisor in the field of investigation, and

2. the project is carried out in an appropriate research facility, and

3. the project is carried out with the utmost regard for the humane care and treatment of the animals involved in the project, and

4. a research plan is developed and approved by the qualified biomedical scientist prior to the start of any research.

Caring for Live Organisms

You will probably order most of the organisms required for the labs in this manual from biological supply houses. Some organisms can also be purchased at pet stores. A few can be collected locally from their natural habitats. All the organisms can be cultured and maintained in a classroom or laboratory setting.

In many schools, all laboratory supplies, including live organisms, must be ordered a year in advance. If this situation exists at your school, you may need to maintain cultures for long periods of time. Cases where long-term care varies from short-term care have been noted in the instructions.

Using Proper Equipment

Careful attention to directions and the use of proper equipment and supplies is important for maintaining live organisms. Be especially careful when using glassware. Be sure that all glassware is clean and free of any soap residue.

Ideally, the glassware you use to culture organisms should be new and untouched by chemicals, including soap. Used laboratory glassware often retains traces of the chemicals it has contacted even after it has been cleaned. Even the faintest trace of some chemicals can have a serious impact on organisms. Because the organisms used in the labs in this manual are relatively hardy, they can be cultured under less-than-ideal conditions. However, you may want to set aside some glassware to use exclusively for culturing organisms and preparing media.

Specific Care Instructions

Algae Order specific species of algae such as *Chlorella* from a biological supply company. The supplier should supply instructions for maintaining the cultures. In general, store algae in loosely capped jars in a cool room beneath fluorescent lights.

Aquatic Plants Aquatic plants such as *Elodea* are common freshwater aquarium plants and are generally available from pet stores. Aquatic plants can also be collected throughout most of the year from ponds and slow-moving streams.

To maintain aquatic plants in a classroom, fill an aquarium or large (4-L) glass jar with pond or spring water. If pond or spring water is not available, fill the container with tap water and set it aside for at least 24 hours before introducing the aquatic plants.

Float aquatic plants loosely on the surface of the water. If aquatic plants are overcrowded they may deteriorate. Replenish the water as necessary as it evaporates. You can provide nutrients for aquatic plants by adding six to eight guppies or a mature duckweed culture to the aquarium. Do not add any snails to the container. The snails will feed on and destroy the plants.

You can also provide nutrients by adding dilute (1%) commercial fertilizer (5–10–5) to the water. Provide a minimum of 15 hours of fluorescent light each day.

Bacteria Order pure cultures of nonpathogenic bacteria from a biological supply company. Familiarize yourself with bacteriological techniques, and collect the necessary supplies and equipment before working with bacteria in the laboratory.

Bacteria are easily cultured in nutrient broth. To prepare the broth, bring 350 mL of distilled water to a boil in a 500-mL beaker. Slowly add 3 g of dehydrated nutrient broth while stirring constantly.

Pour the broth into small test tubes and insert a cotton plug into each tube. Sterilize the tubes for 15 minutes at 15 psi (103.4 kPa) of pressure in an autoclave or pressure cooker. Store the sterilized tubes in a refrigerator until they are needed.

Use an inoculating loop and follow sterile techniques when you transfer bacteria to the tubes of sterile nutrient broth. Store inoculated tubes at room temperature for two to three days to allow the bacteria to grow. The tubes can be incubated at 37°C for 24 hours if you intend to use the cultures immediately. Make subcultures and dilutions of the cultures at two-week intervals. Cultures remain viable for several weeks when stored in a refrigerator.

Bacteria may also be cultured on agar plates or slants. Biological supply companies often provide bacterial cultures on slants. Make subcultures of bacteria as soon as possible after receiving the original cultures. You can extend the life of slant cultures by covering the slants with a thin layer of sterile mineral oil and storing them in a refrigerator. The oil-covered slants will usually survive for several months.

Daphnia Order *Daphnia* from a biological supply house. To culture *Daphnia*, nearly fill a 4-L jar with pasteurized spring water or tap water that has been allowed to stand at room temperature for at least 24 hours.

To prepare pasteurized spring water, place 12 L–16 L of spring water in a large enameled container and heat the water at 65°C for 15 minutes. Store the pasteurized water for up to two weeks in covered plastic containers. After two weeks, you will need to repeat the pasteurization process to control the growth of bacteria that produce hydrogen sulfide.

Add green unicellular algae or 100 mL of an established *Euglena* culture to the water. Add several *Daphnia* to the jar and place the jar near a light source. Replenish the water and *Euglena* culture as necessary. Divide the *Daphnia* culture about every three weeks.

Ferns You can grow ferns in clay pots or in terrariums. Keep the soil moist but not wet. Most ferns prefer medium-intensity light and relatively cool temperatures. Many ferns, such as the bracken fern, should not be placed in direct or strong sunlight. Fern gametophytes take at least six weeks to grow from spores. Culture the spores from crushed sori in flowerpots, on the surface of an inverted flowerpot, or in sterile agar.

Hydra Hydras will grow in a culture dish containing a 5-cm sprig of an aquatic plant and pasteurized spring water. (See the *Daphnia* section for pasteurization instructions.) Place 20 to 30 hydras in the culture dish. Place the dish near a fluorescent light where it can receive 16 hours of light each day.

Providing an adequate food supply is the most difficult aspect of maintaining hydras. Hydras are active, carnivorous feeders that will eat only live food. Feed hydras *Daphnia*, chopped *Tubifex* worms, or the washed larvae of brine shrimp every other day.

Hydras require clean water. About 30 minutes after each feeding, remove uneaten debris from the bottom of the dish with a dropper pipette. Replace the aquatic plant as it deteriorates. When the population reaches 50, begin a new culture with half of the individuals from the existing culture.

Mushrooms When you receive your shipment of spores, read the instructions. Most fungi spores can be stored at room temperature, where they will last for several weeks if kept in subdued light. Keep the culture out of direct sunlight and avoid high temperatures.

Because fungi are aerobic, you need to loosen the caps on tube cultures. Lyophilized (freeze-dried) cultures can be stored at room temperature if you intend to use them within a week. For long-term storage, refrigerate or freeze the cultures.

Planarians Planarians such as *Dugesia* can be collected from the underside of logs and stones in bodies of cold, clear fresh water. They can also be ordered from biological supply houses. Keep planarians in black or opaque containers, such as enameled pans, at a temperature of about 18°C. Change the water frequently. Feed the planarians bits of raw liver, *Tubifex* worms, or egg yolk. After several hours, remove excess food with a dropper pipette to avoid fouling the water.

Snails Freshwater snails will flourish in an established aquarium with aquatic plants provided for food. Remove dead snails immediately to prevent fouling of the water. Place two medium-sized snails in the aquarium for each gallon of water.

Termites You can obtain termites from biological supply companies or collect them from rotting wood. It can be labor-intensive to culture termites for extended periods of time, but it can be done if necessary.

You can obtain most of the materials needed to culture termites from a school wood shop. Start with three 13 × 13 cm squares of pine, 1 cm thick. Drill a hole 8 cm in diameter through the center of one square. Use a router to carve four grooves 0.5 cm deep and 0.5 cm wide into the pine on either side of the square. The grooves should lead from the outside of the square to the circle you drilled in the middle. (The termites will use these grooves to enter and exit the central hole.)

Put the drilled square on top of an intact pine square and pack the hole with wet, unbleached paper towels. Cover the hole with the third pine square.

Next, you need to construct an escape-proof enclosure for the termites. You will need two glass or plastic containers, one of which can fit completely within the other, and both of which can be sealed shut. The small container should have a diameter about twice the diameter of the pine box. Fill the bottom of the smaller container with soil or peat, and place the pine box inside. Fill the remaining space in the small container with popsicle sticks.

Place the small container inside the large container. Fill the large container with enough water to form a 2-cm deep "moat" around the small container. Although termites will not be able to cross the water to escape, termites may be able to chew through thin-walled plastic containers. If they do, the containers will flood, but no termites will escape.

Let the pine box and the popsicle sticks soak in water overnight before you add the termites. Pour the termite media or rotten wood onto the popsicle sticks. Completely seal both containers. Every two weeks, unseal the containers and add water through the hole in the pine box. Add popsicle sticks or paper towels as needed.

Terrestrial Plants You can buy bean seeds at supermarkets. Purchase plants from sources that provide instructions about a plant's need for water, light, and fertilizer. Coleus plants can be easily propagated from stem cuttings.

Yeast To prepare an active culture of yeast, dissolve 0.1 g of dry yeast and 5 g of sucrose in 75 mL of distilled water. Mix thoroughly. Use the yeast culture within two to four days. The culture should provide enough yeast for three classes of 24 students each.

Master Materials List

The *Miller & Levine Biology* program offers many opportunities for students to develop laboratory skills. This materials list summarizes the materials required for the lab skills labs, chapter labs, and additional labs. You can use the Master Materials List to help you plan your activities and order supplies. Materials that are listed in the consumable and nonconsumable charts are available from Science Kit. They can be ordered at www.sciencekit.com, or by calling 800-828-7777.
(See T25–T26 in the Teacher's Edition of the textbook for a Quick Lab Materials List.)

The quantities listed in the Master Materials List are based on a maximum of 24 students in the laboratory. Adjust the quantities if your class size is different or if you decide to change the recommended group size. You will need safety goggles, plastic aprons, and disposable gloves for many of the labs.

Consumable Materials			
Description	**Lab**	**Group Size**	**Quantity per Class**
agar plates, prepared	CL 20	small groups	12
agarose, prepared gel, 0.8%	CL 15	small groups	200-mL bottle
antibiotic disks, penicillin and tetracycline	CL 20	small groups	12 each
Bacillus subtilis or *Staphylococcus epidermidis*	CL 20	small groups	1 culture
bacteria, oil-eating	AL 3	class	1 container
balloons, small round, 5-inch	AL 14	small groups	6
balloons, round, 9-inch	CL 33 AL 14	pairs small groups	24 6
bromthymol blue, 0.04%	AL 5	small groups	8 mL
cheesecloth	CL 12	small groups	1 package
Chlorella	CL 3	small groups	1 culture
chromatography paper strips	CL 8	small groups	13
coverslips	LS 3, AL 4, AL 9, AL 11 CL 5	pairs small groups	60 total 15
Daphnia magna	AL 11, AL 12	pairs	1 culture
dialysis tubing, 1-inch diameter	CL 7	small groups	1 roll
disease-causing agent, simulated	AL 15	individuals	1 packet
disease indicator powder	AL 15	individuals	1 bottle

KEY **CL** Chapter Lab **AL** Additional Lab **LS** Lab Skills

Description	Lab	Group Size	Quantity per Class
dissection trays, disposable	CL 32	pairs	12
DNA samples in microfuge tubes	CL 15	small groups	1 set
DNA stain concentrate	CL 15	small groups	30 mL
Elodea	AL 5	small groups	24 sprigs
Escherichia coli	CL 20	small groups	1 culture
ethanol, 95%	CL 12	small groups	150 mL
filter paper, 15-cm, medium flow	CL 2	small groups	30 pieces
foam stoppers (or cotton balls)	AL 3	class	3
forceps, disposable	CL 20	small groups	36
fructose	CL 9	small groups	5 g
glass beads	CL 20	small groups	60 or more
glucose	CL 7, CL 9, CL 30	small groups	22 g total
glucose test strips	CL 7, CL 30, AL 13	small groups	1 bottle
hydra, brown	AL 12	pairs	1 culture
indole-3-acetic acid (IAA) powder	CL 24	small groups	100 mg
iodine solution, Lugol's	AL 4 CL 7	pairs small groups	12 drops 24 drops
isopropyl alcohol, 70%	CL 8	small groups	60 mL
lactose	CL 9	small groups	5 g
lens paper	CL 1 LS 3, AL 4, AL 9, AL 10 CL 5, CL 10, CL 25	individuals pairs small groups	1 or 2 packages 2–4 packages 1 or 2 packages
Lyme disease test solutions, simulated	CL 35	small groups	1 set
maltose	CL 9	small groups	5 g
micropipette tips	AL 3 CL 15, CL 20, CL 35	class small groups	3 48 total
mushroom-growing kits	CL 21	class	3
nutrient broth	CL 20	small groups	1 package
pH paper, wide-range and precision-range	CL 6 AL 6	small groups small groups	1 package each 24 strips
planaria, brown	CL 10	small groups	1 culture
snails, aquatic	AL 5	small groups	24

Consumable Materials continued			
Description	**Lab**	**Group Size**	**Quantity per Class**
sodium chloride	AL 4 CL 12	pairs small groups	10 g 15 g
spot plates	CL 30	small groups	6
TBE buffer (5× solution)	CL 15	small groups	300 mL
termites	CL 29	pairs	at least 12
weighing paper	AL 3 CL 28, AL 2	class small groups	3 sheets 23 sheets total

Nonconsumable Materials			
Description	**Lab**	**Group Size**	**Quantity per Class**
balances	AL 3 CL 28, AL 2	class small groups	1 6
beakers, 50-mL	CL 2	small groups	30
beakers, 100-mL	CL 35	small groups	6
beakers, 150-mL	CL 23	small groups	6
beakers, 250-mL	CL 7 CL 15, CL 28	small groups small groups	10 6
beakers, 400-mL	CL 5, CL 9, CL 35	small groups	5–6
beaker, 1000-mL	CL 2	small groups	1
beaker tongs	CL 2	small groups	6
cameras, disposable (optional)	CL 22	small groups	6
computers	AL 10 CL 4, CL 22	pairs small groups	12 6
depression slides	AL 11	pairs	12
dissecting pins	CL 27	small groups	36
dissecting probes	CL 27, CL 28 LS 3, AL 4, AL 9, AL 11	small groups pairs	6 12
dissecting scissors	CL 27	small groups	6
electrophoresis chambers with patch cords	CL 15	small groups	6
forceps	CL 29, CL 32, AL 4, AL 9, AL 11 CL 2, CL 7, CL 10, CL 27	pairs small groups	12 6

Nonconsumable Materials continued

Description	Lab	Group Size	Quantity per Class
funnels	CL 12	small groups	6
graduated cylinders, 10-mL	CL 5, CL 8, AL 2 CL 7	small groups small groups	5–6 12
graduated cylinders, 25-mL	CL 2, CL 3, CL 6, CL 12	small groups	6
graduated cylinders, 100-mL	CL 5 CL 15	small groups small groups	1 6
hand lenses	Al 9 CL 6, CL 22, CL 27, CL 28	pairs small groups	12 6
hot plates	CL 2 CL 9	small groups small groups	1 5
lab equipment, assorted, 10 pieces	LS 1	small groups	6 sets
magnetic centromeres, two colors	CL 11	small groups	24 of each color
metersticks	CL 33 CL 4	pairs small groups	12 6
measuring spoon, 1-tbsp	AL 13	small groups	6
measuring tapes	CL 22	small groups	6
micropipettes	AL 3 CL 15 CL 20, CL 35	class small groups small groups	3 24 12
microscopes, compound	CL 1 LS 3, AL 4, AL 9, Al 10, AL 11 CL 5, CL 25	individuals pairs small groups	24 12 5–6
microscope, dissecting	AL 12 CL 10	pairs small groups	12 6
microscope slides	LS 3, AL 4 AL 9 CL 5 CL 10	pairs pairs small groups small groups	12 24 15 6
microtubes	AL 15	individuals	24
molecular model kits	AL 1	pairs	12
petri dishes	AL 12 CL 2, CL 23 CL 10, CL 29	pairs small groups small groups	12 6 24–30

Description	Lab	Group Size	Quantity per Class
pipette bulbs, fillers, or pumps	AL 15 CL 6, CL 9	individuals small groups	24 6–10
pipettes, dropper	LS 3, AL 9, AL 11 AL 12 CL 2, CL 10 CL 3, CL 5	pairs pairs small groups small groups	12 24 6 12–15
pipettes, volumetric, 1-mL	AL 15 CL 9	individuals small groups	24 10
pipettes, volumetric, 5-mL	CL 6	small groups	6
plastic tubing with lock fitting	CL 9	small groups	5
pop beads, two colors	CL 11	small groups	180 of each color
prepared slides, bacteria	CL 1	individuals	24
prepared slides, content optional	LS 3	pairs	12
prepared slides, cross sections of hydra, roundworm, and earthworm	CL 25	small groups	6 sets
prepared slides, plant root or stem	CL 1	individuals	24
prepared slides, pollen with key	AL 10	pairs	12
pressure probes and interface	CL 9	small groups	5
ring stands with test-tube clamps	CL 9	small groups	5
rubber stoppers, one-hole	CL 8 CL 9, AL 14	small groups small groups	13 5–6
rubber stoppers, solid	AL 2	small groups	18
rulers, metric	AL 3 CL 26 CL 31, CL 33 CL 7, CL 8, CL 10, CL 15, CL 20, CL 23, AL 2, AL 5	class individuals pairs small groups	1 24 12 6
rulers, transparent, 15-cm	CL 1	individuals	24
scalpels	CL 10	small groups	6
scissors, general purpose	CL 19 CL 21 LS 3, CL 29, AL 4, AL 9 CL 7, CL 11, CL 24, AL 14	individuals class pairs small groups	24 1 12 6

Nonconsumable Materials continued			
Description	**Lab**	**Group Size**	**Quantity per Class**
scrub brushes	LS 2	small groups	6
spray bottles	CL 21	class	3
stirring rods	CL 5, CL 12, AL 13	small groups	5–6
sucrose	CL 9	small groups	5 g
test tubes, large	CL 3, CL 8	small groups	12
	CL 6	small groups	30
	AL 5	small groups	48
test tubes, medium	CL 5	small groups	10
	CL 9, CL 12	small groups	5–6
	AL 2	small groups	42
test-tube racks	AL 5	small groups	12
	CL 3, CL 5, CL 6, CL 8, CL 9, CL 12, AL 2	small groups	5–6
thermometers	CL 2, CL 9	small groups	4–5
timers (or clock with second hand)	AL 11	pairs	12
	CL 2, CL 15, CL 30, AL 13, CL 17	small groups	6
trays, dissection	LS 2, CL 27	small groups	6
trays, gel casting	CL 15	small groups	6
trays, staining	CL 15	small groups	6
tweezers	CL 22	small groups	6
vials, plastic	AL 3	class	3
	AL 15	individuals	24
well plates	CL 35	small groups	6

Additional Materials			
Description	**Lab**	**Group Size**	**Quantity per Class**
batteries, alkaline, 9-volt	CL 15	small groups	30
Beano (digestive aid)	AL 13	small groups	13 mL
beans, dried	CL 6, AL 13	small groups	1.5 lb total
bean seeds, large	CL 23	small groups	24
bleach, household	AL 3	class	small bottle
	CL 20	small groups	

	Additional Materials continued		
Description	**Lab**	**Group Size**	**Quantity per Class**
blender (or food processor)	CL 2	small groups	1
bones, small and cross sections (chicken, duck, and cow)	CL 28	small groups	6 sets
broccoli	AL 13	small groups	1 head
chicken wings	CL 32	pairs	12
Chinese cabbage, chopped	AL 6	small groups	2 heads
containers, shallow	CL 2, CL 24	small groups	4–6
cornstarch	CL 7	small groups	1 g
cotton balls	Al 11	pairs	12
	CL 3	small groups	12
cups, small plastic	AL 13	small groups	30
detergent, liquid dishwashing	CL 12	small groups	100 mL
detergent, powder (3 brands)	AL 2	small groups	small packages
fern fronds	AL 9	pairs	12
fertilizer, high nitrogen content	CL 3	small groups	1 teaspoon
field guides for plants	CL 22	small groups	several
food coloring	CL 6	small groups	1 set
gelatin	AL 2	small groups	16 0.25-oz packets (108 g)
glass-marking pencils	AL 3	class	1
	CL 3, CL 6, CL 8, CL 10, CL 20, AL 2, AL 5, AL 13	small groups	6
grape juice, white	CL 5	small groups	125 mL
graph paper	CL 16	individuals	24 sheets
	LS 1, AL 11	pairs	24 sheets total
	CL 2, CL 4, CL 5, CL 6, AL 6	small groups	86 sheets total
grow light	CL 3	small groups	1 or 2
hacksaw	CL 28	small groups	1
highlighters, light-colored	CL 16	individuals	24
hydrogen peroxide, 3%	AL 9	pairs	1 small bottle
	CL 2	small groups	
ice cubes	CL 2, CL 12	small groups	2–3 trays (1 bag)

Description	Lab	Group Size	Quantity per Class
knives	LS 2	small groups	6
labels, stick-on	LS 1, CL 6, CL 22	small groups	150 total
lactase, liquid	CL 30	small groups	small bottle
lanolin	CL 24	small groups	25 g
leaves, spinach and red kale	CL 8	small groups	6 each
liver, raw	CL 2	small groups	0.5 lb
markers, permanent, fine tip	AL 15 LS 2, CL 23, CL 24, CL 35, AL 6	individuals small groups	12 (shared) 6
measuring spoons, ½-teaspoon	AL 6	small groups	6
microwave oven	CL 15	small groups	1
milk	CL 30	small groups	4 mL
moss, clumps	AL 9	pairs	12
newspapers	LS 3	pairs	12 sheets
notepads or notebooks	CL 22	small groups	6
paintbrushes, small	CL 29 CL 10	pairs small groups	12 6
paper, large	CL 11	small groups	6 sheets
paper clips	CL 31 CL 8	pairs small groups	24 13
paper plates, large	CL 17	small groups	12
paper plates, small	AL 3 CL 17	class small groups	3 30
paper towels	LS 2, CL 2, CL 6, CL 23 AL 3	small groups pairs	66 sheets total 12 small pieces
pencils, colored (assorted colors)	LS 1, CL 32, AL 8 CL 8, CL 11, CL 25	pairs small groups	12 sets 6 sets
pens, ballpoint, red (Bic or Papermate)	CL 29	pairs	12
pens, ballpoint, rollerball, and felt-tip (assorted brands and colors)	CL 29	pairs	24
plants, leafy	CL 24	small groups	6
plastic bags with twist ties	LS 2	small groups	12

Description	Lab	Group Size	Quantity per Class
plastic bags, freezer, self-sealing	CL 12	small groups	6
plastic bags, zip-close	CL 6, CL 15, CL 22, AL 6	small groups	1 or 2 packages
plastic bottles, small	AL 14	small groups	6
plastic pots, 4-inch	CL 24	small groups	6
potatoes, medium-sized	LS 2	small groups	6
potting soil	CL 24	small groups	1 bag
red onions	AL 4	pairs	2 or 3
quarters	CL 8	small groups	6
scissors, gardening	CL 22	small groups	6
seeds, large and small	CL 17	small groups	500 each
squid, whole (fresh or frozen)	CL 27	small groups	6
strawberries, ripe	CL 12	small groups	6
string	CL 24	small groups	1 ball
table salt, noniodized	AL 6	small groups	3 teaspoons
tape, masking	CL 20, CL 23, CL 24	small groups	1 roll
tape, strapping	CL 15	small groups	1 roll
tools, assorted	CL 17	small groups	12
toothpicks	AL 12 CL 24, CL 30	pairs small groups	12 30 total
twist ties	CL 7	small groups	24
vegetable oil	CL 9	small groups	15 mL
vinegar, white	CL 6	small groups	1 mL
water, bottled spring	AL 11 CL 3, CL 10, AL 5	pairs small groups	675 mL 2–3 liters
water, distilled	AL 15 AL 4 CL 2, CL 6, CL 15, CL 35, AL 2	individuals pairs small groups	360 mL 24 drops 4–5 liters
wire cutter or pliers	CL 31	pairs	1
work gloves, protective	CL 22	small groups	24
yeast, dried	CL 5, CL 9	small groups	2 packets

Biology

Miller & Levine

Laboratory Manual A

Copyright © Pearson Education, Inc., or its affiliates. All Rights Reserved. Printed in the United States of America. This publication is protected by copyright, and permission should be obtained from the publisher prior to any prohibited reproduction, storage in a retrieval system, or transmission in any form or by any means, electronic, mechanical, photocopying, recording, or likewise. To obtain permission(s) to use material from this work, please submit a written request to Pearson Education, Inc., Upper Saddle River, New Jersey.

Pearson, Prentice Hall, and Pearson Prentice Hall are trademarks, in the U.S. and/or other countries, of Pearson Education, Inc., or its affiliates.

Boston, Massachusetts   Chandler, Arizona   Glenview, Illinois   Upper Saddle River, New Jersey

ISBN-13: 978-0-13-368712-5
ISBN-10: 0-13-368712-0

1 2 3 4 5 6 7 8 9 10   13 12 11 10 09

Contents

Safety in the Biology Laboratory vi
Lab Skills 1   Lab Equipment and Safety 1
Lab Skills 2   Applying Scientific Methods 5
Lab Skills 3   Using a Compound Microscope 9

Chapter Labs

Unit 1 The Nature of Life
1 Using a Microscope to Estimate Size 17
2 Temperature and Enzymes 21

Unit 2 Ecology
3 The Effect of Fertilizer on Algae 25
4 Abiotic Factors and Plant Selection 29
5 The Growth Cycle of Yeast 35
6 Acid Rain and Seeds 39

Unit 3 Cells
7 Detecting Diffusion 45
8 Plant Pigments and Photosynthesis 49
9 Comparing Fermentation Rates of Sugars 55
10 Regeneration in Planaria 61

Unit 4 Genetics
11 Modeling Meiosis 67
12 Extracting DNA 73
13 From DNA to Protein Synthesis 77
14 Using DNA to Identify Human Remains 81
15 Using DNA to Solve Crimes 89

Unit 5 Evolution
16 Amino Acid Sequences: Indicators of Evolution 95
17 Competing for Resources 101
18 Dichotomous Keys 107
19 Using Index Fossils 115

Unit 6 From Microorganisms to Plants

20 Controlling Bacterial Growth 125
21 Mushroom Farming 129
22 Exploring Plant Diversity 135
23 Identifying Growth Zones in Roots 141
24 Plant Hormones and Leaves 147

Unit 7 Animals

25 Comparing Invertebrate Body Plans 151
26 Investigating Hominoid Fossils 157
27 Anatomy of a Squid 163
28 Comparing Bird and Mammal Bones 169
29 Termite Tracks 173

Unit 8 The Human Body

30 Digestion of Dairy Products 179
31 Testing Sensory Receptors for Touch 183
32 Comparing Limbs 189
33 Tidal Volume and Vital Capacity 195
34 Diagnosing Endocrine Disorders 203
35 Detecting Lyme Disease 207

Additional Labs

1   Making Models of Macromolecules 213
2   Enzymes in Detergents 219
3   Oil-Eating Bacteria 223
4   Osmosis 227
5   Photosynthesis and Cellular Respiration 233
6   Investigating the Fermentation of Kimchi 239
7   Independent Assortment and Gene Linkage 243
8   Ecosystems and Speciation 249
9   Comparing Adaptations of Ferns and Mosses 255
10 Using Pollen to Solve Crimes 259
11 The Effect of Chemicals on Heart Rate 265
12 Observing Hydra 271
13 Reducing Excess Gas 275
14 Modeling Breathing 279
15 Modeling Disease Transmission 283

Selected Quick Labs

2.1   Model an Ionic Compound 289

7.2   Making a Model of a Cell 291

10.1   Modeling the Relationship Between Surface Area and Volume 293

11.2   How Are Dimples Inherited 301

15.2   Inserting Genetic Markers 303

20.1   How Do Viruses Differ in Structure 305

Appendix A   How to Form a Hypothesis 307

Appendix B   Presenting Data 310

Appendix C   Measurements and Calculations 315

Appendix D   Laboratory Techniques 318

Appendix E   Science and Technology 323

Safety in the Biology Laboratory

Working in the biology laboratory can be exciting, but it can also be dangerous if you do not follow the proper safety guidelines. You are responsible for helping to maintain a safe environment in the laboratory. Unsafe practices endanger not only you but also the people who work near you.

Safety Rules

To prepare yourself for a safe year in the laboratory, review the following safety rules. Make sure you understand each rule. Ask your teacher to explain any rules you do not understand.

Dress Code

- To protect your eyes, wear safety goggles when you see the safety goggles symbol. This symbol will appear when you work with chemicals that are corrosive, such as acids or bases. The symbol will also appear when a chemical has irritating vapors.

    Avoid wearing contact lenses when you work with chemicals. If you need to wear contact lenses in the lab to see clearly, talk with your teacher about your need.

- Wear a laboratory apron or coat when you are working with chemicals that are corrosive or can stain your clothing. Also wear an apron when you are heating materials.

- Tie back long hair to avoid contact with chemicals, flames, or biological cultures.

- Remove, tie back, or avoid wearing any clothing or jewelry that can hang down and touch chemicals, flames, or cultures.

- Do not wear sandals or open-toed shoes in the laboratory. Never walk around barefoot or in stocking feet in the laboratory.

General Safety Rules

- Read the procedure for a lab in advance. Follow the steps of the procedure exactly as they are written unless your teacher tells you otherwise. If you do not understand a step, ask your teacher for help.

- Never do an experiment that your teacher has not approved. Do not use any lab equipment without permission or without the supervision of your teacher.

- Never eat or drink anything while you are in the laboratory. Do not bring food into the lab that you intend to eat later. Do not chew gum. Do not apply cosmetics.

- If you spill a chemical, check with your teacher right away about the proper cleanup procedure.

- Do not pour chemicals or other materials into the sink or place items in a trash container unless specifically instructed to do so by your teacher.

Emergencies and First Aid

- Know the location and proper use of safety equipment such as the fire extinguisher, fire blanket, eye-wash station, and first-aid kit.

- Learn what to do in response to specific emergencies, such as cuts, burns, or contact with chemicals.

- Immediately report all accidents, no matter how minor, to your teacher.

- Your teacher will help you determine the proper response to an accident. He or she may administer first aid, send you to the school nurse, or call a physician.

- Report any fires to your teacher at once. Know the location of the fire alarm and know where and how to report a fire or other emergency requiring outside assistance.

Heating and Fire Safety

- Always wear safety goggles when you use a candle or gas burner as a heat source.
- Make sure you know how to safely light a gas burner. Your teacher will demonstrate the proper procedure for lighting a burner. Also refer to the section in Appendix D on gas burners.
- If the flame leaps out of a burner toward you, turn the gas off immediately. Do not touch the burner, which may be hot.
- Never leave a lighted burner unattended.
- Never reach across a flame.
- Never heat a chemical that you are not told to heat. A chemical that is harmless when cool can be dangerous when heated.
- Make sure that there are no open containers of flammable liquids in the laboratory when flames are being used.
- When you heat a test tube with a flame, point the opening of the tube away from yourself and others. Chemicals can splash or boil out of a heated test tube.
- Never heat a closed container. Expanding gases inside the container may cause the container to blow apart, causing injury to you or others working nearby.
- Never pick up a container that has been heated without first holding the back of your hand near it. If you can feel the heat on the back of your hand, the container may be too hot to handle. Use a clamp or tongs when handling hot containers, or, if appropriate, wear heat-resistant gloves.
- Maintain a clean work area and keep materials other than the ones you are heating away from flames or hot plates.

Using Chemicals Safely

- Never mix chemicals for the "fun of it." You might produce a dangerous, possibly explosive, substance.
- Chemicals used in labs may be poisonous. Never touch, taste, or smell a chemical that you do not know for a fact is harmless. If you are instructed to smell the fumes in an experiment, gently wave your hand over the opening of a container and direct the fumes toward your nose. Do not inhale the fumes directly from the container.
- Use only those chemicals needed in the investigation. Keep all lids closed when a chemical is not being used. Notify your teacher whenever chemicals are spilled.
- Dispose of all chemicals as instructed by your teacher. To avoid contamination, never return chemicals to their original containers.
- Be extra careful when working with acids or bases. Pour such chemicals from one container to another over the sink, not over your work area.
- When diluting an acid, pour the acid into water. Never pour water into the acid.
- Notify your teacher immediately if you spill an acid or a base.
- Use a continuous stream of water from the tap to rinse acid or bases off your skin or clothing.
- If an acid or base splashes in your eyes, go to the eye-wash station immediately to flush the liquid from your eyes.

Using Glassware Safely

- Before you heat a beaker or other glass container, make sure the outside of the container is dry.

- If you use a gas burner as a heat source, use a wire screen to protect glassware from the flame.

- Keep in mind that hot glassware will not appear hot. Never pick up a heated glass object without first checking to see if it is hot. If you can feel the heat on the back of your hand, use a clamp or tongs to handle the container or wear heat-resistant gloves if appropriate.

- Never use broken or chipped glassware.

- If a glass object breaks, notify your teacher. Then use a brush and dustpan to collect and dispose of the broken glass in the proper trash container. Never pick up broken glass with your hands.

- Never eat or drink from laboratory glassware. Thoroughly clean glassware before putting it away.

- If you need to insert a glass tube into a rubber stopper or rubber tubing, use a lubricant and a gentle turning motion to reduce the risk of breaking the glass.

Using Sharp Instruments

- Handle scalpels, scissors, and knives with extreme care. Always cut away from yourself.

- Always use sharp instruments only as instructed.

- Notify your teacher immediately if you cut yourself while working in the laboratory.

Working With Live Organisms

- No experiments that will cause pain, discomfort, or harm to animals should be done in the classroom or at home.

- Treat all living organisms with care and respect. Limit your interaction with organisms to only what is required to complete an experiment.

- Pay close attention to the instructions in the procedure and any additional instructions from your teacher.

- Use sterile procedures, as instructed by your teacher, when working with microbes.

- Wash your hands thoroughly after you handle any organisms or their containers.

End-of-Experiment Rules

- Before you leave the laboratory, clean up your work area and return all equipment to its proper place.

- Make sure you turn off and disconnect burners from the gas supply. Also turn off and unplug hot plates.

- Wash your hands thoroughly with soap and warm water before you leave the lab.

Safety Alerts

All the labs in this manual have been designed with safety in mind. When appropriate, you will find a paragraph about safety after the list of materials. Some of the safety symbols shown on the next page will also be included to alert you to possible dangers and to remind you to work carefully.

Watch for statements within a procedure that are labeled "CAUTION." These statements focus on possible risks related to specific steps in the procedure. The possible risk may be to yourself, to an organism, or to equipment.

Safety Contract

Once you have read the information on pages vi–ix and are sure you understand all the rules, fill out the safety contract below. Signing this contract tells your teacher that you are aware of the safety rules and agree to follow them. Return your signed contract to your teacher. You will not be allowed to work in the laboratory until you have signed the contract.

Safety Contract

I, _____,

- agree to be responsible for my own safety and behavior in the lab and to do everything I can to ensure the safety of others.

- agree to read all labs in advance and come to class fully prepared and dressed appropriately.

- agree to follow all written instructions in the manual and any additional instructions given to me by my teacher.

- agree to use great caution when handling items that are potentially dangerous including glassware, sharp instruments, heat sources, and chemicals.

- agree to treat all living organisms with care and respect.

- agree that I know the locations and use of all safety equipment.

Signature _____ Date _____

Lab Skills 1 Lab Equipment and Safety

Problem
What can you do to ensure that you work safely and efficiently in the science laboratory?

Introduction
Lab activities provide an opportunity to practice the process of science. They allow you to do what scientists all over the world do in research laboratories and in the field. Like all scientists, you must follow procedures that ensure your safety. These procedures also ensure that the data you collect is reliable. Unlike most scientists, you will need to fit your experiments into a specific block of time. Thus, your ability to work efficiently will be essential to your success.

In this lab, you will draw a map of the room in which you will do labs. You will note the locations of safety equipment and other supplies. Finally, you will identify some pieces of equipment that may be unfamiliar and infer the purpose of these items.

Skills Focus
Observe, Infer, Compare and Contrast

Materials
- graph paper
- colored pencils

Pre-Lab Questions

1. **Infer** Why is it important to know the location of equipment, such as a fire extinguisher, before you begin working in the lab?

   Sample answer: If you know exactly where each piece of safety

   equipment is located, then you can respond quickly to an emergency

   and minimize the damage.

   _____

2. **Relate Cause and Effect** How could reading a lab in advance contribute to both safety and efficiency?

   Sample answer: After I read the procedure, if I do not understand a step

   I can ask questions and possibly prevent a dangerous mistake. I also can

   get started without any delay.

Big Idea
Preparation is the key to staying safe during scientific activities.

Skills Objectives
Students will be able to
- identify the locations of equipment in the science lab.
- identify less-familiar pieces of equipment and infer their use.

Preparation Time
20 minutes

Class Time
30–40 minutes

Group Size
Part A: Pairs
Part B: Small groups

Safety
Warn students to handle equipment with care and to avoid jostling other students.

Advance Preparation
Part A: Label closed cabinets and drawers with the names of the items they contain.
Part B: Gather and label the items you decide to use. Place a labeled set on each lab bench or distribute one set around the room to avoid congestion. Prepare a list of items to distribute to students.

Teaching Tip
To assess prior knowledge, ask students, "What types of lab equipment have you used in the past, and what precautions did you have to take while working with those types of equipment?"

---

3. Use Analogies Give an example of an activity that takes place outside of school in which people are expected to review safety precautions before taking part in the activity.

Examples include airplane flights, amusement park rides, and installing

electronic equipment.

_____

Procedure

Part A: Mapping the Lab

Part A
You may wish to add or subtract items from the lists in Step 2 and Step 4.

Use a sheet of graph paper to make a map of your science lab. To avoid having a cluttered map, use abbreviations instead of full names to record the locations of items. Use the space below to construct a key with abbreviations, such as FB for fire blanket.

1. Start by marking the locations of doors, windows, lab benches, and any desks.

2. Next, walk around the room and locate the following safety equipment: safety goggles, fire extinguisher, fire blanket, safety shower, eyewash station, fume hood, latex gloves, first-aid kit, and broken glass disposal box. Use a red pencil to record the locations of these items on the map.

3. Then, find the locations where common lab equipment such as beakers, graduated cylinders, microscopes, and thermometers are stored. Use a green pencil to mark these locations on your map. Add the abbreviations you choose to your key.

4. After each lab period, your lab station should be cleaned and organized. To help achieve this goal, use a blue pencil to mark the locations for items such as the following on your map: sink, sponge, paper towels, test-tube brush, hand soap, and dishwashing liquid. Add the abbreviations for these items to your key.

Key to Map Abbreviations

Part B: Identifying Lab Equipment

5. Your teacher will place ten pieces of less-familiar lab equipment labeled A–J on your lab bench or table. Choose a name for each item from the list that your teacher will give you.

6. Identify at least one way each item might be used in an experiment.

7. In the column titled Safety Issues, note which items might require one or more of the following safety warnings: safety goggles, breakage, electric shock, sharp object, and disposal.

Part B
Choose items to display that you intend to use in labs at some point in the year.

Step 7
Refer students to the front of the lab manual for a description of the safety symbols.

Sample Data

Data Table			
Item	Name	Possible Use	Safety Issues
A	Transfer pipette	Transfer liquids from one container to another.	Safety goggles, breakage
B	Well plate	Do an experiment with small amounts of reactants.	Safety goggles, disposal
C	Electrophoresis chamber	Separate a mixture.	Safety goggles, electric shock
D	Gas sensor probe	Detect the presence of gases.	Safety goggles, electric shock
E	Scalpel	Slice a preserved specimen.	Safety goggles, sharp object
F	Dialysis tubing	Observe diffusion.	Safety goggles
G	Mortar and pestle	Grind up solids.	Safety goggles, disposal
H	Petri dish	Grow bacterial cultures or observe small live organisms.	Safety goggles, disposal
I	Cheesecloth	Filter liquids.	Safety goggles
J	Calipers	Measure the diameter of an object.	Safety goggles

Analyze and Conclude

1. **Infer** Why is there a general safety rule to never bring food or drinks into the lab?

   Sample answer: The food or drinks may become contaminated by a chemical that is present in the air, on surfaces, or on the hands.

2. **Sequence** Describe what you would do if a glass beaker drops and breaks. List the appropriate steps in order.

   Sample answer: Notify my teacher and anyone working nearby. Collect a brush and dustpan to sweep up the broken glass and deposit the pieces in the broken glass deposit box. If the beaker contained a liquid, wipe up the spill.

3. **Design an Experiment** Graduated cylinders, beakers, and pipettes are all used to measure liquids. Identify two factors that would determine which item to choose in a given situation.

   Sample answer: Two factors are the amount of liquid and the degree of accuracy required for the measurement.

4. **Compare and Contrast** Use the example of heating water with a burner or a hot plate to explain how safety precautions may need to be adjusted when the method used to perform a task changes.

   With the hot plate, students need to avoid tangled cords and electric shock. With the burner, students need to tie back loose hair and clothing and avoid using flammable materials. (In both cases, students must wear safety goggles and use heat-resistant gloves.)

5. **Predict** Why do scientists include a detailed description of their procedures when they publish the results of experiments?

   Sample answer: Including the procedure allows other scientists to repeat an experiment and confirm the results.

Extend Your Inquiry

Biologists develop detailed safety plans, or protocols, to protect themselves and the organisms they are studying. Each of the fields described on pages 22–23 of your textbook has different safety issues. Work in small groups to research a safety protocol for one of these fields. Consult with your teacher about possible topics.

Help students choose a topic for which information is readily available and not overly technical. Some possible suggestions are sterile techniques when working with bacteria, the use of clean rooms in biotechnology, safety protocols for divers doing deep-sea explorations, or protocols for tagging wildlife.

Lab Skills 2 Applying Scientific Methods

Problem

How will light affect the sprouting of eyes on a potato?

Introduction

Scientific methodology is a general style of inquiry that is used to gather data and test ideas. Biologists use this type of inquiry to learn about living things. Doing experiments is a central part of scientific inquiry. For a controlled experiment, you need both an experimental setup and a control setup. The setups must be exactly the same except for the independent variable. With this approach, you will know that your results are due to that variable.

In this lab, you will use a potato to do a controlled experiment. Potato plants store starch in structures, known as potatoes, that people dig up and eat. Figure 1 shows where the potatoes are located in relation to the rest of the growing plant. Along the surface of a potato are buds, or "eyes," which look like small dimples in the potato skin. The eyes in a potato can sprout and grow into new potato plants. In your experiment, you will determine whether more eyes sprout in the dark or in the light.

Big Idea
Scientific methodology is an organized way to answer questions about the natural world.

Skills Objectives
Students will be able to
• distinguish an experimental setup from a controlled setup.
• explain the importance of a controlled experiment.

Class Time
30 minutes for setup; 15 minutes for observations after one week

Group Size
Small groups

Figure 1 Potato plant

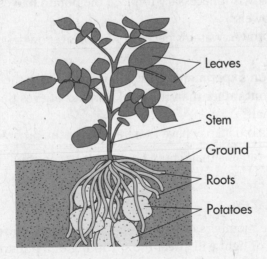

Leaves

Stem

Ground

Roots

Potatoes

Skills Focus

Form a Hypothesis, Control Variables, Organize Data

Materials

- medium-sized potato
- scrub brush
- knife
- dissection tray
- 2 paper towels
- 2 plastic bags with twist ties
- permanent marker

Safety

When using the knife to cut the potato, keep your fingers out of the path of the blade. Wash your hands thoroughly with soap and warm water after handling the potatoes.

Pre-Lab Questions

1. **Control Variables** How does cutting one potato in half help control the variables in this experiment?

   Sample answer: Because the two halves come from the same potato, you ensure that the ability to sprout is not a variable.

2. **Infer** Why is it necessary to place the potato halves on moist paper towels?

   Sample answer: Water is necessary for plant growth.

3. **Design an Experiment** Why will you compare the percentage of eyes that sprout rather than the total number of eyes that sprout on each potato half?

   One potato half may have more eyes than the other. (The number of eyes is a variable that would be difficult to control.)

Procedure

1. With the members of your group, discuss how the presence or absence of light will affect the sprouting of a potato. Record the hypothesis you will test to answer this question.

   Hypothesis: *Sample answer:* More eyes will sprout when the potato is in the dark (or fewer will sprout when the potato is in the light).

2. Put on your safety goggles and lab apron. Scrub the potato with a firm brush to remove any wax coating that may be on the potato.

3. Using a dissection tray, carefully cut the potato lengthwise into equal halves. Assign one half to be put in the dark and one half to be kept in the light. Count the number of eyes on each potato half and record this information in the data table below.

4. Fold each paper towel until you have rectangles about equal in size to your potato halves. Moisten the towels with water. Place a folded paper towel in each plastic bag.

5. Place a potato half in each plastic bag with the cut surface on the paper towel as shown in Figure 2. Tie each bag with a twist tie. Use a permanent marker to label one bag Light and the other Dark.

Figure 2 Potato half in plastic bag

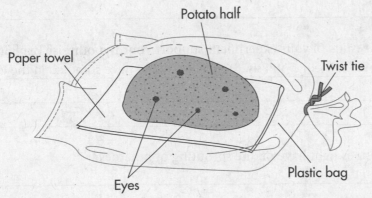

Potato half

Paper towel

Twist tie

Eyes

Plastic bag

Step 3
Make sure students know how to recognize an eye.

Teaching Suggestion
To reduce the risk of microbial contamination, students could use tongs to dip the potato halves in dilute bleach for 30 seconds. Then, have students rinse the halves thoroughly with running water before placing them in the plastic bags. Students should wear plastic gloves while working with bleach.

6. Your teacher will designate a cool, dark place where you will keep one potato half and a cool, well-lit place where you will keep the other. Place the bags in the appropriate locations. Make sure that the potato halves are resting on top of the paper towels after you place the bags.

7. After one week, open the bags and count the number of sprouts on each potato. Record these numbers in the data table.

8. To calculate the percentage of eyes that sprouted, divide the number of sprouts by the number of eyes and multiply the result by 100. Record your answers in the data table.

9. When the experiment is over, follow your teacher's instructions for cleanup and disposal of materials.

Step 6
Find a cool, dark place and a cool, well-lit place where students can store their potato halves. These locations should be roughly the same temperature and should remain at this temperature for the duration of the experiment.

Data Table			
Location of Potato	Number of Eyes	Number of Sprouts	Percentage of Eyes Sprouted
Dark			
Light			

Analyze and Conclude

1. **Design an Experiment** What was the independent variable in this experiment? What was the dependent variable?

   The independent variable was the amount of light. The dependent variable was the percentage of eyes that sprouted.

2. **Design an Experiment** Which was the experimental setup in this investigation? Which was the control? Explain.

   Because the question being investigated was the effect of light on the sprouting of potato eyes, the setup in the light was the experimental setup and the setup in the dark was the control.

3. **Evaluate** Did the results of your experiment support your hypothesis? Explain.

   Answers will depend on the hypothesis. More eyes should have sprouted in the dark than in the light.

4. **Infer** What effect does light have on the sprouting of potatoes?

   Light reduces (inhibits) sprouting in potatoes.

5. **Control Variables** Why was it important to keep both the control setup and the experimental setup at the same temperature throughout the experiment?

   Sample answer: Keeping the temperature constant ensures that the results of the experimental setup were due only to the absence or presence of light and not differences in temperature.

Extend Your Inquiry

Design an experiment to investigate whether temperature or amount of water affects the percentage of sprouts. Before you begin, have your teacher approve your plan.

For both variables, moderate levels should produce the highest percentage of sprouts. Growth will be inhibited by too much or too little water, or by temperatures that are too high or too low.

Lab Skills 3 Using a Compound Microscope

Problem

What is the proper way to use a compound microscope and prepare a wet-mount slide?

Introduction

A microscope is a device that magnifies objects that are too small to be seen by the eye alone. A compound microscope has three main parts that work together to bring a magnified image to your eye. A light source illuminates the object being observed. A lens on the nosepiece magnifies the image of the object. A lens in the eyepiece further enlarges the image and projects the image into your eye.

Thin glass plates, or slides, are used to observe biological specimens under a microscope. The slides are made in one of two ways. A prepared slide is made by encasing a specimen in glass. This permanent slide can be stored and viewed many times. A wet-mount slide is made by enclosing a drop of liquid containing the specimen between the slide and a thin glass coverslip. This temporary slide is made to last only a short time—usually one laboratory period.

The microscope you will use will be similar to the one shown in Figure 1. A microscope is a precision instrument that requires careful handling. In this lab, you will learn how to use a compound microscope. You will also learn how to prepare a wet-mount slide.

Big Idea
Each new technology allows scientists to ask more questions about the natural world.

Skills Objectives
Students will be able to
• use a microscope properly.
• prepare a wet-mount slide.

Preparation Time
10 minutes

Class Time
45 minutes

Group Size
Pairs

Advance Preparation
Check that all microscopes were stored with the low-power objective in position.
Students with astigmatism who wear glasses may need to wear the glasses while using the microscope. Have rubber lens protectors available for those students to protect both the glasses and the eyepiece lens.

Figure 1 Parts of a microscope

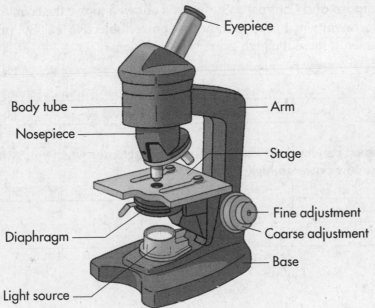

- Eyepiece
- Body tube
- Nosepiece
- Arm
- Stage
- Fine adjustment
- Coarse adjustment
- Diaphragm
- Base
- Light source

Skills Focus

Observe, Calculate, Compare and Contrast

Materials

- compound microscope
- lens paper
- prepared slide
- scissors
- newspaper
- microscope slide
- dropper pipette
- coverslip
- dissecting probe

Safety

To avoid damaging a microscope, follow the rules that are stated in this lab. Handle slides gently to avoid breaking them and cutting yourself. Alert your teacher if you break a glass object. To avoid electrical shocks, make sure that cords, plugs, and your hands are dry when using the light source. Use the scissors only as instructed. Do not direct the points of the scissors toward yourself or others.

Pre-Lab Questions

1. **Infer** Why is it important to keep a microscope at least 10 cm from the edge of the table?

   Sample answer: If the microscope is too close to the edge of the table, you increase the risk of knocking the microscope off the table.

2. **Compare and Contrast** Why are you allowed to use the coarse adjustment when you focus the low-power objective lens but not when you focus the high-power objective lens?

   Sample answer: Because the high-power objective is longer than the low-power objective, there is a greater risk of damaging the slide or objective when using the coarse adjustment to move the nosepiece.

3. **Predict** How will the image of the letter *e* change when you switch from low power to high power?

   Sample answer: The image will be larger, and less of the letter will be visible when I look through the eyepiece.

Procedure

Part A: Practice Using the Microscope

1. Collect a microscope and bring it to your workstation.

   RULE 1: Always carry a microscope with both hands. Grasp the arm of the microscope with one hand, and place your other hand under the base. Hold the microscope in an upright position so that the eyepiece cannot fall out. Place the microscope at least 10 cm from the edge of your table or desk with the arm facing you.

2. The magnification for a lens is etched on the side of the objective. In Figure 2, the lens has a 10× magnification, which means that it will produce an image that is ten times the actual size of the object being viewed. Find the magnification for each objective lens and record this data in the table. Then find and record the magnification for the eyepiece. To find the total magnification under each power, multiply the objective magnification by the eyepiece magnification. Record the results in the table.

Step 1
Before students begin the procedure, demonstrate how to carry a microscope.

Figure 2 Nosepiece with objective lens

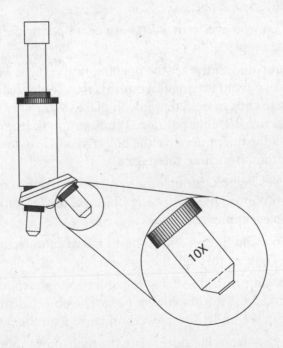

Sample Data

Data Table			
Objective	Objective Magnification	Eyepiece Magnification	Total Magnification
Low power	4×	10×	40×
Medium power	10×	10×	100×
High power	40×	10×	400×

3. Before you use a microscope, you should clean the objective lenses and the lens in the eyepiece.

RULE 2: To avoid scratching the lenses, always use lens paper to clean the lenses. Use a new piece of lens paper for each lens because dust picked up from one lens could scratch the next lens. Never touch a lens with your finger. Oils on your skin can attract dust that could scratch the lens.

4. Look at the microscope from the side. The low-power objective should be about 3 cm from the stage. Rotate the nosepiece until you hear the high-power objective click into position. Note that the high-power objective is longer than the low-power objective.

RULE 3: Always view the microscope from the side when you move an objective to avoid damaging the lens or a slide.

5. Rotate the nosepiece until the low-power objective clicks into position. Find the coarse adjustment knob and practice using it to raise and lower the nosepiece.

Step 6
If you have any microscopes with mirrors, show students how to adjust the mirrors and caution them to never use the sun as a direct light source.

6. Plug in the cord attached to the light source. Look through the eyepiece. Practice using the diaphragm to adjust the amount of light entering the microscope.

RULE 4: To avoid eyestrain, keep both eyes open while looking through the eyepiece.

7. Center a prepared slide over the opening in the stage. Hold the slide by its edges to avoid leaving fingerprints that could distort the image. Use the stage clips to hold the slide in place. Make sure the low-power objective is still in position. While you look from the side, use the coarse adjustment to move the objective as close to the stage as possible without touching the stage.

Step 8
A student's inability to bring an object into focus may have one or more causes: dirt on a lens or slide, a slide not centered over the stage opening, an incorrect amount of light, an improperly aligned objective, an objective that is raised too high, or one that is not raised high enough.

8. Use both eyes to look through the eyepiece. Turn the coarse adjustment to move the low-power objective *away* from the stage until the object comes into focus.

RULE 5: To avoid hitting a slide, never move an objective toward the stage while looking through the eyepiece.

9. Use the fine adjustment to bring the object into sharp focus. You may need to adjust the diaphragm to see the object clearly. Draw what you can see under low power in Figure 3 on the next page.

10. While you look from the side, rotate the high-power objective into position. Look through the eyepiece and use the fine adjustment to bring the object into focus. Draw what you can see under high power in Figure 3.

RULE 6: Never use the coarse adjustment when you are using a high-power objective.

11. Move the low-power objective back into position. Remove the slide from the stage.

Figure 3 Prepared slide under low power and high power

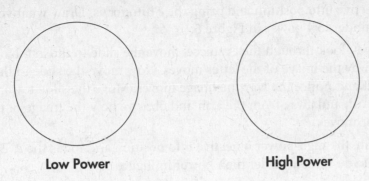

Low Power   High Power

Part B: Prepare a Wet-Mount Slide

12. Look for the smallest lowercase letter *e* you can find in a newspaper. Cut out the letter and place it on the center of a slide. Use a dropper pipette to place one drop of water on the letter, as shown in Figure 4.

13. Place a coverslip so that one edge touches the side of the drop at a 45° angle, as shown in Figure 4. Use a dissecting probe to slowly lower the coverslip onto the paper. This slow movement should prevent air bubbles from being trapped between the slide and the coverslip, which could distort the image.

Step 13
Use a projector to demonstrate how to hold and place the coverslip. Also show students how to remove an air bubble from a slide by gently tapping the surface of the coverslip directly over the air bubble with a pencil eraser.

Figure 4 How to prepare a wet-mount slide

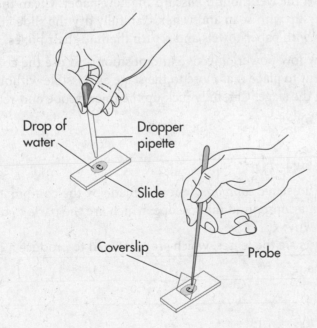

Drop of water — Dropper pipette

Slide

Coverslip — Probe

14. If necessary, use a paper towel to dry the bottom of the slide. Center the slide on the stage with the *e* right side up. Rotate the low-power objective into position and bring the *e* into focus. Draw what you can see under low power in Figure 5.

15. As you look through the eyepiece, move the slide to the left. Notice the way the image of the letter moves. Now move the slide to the right and notice the way the image moves. Move the slide toward the arm and away from the arm and observe how the image of the letter moves.

16. Rotate the high-power objective into position and focus the *e*. Draw what you can see under high power in Figure 5.

Figure 5 Wet-mount slide under low power and high power

Low Power

High Power

17. Take apart the wet mount. Discard the newspaper. Clean the slide and coverslip with soap and water. Carefully dry the slide and coverslip with paper towels and return them to their boxes.

18. Rotate the low-power objective into position and use the coarse adjustment to place it as close to the stage as possible without touching the stage. Carefully pick up the microscope and return it to its storage area.

Analyze and Conclude

1. **Apply Concepts** The adjective *compound* means "made by the combination of two or more parts." In a compound microscope, which are the parts that are being combined, and why?
   Sample answer: The parts are the lenses, which are combined to produce a greater
   magnification of an image.

_____

_____

2. **Compare and Contrast** How is the image of an object seen through a high-power objective different from the image seen through a low-power objective?

The image seen through the high-power objective will be larger and contain more

detail than the same image seen through the low-power objective.

3. **Observe** How did the position of the *e* appear to change when it was viewed through the microscope?

The image of the letter was upside down and backward when compared with the

actual letter.

4. **Draw Conclusions** You observe an ant through the eyepiece of a microscope. The ant moves toward the bottom of the slide and then it moves to the right. What do these observations tell you about the actual movement of the ant?

Because objects viewed through a microscope appear to move in a direction exactly

opposite to that of their actual movement, the ant must have moved toward the top

of the slide and then to the left.

5. **Form a Hypothesis** Why must scientists cut a thin slice from a biological specimen before they can view it under a microscope?

Sample answer: Light must be able to pass through the specimen for an image of the

object to form.

Extend Your Inquiry

Use the microscope to view a small piece of a color photograph from a magazine or newspaper. Draw or describe the details you are able to see when the photograph is magnified.

Students should see the colored dots that combine to form the photograph.

Chapter 1 Lab # Using a Microscope to Estimate Size

Problem

How can you use a microscope to estimate the size of an object?

Introduction

When you view objects with a microscope, the objects appear to be much larger than they really are. When an object is magnified, you can get a false sense of its actual size.

You can estimate the size of magnified objects if you know the size of the field of view. The field of view is the brightly lit circle you see as you look through the eyepiece of a microscope. The size of the field depends on which objective lens you are using. When you switch from a low-power to a high-power lens, you zoom in on an object. The field of view decreases as you zoom in.

In this lab, you will determine the diameter of the field of view for each objective lens. Then you will use your results to compare the sizes of a plant cell and a bacterial cell.

Skills Focus

Observe, Measure, Calculate, Predict

Materials

- compound microscope
- transparent 15-cm plastic ruler
- prepared slide of a plant root or stem
- prepared slide of bacteria

Safety 🔲 🔥

Handle slides gently to avoid breaking them and cutting yourself. Alert your teacher if you break a glass object. Review the rules for handling a microscope. To avoid electrical shocks, make sure that cords, plugs, and your hands are dry when using the light source.

Big Idea
Science is a way of knowing.

Skills Objectives
Students will be able to
• measure the diameter of a field of view.
• estimate the size of objects.

Class Time
30–40 minutes

Group Size
Individuals

Advance Preparation
Students should know how to use and care for a microscope before they do this lab. See Lab Skills 3: Using a Compound Microscope.

Teaching Tips
To give students a sense of the size of cells, compare cells to familiar objects. A baseball is about 10 times the length of a marble, which is about 10 times the length of a grain of salt, which is about 1000 times the length of a bacterial cell.

The Molecular Expressions Web site offers students a trip from the Milky Way to a quark by decreasing powers of ten.

Pre-Lab Questions

1. **Review** Which lens provides more magnification—a low-power lens or a high-power lens? Which lens provides the larger field of view?

   The high-power lens provides more magnification. The low-power lens provides the larger field of view.

2. **Use Analogies** A photographer may take wide views and close-ups of the same scene. How are these views similar to the low-power and high-power lenses on a microscope? What is an advantage of each view?

   A wide view and low power can show the relationship between objects in space. A close-up view and high power can reveal more details about an object's structure.

3. **Calculate** Eight cells fit across a field of view of 160 μm. What is the width of each cell?

   20 μm

4. **Predict** Which cell do you think will be larger, the plant cell or the bacterial cell? Give a reason for your answer.

   Accept any answer for which a student provides a logical reason. For example, some students may predict that plant cells are smaller because a plant has more than one cell.

Procedure

Part A: Determine a Field of View for Each Objective Lens

Step 1
Make sure students are using the low-power objective.

1. Make sure the low-power lens is in place. Place the ruler on the microscope stage so that the millimeter marks are lined up on the diameter of the lit circle.

2. Look through the eyepiece of the microscope. Focus on the millimeter marks. Slowly move the ruler until a millimeter mark is lined up with the left edge of the circle.

Step 3
Students may need help converting from millimeters to micrometers.

3. Count the number of whole millimeters you see. Estimate what fraction of the partial millimeter is visible. Record the diameter in millimeters in the data table on page 19. Then convert the data to micrometers. (There are 1000 micrometers in a millimeter.)

4. Record the power of the low-power, medium-power, and high-power objective lenses in the data table.

5. Divide the power of the low-power lens by the power of the medium-power lens. Multiply the result by the diameter of the low-power field of view to calculate the diameter of the medium-power field of view.

6. Repeat Step 5 for the high-power lens.

Sample Data

Data Table			
Objective	Power	Diameter (mm)	Diameter (μm)
Low power	4×	1.4	1400
Medium power	10×	0.56	560
High power	40×	0.14	140

Part B: Compare the Size of a Plant Cell and a Bacterial Cell

7. Examine a prepared slide of a plant stem or root at low power and at high power. The small round shapes you see are cells. Decide whether to estimate the size of a plant cell at low power or at high power. Using the diameter of the field of view you choose, estimate and record the size of a typical plant cell.

The width should fall within the range of 10–100 μm.

8. Repeat Step 7 with a prepared slide of bacteria. Estimate and record the size of a typical bacterial cell.

A typical bacterial cell has a width of about 2 μm.

Analyze and Conclude

1. **Infer** Why didn't you use the ruler to measure the field of view of the medium-power and high-power lenses?

At the greater magnification, you would not be able to see even one entire millimeter.

2. **Classify** Are bacteria unicellular organisms or multicellular organisms? Provide evidence for your answer.

When I viewed the prepared slide of bacteria, I noticed spaces between the individual cells.

Expected Outcome
Usually the plant cell is about 10 times the size of the bacterial cell.

Teaching Tip
If all the microscopes you use are the same, display the data for field of view in a central location after all your students have completed this lab.

Disposal
If a slide should break, follow your school's guidelines for cleanup and disposal of broken glass.

3. Control Variables How did you decide which lens to use to estimate the size of the plant cell? The size of the bacterial cell?

Sample answer: I used the low-power lens for the plant cells, which were too large to view at high power. I used the high-power lens for the bacteria so that I could see the smaller cells.

4. Predict Some plant diseases are caused by bacteria. Could bacteria injure plant cells by surrounding and eating them? Could bacteria injure plant cells by entering them? Explain your thinking.

Because bacteria are much smaller than plant cells, bacteria most likely injure plant cells by entering the cells.

Extend Your Inquiry

With your teacher's permission, use the microscope to observe a hair from your head. Use the data you collect to estimate the width of the hair. You and your classmates might want to pool your data to establish a range of widths for human scalp hair.

Human scalp hair can range from very fine (40–50 μm) to very coarse (110–120 μm). Students will probably need to use the high-power lens to do this extension. (Before doing this activity, make sure your school does not prohibit the plucking of human scalp hair.)

Chapter 2 Lab **Temperature and Enzymes**

Problem

How does temperature affect the rate of an enzyme-catalyzed reaction?

Introduction

Some cells in your body can produce hydrogen peroxide to help fight infections. Hydrogen peroxide (H_2O_2) is one of many chemicals that can help cells at low levels and harm them at high levels. So the level of hydrogen peroxide in a cell must be controlled.

Hydrogen peroxide can break down into water (H_2O) and oxygen gas (O_2). An enzyme called catalase helps speed up this reaction. In this lab, you will observe this enzyme-catalyzed reaction. Then you will design an experiment to determine the effect of temperature on the reaction.

Skills Focus

Form a Hypothesis, Design an Experiment, Measure, Interpret Graphs

Materials

- raw liver
- forceps
- petri dish
- dropper pipette
- 1% hydrogen peroxide solution
- 25-mL graduated cylinder
- 50-mL beakers
- pureed liver
- filter-paper disks
- paper towels
- timer or clock with second hand
- water baths
- thermometers
- beaker tongs
- graph paper

Safety 🧤🥼🧤🥽🔥🧤

Hydrogen peroxide solution can be irritating. If the solution gets in your eye, tell your teacher and immediately use the eye wash fountain. Rinse off any solution that spills on your skin or clothing. If you have glass beakers or cylinders, check for cracks or chips. Alert your teacher if you break a glass object. To avoid electrical shock, make sure that cords, plugs, and your hands are dry when using a hot plate. Wash your hands thoroughly with soap and warm water before leaving the lab.

Big Idea
Enzymes affect how matter and energy interact in cells.

Skills Objectives
Students will be able to
• form a hypothesis about the effect of temperature on enzymes.
• design an experiment to test the hypothesis.

Preparation Time
30 minutes

Class Time
45 minutes

Group Size
Small groups

Materials
Each team will need at least 5 beakers and 5 filter-paper disks. Use shallow containers, such as plastic dishpans, for the water baths. You may need a hot plate and a large glass container for heating water, heat-resistant gloves for handling the container, and ice.

Advance Preparation
Have volunteers make small filter-paper disks that will fit in the beakers. All the disks need to have about the same diameter to control the mass of puree.

In a blender, mix pieces of raw liver with a little distilled water. Use the lab procedure to test the concentration of catalase in the puree. Dilute the puree until you are able to measure the time needed to float the disks.

Mix 320 mL of distilled water with 160 mL of 3% hydrogen peroxide solution.

Safety
Caution students to slowly pour the hydrogen peroxide solution from the graduated cylinder into the beaker to avoid splashes.

Pre-Lab Questions

1. Relate Cause and Effect How will you know that a chemical reaction is taking place in Part A? How will you know in Part B?

I will observe bubbles of oxygen on the surface of the liver. The filter paper disk will rise to the top of the liquid.

_____

2. Control Variables In Part B of the lab, which variable will you manipulate? Which variable is the dependent variable?

temperature; reaction time

_____

3. Relate Cause and Effect How is the time required for the filter-paper disk to float related to the activity of the enzyme?

Oxygen produced in the reaction causes the disk to float. The rate of the reaction that produces the oxygen depends on the activity of the enzyme. The more active the enzyme, the faster the oxygen is produced, and the quicker the disk will rise.

Procedure

Part A: Observe the Catalase Reaction

1. Put on your apron, gloves, and safety goggles. Use forceps to place a small piece of raw liver in an open petri dish. Liver cells contain catalase. Use a dropper pipette to put a drop of hydrogen peroxide solution on the liver. Observe what happens. **CAUTION:** Rinse off any solution that spills on your skin or clothing or splashes in your eye.

2. With your teacher's guidance, select the proper equipment to measure the rate of the reaction—either a filter-paper disk or an oxygen probe. If you will be using an oxygen probe, see your teacher for instructions.

3. Use a graduated cylinder to place 25 mL of hydrogen peroxide solution in a 50-mL beaker.

4. Use forceps to dip a filter-paper disk in liver puree. Place the filter-paper disk on a paper towel for 4 seconds to remove any excess liquid.

5. Use the forceps to place the filter-paper disk at the bottom of the 50-mL beaker. Observe the filter-paper disk, and record the number of seconds it takes to float to the top of the liquid.

Number of seconds: _____

Part B: Design an Experiment

6. Form a Hypothesis How will changing the temperature affect the rate of the hydrogen peroxide reaction? Record the hypothesis you will test to answer this question.

Hypothesis: *Sample answer:* As the temperature increases, the rate of the reaction will increase.

7. Describe Your Plan Describe the procedure you will use to test your hypothesis. You will use some steps from Part A. Other steps in your procedure will be new. Focus on the new steps in your description. Include any necessary safety cautions.

Experimental Plan: _____

_____

_____

_____

_____

_____

Step 7
Check students' experimental designs before they begin doing their experiments. Demonstrate how to use the beaker tongs to hold a beaker in a water bath.

8. Organize Data Construct a data table in the space below. You will need room to record your measurements for two variables. Also include a column for observations. Make as many rows for recording data as the number of trials you plan to do.

9. Disposal When you are done with your trials, follow your teacher's instructions for cleanup and disposal of materials. Wash your hands thoroughly with soap and warm water.

Disposal
Once paper disks are removed, contents of beakers can be flushed down the drain.

10. Graph Use the data you collected to make a graph of your results. Plot the independent variable on the *x*-axis and the dependent variable on the *y*-axis. Ask your teacher whether you should use graph paper, a graphing calculator, or graphing software.

Sample Data Table

Data Table		
Temperature (°C)	Time (seconds)	Observations

Analyze and Conclude

1. **Interpret Graphs** How did increasing the temperature affect the reaction time?

At first, the reaction time increased as the temperature increased. But at the highest temperature, the reaction time decreased.

2. **Draw Conclusions** How did increasing the temperature affect the activity of the enzyme? At what temperature was the enzyme most active? Why is this temperature significant?

Sample answer: The change in reaction time shows that the activity of the enzyme increased as the temperature increased until about 46°C. The enzyme was most active around 37°C, or normal body temperature.

3. **Infer** Why was raw liver used in this experiment rather than cooked liver?

Sample answer: The enzyme could break down at the high temperature required to cook the liver.

4. **Apply Concepts** Why is it important for your body to maintain a stable internal temperature?

Sample answer: If the temperature rises too high, enzymes in your cells will either not be as active or may not be active at all. Without enzymes, reactions in cells will slow down or may even stop.

5. **Perform Error Analysis** Identify at least one source of error in your procedure.

Sample answer: The amount of catalase in the liver may vary among trials. Students may not be able to pinpoint the temperature at which enzyme activity begins to decline because of the limited number of data points.

Extend Your Inquiry

How can pH affect catalase activity? Design an experiment to test your hypothesis. Ask your teacher for comments on your design. If necessary, revise the procedure. With your teacher's permission and supervision, carry out your experiment.

The optimal pH for catalase is around 7.0. The pH of fluids within most body cells is maintained at between 6.6 and 7.5.

Chapter 3 Lab The Effect of Fertilizer on Algae

Problem

How do excess nutrients affect the growth of algae?

Introduction

As primary producers, algae form the base of the food web in the upper layers of the ocean and in freshwater lakes and ponds. The term algae is used to describe a range of organisms from the large brown kelp found attached to rocks at the seashore to the tiny green algae found in fish tanks. Like other plants, green algae need nitrogen, phosphorus, and potassium in order to grow. All three nutrients must be available for the algae to thrive and reproduce.

Have you ever seen a pond with a thick, green layer of algae on its surface? This layer is a sign that the homeostasis of the ecosystem has been disturbed by the presence of too much nitrogen or phosphorus in the water. Fertilizers and animal waste contain these nutrients, which can be transferred to bodies of water when rainfall flows downhill from farms.

In this lab, you will work with *Chlorella*, a type of algae that is commonly found in ponds and aquariums. You will compare the growth of *Chlorella* when nutrients are limited and when nutrients are abundant.

Skills Focus

Predict, Compare and Contrast, Infer

Materials

- 2 test tubes
- glass-marking pencil
- test-tube rack
- 2 dropper pipettes
- algae culture
- 25-mL graduated cylinder
- spring water
- fertilizer
- 2 cotton balls
- grow light

Safety

Wear safety goggles and plastic gloves when handling cultures. If you have glass test tubes or cylinders, check for cracks or chips. Alert your teacher if you break a glass object. Wash your hands thoroughly with soap and warm water before leaving the lab.

Big Idea
The primary production of an ecosystem may be limited by the supply of nutrients.

Skills Objectives
Students will be able to
- compare the productivity of a culture when nutrients are limited and when nutrients are abundant.
- infer how excess nutrients might affect an ecosystem.

Preparation Time
30 minutes

Class Time
30 minutes for setup; 5 minutes a day for 4 days for observation

Group Size
Small groups

Materials
Use a high-nitrogen fertilizer with N-P-K rating of 24-8-16. Use bottled spring water instead of pond water. Do not use tap water or distilled water.
   You can substitute a sunny windowsill for a grow light. However, the number of days required to see results may vary.

Advance Preparation
Obtain *Chlorella* from a science supply house. To make a stock solution of fertilizer, add an eighth of a teaspoon of fertilizer to a liter of bottled spring water.

Pre-Lab Questions

1. **Design an Experiment** What is the independent variable in this experiment?

The independent variable is the presence of fertilizer.

2. **Predict** After four days, how will you be able to tell which test tube has more algae?

Sample answer: In the test tube with more algae, the liquid will have a darker green color and be less transparent to light.

3. **Control Variables** Why will you grow *Chlorella* in spring water instead of pond water?

Sample answer: Pond water is likely to contain many species of algae. Using spring water ensures that both test tubes have *Chlorella*, and that neither test tube has a different algal species.

Procedure

Step 2
To ensure that the number of algae cells is not a variable, students need to start with approximately the same number of algae in each test tube. Show students how to avoid picking up clumps of algae with the pipette. Before students collect the algae, shake the sealed container vigorously until the mixture is as homogeneous as possible.

Step 6
If you are using a single grow light, consolidate the test tubes into a few test-tube racks.

1. Use a glass-marking pencil to label one test tube Control and the other Fertilizer. Place the test tubes in a test-tube rack.

2. Put on your safety goggles and plastic gloves. Use a dropper pipette to add 20 drops of algae culture to each test tube.

3. Add 19 mL of spring water to each test tube.

4. Use a second dropper pipette to add 4 drops of fertilizer solution to the test tube labeled Fertilizer.

5. Loosely plug each test tube with a cotton ball to slow the evaporation of the water.

6. Place the test-tube rack under a grow light. Turn on the light. Position the rack so that each test tube will receive an equal amount of light.

7. Observe the test tubes each day for the next four days. Record your observations in the data table.

Data Table		
Day	Control	Fertilizer
1		
2		
3		
4		

Analyze and Conclude

1. **Compare and Contrast** Summarize your observations of the two test tubes over four days.

   The green color was noticeable in the test tube with the fertilizer before it was

   noticeable in the control. After four days, the color in the test tube with the fertilizer

   was darker than in the control.

2. **Draw Conclusions** How did the addition of fertilizer affect the growth of the algae?

   Adding fertilizer caused the number of algae to rapidly increase.

3. **Infer** In Step 5, why did you use cotton balls instead of rubber stoppers to plug your test tubes? *Hint:* Review the diagram of the carbon cycle on page 83 of your textbook.

   Sample answer: Green algae need carbon dioxide for photosynthesis. A stopper

   would prevent a fresh supply of air from flowing into the test tube to replace carbon

   dioxide used during the experiment.

4. **Apply Concepts** How could a thick layer of algae on the surface of a pond affect producers that live on or near the bottom of the pond?

   Sample answer: The layer of algae could keep sunlight from reaching producers

   that live on the bottom of the pond, which would slow down or even stop their

   productivity.

Extend Your Inquiry

Design an experiment to see whether the proportion of nitrogen in a fertilizer affects the growth of *Chlorella*. Compare the fertilizer you used in this lab, which has a high proportion of nitrogen, with a low-nitrogen fertilizer. Ask your teacher for instructions on preparing a stock solution of fertilizer.

Chlorella grows best in a fertilizer that has a high nitrogen content. The algae should grow slightly less abundantly when provided with the same amount of a low-nitrogen fertilizer. To keep phosphorous and potassium levels roughly constant while reducing the nitrogen level, you may need to use a different overall quantity of a fertilizer, e.g., twice the amount of a 7-4-10 fertilizer.

Open-Ended Inquiry • Real-World Lab

Chapter 4 Lab Abiotic Factors and Plant Selection

Problem

How can you decide which plants will thrive in a garden?

Introduction

The first humans arrived in New Zealand about 1000 years ago. They crossed the Pacific Ocean from Polynesia in large canoes. The climate in Polynesia is tropical, with abundant rainfall and warm temperatures. New Zealand has a more temperate climate. The days and nights tend to be cooler, and there is much less rainfall.

The immigrants brought crops with them, such as yams, taro, and gourds, that they wanted to grow in their new home. They looked for regions in New Zealand where the soil conditions and other abiotic factors were similar to those in their former home. Sometimes the farmers had to adjust the soil to make it easier for the plants to thrive.

Modern gardeners deal with some of the same issues. They need to find a location where the conditions are right for the plants they want to grow, or they need to select plants that will grow successfully in the existing conditions.

In this lab, you will collect data about abiotic factors in your region. Then, you will plan a small garden and select plants that can grow successfully in that garden.

Skills Focus

Classify, Analyze Data, Use Models

Materials

- plant hardiness zone map
- plant catalogs
- graph paper
- tape measure or metersticks

Big Idea
Abiotic factors such as climate and soil type influence the success or failure of plant growth.

Skills Objectives
Students will be able to
- identify regional and local abiotic factors.
- plan a garden based on local abiotic factors.

Class Time
Part A: 25 minutes
Part B: 45 minutes
Part C: 40 minutes

Group Size
Small groups

Materials
Students will need access to online or printed seed catalogs. Many online suppliers include a plant hardiness zone map. The USDA Web site has a map which further subdivides the zones, but this site does not have data on the last frost.

Advance Preparation
Students will need sites where they can safely observe and make measurements. A site near the school would be ideal. In areas without much open land, students could plan a balcony garden with planters or a set of window boxes.

Pre-Lab Questions

1. **Predict** How will knowing the plant hardiness zone for your area help you plan a garden?

   Sample answer: Knowing the plant hardiness zone will provide information about some abiotic factors. (Some students may know that suppliers of seeds and plants usually provide a range of hardiness zones for each species.)

2. **Relate Cause and Effect** What is the relationship between the last frost and the length of the growing season?

   Sample answer: The earlier the last frost occurs, the longer the growing season.

3. **Infer** A plant species grows well in one location in a small garden but does not grow as well in another location. Suggest one possible reason for this difference.

   Sample answer: One location may have direct sunlight all day, and the other may be in the shade for most of the day.

Procedure

Part A: Investigate Your Area

Before you can decide which plants are suitable for your garden, you need to research several abiotic factors for your area. Record the data you collect in the data table on the next page.

Step 3
If students use a USDA map, they will not find data for the last frost. This information is available on commercial sites and in almanacs.

Some maps use "last frost-free date" instead of "last frost date," which can be confusing. "Last frost-free date" means the *latest* date in the year when the nights will be frost-free.

Step 4
Students may wonder why they have been asked to find average annual rainfall, not average annual precipitation. Point out that gardeners are concerned with the amount of water during the growing season.

1. Use a plant hardiness zone map to identify your area's plant hardiness zone. In the lower 48 states of the United States, there are 8 hardiness zones, numbered 3 through 10. Some parts of Alaska are in Zones 1 and 2. Most of Hawaii is in Zone 11.

2. Find your region's average lowest temperature. This data will be presented as a temperature range. From this information, you can infer whether the soil in your region is likely to freeze in winter and how quickly frozen soil will thaw in the spring.

3. Identify the time of year when your area will typically have its last frost. From this information, you can tell when it is safe to plant seeds or seedlings and you can estimate the length of your growing season.

4. Use an almanac or an online resource to find the average annual rainfall for your area.

Sample Data for Minneapolis

Data Table: Local Abiotic Factors	
Plant Hardiness Zone	4
Lowest Average Temperature	−30°C to −25°C (−25°F to −20°F)
Last Frost	Early June
Average Annual Rainfall	66 cm (26 inches)

Part B: Investigate Your Garden Site

Within a hardiness zone, abiotic factors will vary from community to community. They will also vary at different locations within a community. When you select plants for a garden, you have to consider local conditions as well as regional factors. Your teacher may select a site that you can use to plan a garden. Or your teacher may ask you to suggest some possible sites.

5. Once you have agreed on a site, members of your group need to visit the site. Ideally, you should visit the site at different times of day to make observations. Here are some issues to consider. Will any parts of the site be in shade for most of the day? Is the site flat or sloped? Is the site exposed to wind, or is it sheltered from the wind? Record your observations in the space below.

Observations: _____

_____

_____

_____

_____

_____

_____

_____

_____

_____

6. As a group, use a sheet of graph paper to make a scale drawing of your site. Note the location of large objects, such as trees or fences. Record where north is in relation to your site. You will be adding information to the drawing in Part C. If you will be working as individuals on Part C, make a copy of the drawing for each team member.

Part C
If students work separately, it might be useful for the team to compare the results to see the variety of possible solutions.

Part C: Plan Your Garden

For Part C, your teacher may ask you to work as a team or as individuals.

7. Decide what type of garden you want to plan—a vegetable garden or a flower garden. Then browse through plant catalogs, looking for plants that can thrive at your site.

8. List the plants you choose below. Include relevant information about each plant, such as whether it needs direct sunlight, indirect sunlight, or shade. For vegetables, include the number of days from when seeds or seedlings are planted until the vegetable can be picked.

_____

_____

_____

_____

_____

_____

_____

_____

_____

_____

_____

_____

_____

_____

9. Update your scale drawing of the garden site to show where each species would be planted. Use different colors or symbols to represent each species and include a key.

Analyze and Conclude

1. Infer What abiotic factor was used to classify regions into plant hardiness zones? Why do you think this factor was chosen?

Sample answer: The major factor was temperature, specifically average lowest temperature. This factor was chosen because it will determine whether plants can survive outdoors during the winter.

2. Relate Cause and Effect In general, what is the relationship between the distance of a region from the equator and its plant hardiness zone?

The number of the zone (and the average lowest temperature) tends to increase as a region gets closer to the equator.

3. Evaluate Which of the local factors that you identified in Part B had the greatest effect on which plants you chose, and why?

Answers will vary, but amount of sunlight is a likely choice because it cannot be adjusted for without changing the site.

4. Control Variables How do people who live in dry regions grow plants that typically thrive in wetter regions? How do people who live in temperate regions grow plants that typically thrive in tropical regions?

People in dry regions can compensate for a lack of rainfall by watering the plants. People in temperate regions can grow plants that typically thrive in tropical regions indoors.

5. Infer Why would someone living in Zone 3 or Zone 4 decide to plant seedlings rather than seeds?

Sample answer: Zones 3 and 4 have relatively short growing seasons. Planting seedlings will save several weeks of growing time.

Extend Your Inquiry

Some people make their living growing crops. Besides abiotic factors, what factors must a farmer consider when he or she chooses to plant a particular crop?

Farmers have to consider the market demand for the crop, what price they can charge, and whether they can make a profit after their expenses (seeds, fertilizer, equipment, labor).

Chapter 5 Lab **The Growth Cycle of Yeast**

Problem

What type of population growth occurs in a yeast culture?

Introduction

Yeast have two traits that make them a good choice for laboratory studies of population growth. Large numbers of these tiny organisms can live in a small space, and yeast are able to reproduce quickly.

Your teacher has prepared five yeast populations, or cultures, by adding yeast to diluted white grape juice. The cultures were grown under similar conditions. The youngest culture is three days old; the oldest culture is seven days old. Your team will be assigned one culture. You will use the microscope to count yeast cells in your culture, and then share your data with the rest of the class. As part of your analysis, you will graph the class results.

Skills Focus

Measure, Calculate, Interpret Graphs

Materials

- yeast culture
- stirring rod
- 3 dropper pipettes
- 3 microscope slides
- 3 coverslips
- microscope
- 10-mL graduated cylinder
- 2 test tubes
- test-tube rack
- graph paper

Safety 🔶 ⚗️ 🧼

Handle slides and coverslips carefully to avoid breaking them and cutting yourself. If you have glass cylinders or test tubes, check for cracks or chips. Alert your teacher if you break a glass object. Review the rules for use of a microscope. To avoid electrical shocks, make sure the cords, plugs, and your hands are dry when using the light source. Wash your hands thoroughly with soap and warm water before leaving the lab.

Big Idea
As resources become limited, population growth slows or stops.

Skills Objectives
Students will be able to
- prepare serial dilutions of a yeast culture.
- use cell counts to compare the size of yeast populations.
- graph a growth curve.

Preparation Time
45 minutes

Class Time
45 minutes

Group Size
Small groups

Materials
In addition to the materials listed for the students, you will need a packet of yeast, a balance, white grape juice, a 100-mL graduated cylinder, and five 400-mL beakers or large drink cups.

Advance Preparation
To make a stock yeast culture, mix 0.2 g of dried yeast with 100 mL of tap water. To make a culture medium that is 25% grape juice by volume, add 25 mL of grape juice to 75 mL of tap water for each 100 mL of medium.

To start a lab yeast culture, add 1 mL of the stock culture to 100 mL of the culture medium. Prepare the culture in a large beaker or drink cup.

Make an identical culture for each of five days. Start on a Monday so the cultures can be used the next Monday. Label a culture with the age it will be on lab day (7 days, 6 days, and so on). Choose a storage location with a temperature of at least 20°C.

Teaching Tips
Show students photographs of yeast cells before the lab.

Explain that you prepared five yeast cultures with different ages so all the data could be collected during one lab period.

Select five microscopes that have the same field of view. Otherwise, you will need to adjust the data to reflect the different areas observed.

Pre-Lab Questions

1. Infer Why was grape juice used to prepare the yeast cultures instead of plain water?

Sample answer: The grape juice contains nutrients that the yeast need to grow and reproduce.

_____

2. Form a Hypothesis Why will you locate the yeast cells under low power, but switch to high power to count the cells?

Sample answer: With low power, the field of view is larger, which makes finding the cells easier. With high power, the magnification is greater, which makes counting the cells easier.

3. Calculate Suppose you have to do one dilution of your culture before you are able to count the yeast cells. If you count 21 yeast cells in the diluted sample, how many yeast cells were in the same area of the undiluted sample?

21×10 or 210 yeast cells

4. Predict What do you think will happen to the yeast populations between Day 3 and Day 7? Give a reason for your answer.

Some students may assume that the nutrients are sufficient to sustain rapid growth through Day 7. Others may assume that a lack of nutrients will begin to slow down growth by Day 7.

Procedure

You may see both single oval-shaped yeast cells and colonies of yeast cells in which several cells are attached together.

Step 1
Students need to stir the cultures because yeast cells tend to settle.

Step 2
The instruction to start with low power assumes a low-power objective with a magnification of at least 10×.

Step 3
Suggest that students dilute samples with counts above 50.

1. Stir the yeast culture well with a stirring rod. Then use a dropper pipette to place a small drop of the culture on a slide. Add a coverslip and place the slide on the microscope stage.

2. First view the drop under low power. Once you locate some yeast cells, switch to high power and focus with the fine adjustment.
CAUTION: When you move an objective lens, always observe the movement from the side of the microscope.

3. If there are too many yeast cells to count, do Steps 4 and 5. If you can count the yeast cells in your field of view, skip to Step 6.

4. Stir the culture. Use a clean dropper pipette to transfer 1 mL of culture into a 10-mL graduated cylinder. Add 9 mL of tap water to the graduated cylinder. Empty the graduated cylinder into a test tube. This procedure dilutes the culture by a factor of 10.

5. Examine the diluted sample under the microscope as in Step 2. If there are still too many yeast cells to count, repeat Step 4. This procedure dilutes the original culture by a factor of 100. You can repeat Step 4 as often as necessary as long as you multiply the dilution factor by 10 each time. Stop diluting the sample when you are able to count the yeast cells.

6. Find an area that is representative of the sample as a whole. Count and record the number of yeast cells. Include both single cells and cells in colonies. Record the count in the appropriate row of the data table. If you had to dilute the culture, also record the dilution factor. If you did not have to dilute the culture, record 1 as the dilution factor.

7. To determine the number of yeast cells present, multiply the observed count by the dilution factor.

8. To complete the data table, collect data from the other teams.

Step 5
In case students need to do more than two dilutions, have extra pipettes, slides, coverslips, and test tubes available.

Step 6
If you have time, have each student in a group do a count. The group can exclude outliers and calculate and record a mean.
 If the distribution is not homogeneous, students could also sample different areas.

Expected Outcome
Growth will be exponential at first. The count should decline by Day 7, but if it does not, the rate of growth should be slower.

Disposal
Yeast cultures can be flushed down the sink.

Sample Data

Data Table			
Age of Culture	Yeast Cells Observed	Dilution Factor	Yeast Cells Present
3 days	10	10	100
4 days	22	10	220
5 days	26	10	260
6 days	25	10	250
7 days	16	10	160

Analyze and Conclude

1. **Graph** Determine which variable is the independent variable and which is the dependent variable. Then make a graph of the class results.

Independent Variable: age of the culture

Dependent Variable: number of yeast cells present

2. **Interpret Graphs** Compare your graph to the graph of logistic growth in Figure 5–5 on page 134 of your textbook.

Sample answer: The graph shows the exponential growth of Phase 1 and

the slowdown of growth of Phase 2. However, instead of leveling off in

Phase 3, the population size declined.

3. **Form a Hypothesis** What density-dependent limiting factor might cause a yeast population to decline rather than level off?

Sample answer: Competition for limited nutrients, such as those in white grape juice, could cause the death of yeast cells. (Yeast cells might also die as toxic waste products build up in the container.)

4. **Design an Experiment** Describe how you could modify the procedure to ensure that the results were not affected by any variables other than age.

Sample answer: I could use one culture and test a sample of that culture every day for five days beginning on Day 3.

5. **Perform Error Analysis** You do not notice a yeast cell near the edge of your field of view. What effect would the dilution factor have on the size of the error?

Sample answer: Any error is multiplied by an increase in the dilution factor. (With a dilution factor of 10, the number of yeast cells present will be off by 10. With a dilution factor of 100, the number of yeast cells present will be off by 100.)

Extend Your Inquiry

For the cultures you observed in this lab, your teacher used a culture medium that was 25 percent grape juice by volume. How would changing the concentration of the grape juice affect the rate of growth? Form a hypothesis and design an experiment to test your hypothesis. Ask your teacher to approve your design and provide instructions for preparing the cultures.

If students want to test more concentrated solutions of grape juice, they will need to modify the procedure because the exponential growth is likely to occur sooner. They could, for example, begin collecting data after only 24 hours.

Open-Ended Inquiry • Design Your Own Lab

Chapter 6 Lab **Acid Rain and Seeds**

Problem

How does acid rain affect seed germination?

Introduction

Every seed contains a tiny living plant and a food supply to nourish that plant when it first begins to develop. The plant and the food supply are enclosed in a protective coat, which keeps the contents of the seed from drying out. The tiny plant can survive for weeks, months, or even years. Factors such as temperature and moisture determine when the plant within the seed will start to grow again. This resumption of growth is called germination.

Before seeds can germinate, they must absorb water, which causes the food-storing tissues to swell and crack the seed coat. The root is the first part of the plant to emerge from the seed.

All rain is mildly acidic because carbon dioxide forms a weak acid when it dissolves in water vapor. If the pH of rain falls below 5.0, the rain is usually classified as acid rain. In this lab, you will design an experiment to determine whether the pH of the water that a seed absorbs can affect germination.

Skills Focus

Design an Experiment, Organize Data, Measure, Graph

Materials

- 5 large test tubes
- test-tube rack
- glass-marking pencil
- 25-mL graduated cylinder
- 60 mL distilled water
- 20 mL vinegar solution
- food coloring
- pipette
- pH paper
- 120 dried beans
- paper towels
- zip-close plastic bags
- stick-on labels
- hand lens
- graph paper

Big Idea
Humans affect regional and global environments through agriculture, development, and industry.

Skills Objectives
Students will be able to
- form a hypothesis about the effect of acid rain on seed germination.
- design an experiment to test the hypothesis.
- do a serial dilution.

Preparation Time
30 minutes to prepare all the solutions and 10 minutes to prepare just the stock solution

Class Time
Part A: 25 minutes
Part B: 20 minutes to design, 15 minutes to set up, and 15 minutes to collect data and clean up

Group Size
Small groups

Materials
If you are not using probes, provide both wide range and precision-range pH paper.
If you have test tubes with screw tops, students can mix the solutions by shaking. Stopper test tubes without screw tops if you store the solutions overnight.

Advance Preparation
To make 400 mL of stock solution with a pH close to 4, mix 0.3 mL of vinegar with 400 mL of distilled water.
Time the initial setup for Part B so that students can collect data after 72 hours.

Teaching Tip
To help review pH, ask students whether they could use vinegar to make a solution with a pH of 8.0. (A solution with a pH of 8.0 is a basic solution. Even a very dilute vinegar solution will still have more hydrogen ions than hydroxide ions. Its pH can approach 7.0 but cannot be equal to or greater than 7.0.)

Safety

Wear goggles and a lab apron when you handle the vinegar. Rinse off any solution that spills on your skin or clothing. If you use glass test tubes or graduated cylinders, check for cracks or chips. Alert your teacher if you break a glass object. Wash your hands thoroughly with soap and warm water before leaving the lab.

Pre-Lab Questions

1. Design an Experiment What do you think the purpose is of adding food coloring to the vinegar in Part A?

Sample answer: As the vinegar is diluted with water, the intensity of the color will decrease. The food coloring provides a visual indicator for the decreased concentration of acid (H^+ ions) in the solutions.

2. Infer How will you know that a seed has germinated?

Sample answer: The seed coat will crack and a root will be visible.

3. Use Models What do the solutions represent?

Sample answer: The solutions represent rain with different concentrations of acid.

Procedure

For your experiment, you will need a set of solutions with different pH values. Your teacher may have prepared the solutions in advance, or you may have to prepare the solutions yourself. Either way, read Part A of the procedure to understand how to do a serial dilution. A serial dilution is the process that is used to make a set of solutions in which the concentration decreases by the same increment from one solution to the next.

Part A: A Serial Dilution of Vinegar

The white vinegar sold in stores contains about 5 percent acetic acid and has a pH of about 2.4. The stock solution of vinegar you will use has a pH of about 4. You will use the stock solution to make a series of solutions with different pH values. Each solution in the series will be 4 times as dilute as the previous solution.

1. Put on your safety goggles and apron. Place 5 large test tubes in a rack. Label the test tubes Stock, 4×, 16×, 64×, and 256×.

2. Use the graduated cylinder to place 15 mL of distilled water in the test tubes labeled 4×, 16×, 64×, and 256×. **CAUTION:** Do not add distilled water to the test tube labeled Stock.

3. Use the graduated cylinder to add 20 mL of the stock solution to the test tube labeled Stock. Then add 4 drops of food coloring.

4. Use a pipette to transfer 5 mL of the stock solution into the test tube marked 4×. You can mix the solution by quickly pumping a small amount of solution into and out of the pipette a few times. **CAUTION:** Rinse off any solution that spills on your skin or clothing.

5. Transfer 5 mL of the 4× solution into the 16× test tube and mix.

6. Repeat the transfer of 5 mL of solution from one text tube to the next until 5 mL of solution has been added to the test tube labeled 256× and the solution mixed.

7. Remove and discard 5 mL from the text tube labeled 256×.

8. With your teacher's guidance, select the proper equipment to measure the pH of each solution—either pH paper or a pH probe. If you will be using a probe, see your teacher for instructions. Record the results in Data Table 1.

Step 7
At the end of this step students should have 15 mL of solution in each test tube.

Data Table 1: pH of Solutions	
Dilution	pH
Stock	
4×	
16×	
64×	
256×	

Part B: Design an Experiment

9. **Form a Hypothesis** How will changing the pH of a water-based solution affect the percentage of seeds that germinate? Record the hypothesis you will test to answer this question.

Hypothesis: _Sample answer:_ As the pH of the solution increases, the percentage of seeds that germinate will increase.

10. **Control Variables** What will your independent variable be? What will your dependent variable be?

Independent Variable pH of solution

Dependent Variable: percentage of seed germination

11. **Describe Your Plan** Record the details of your plan. You will have 120 dried beans and the solutions from Part A. Which variables will you need to control? Before you begin, have your teacher review your plan.

Experimental Plan: Students will need to control the number of seeds, the amount of solution, the time, and where the seeds are stored. Students can wrap the seeds in a paper towel, soak the towel with 15 mL of solution, and store the towel in a labeled zip-close plastic bag. Make sure there is no standing water in the bag and that there is air in the bag before it is sealed. The seeds can be stored in a warm location without direct sunlight.

_____

_____

_____

_____

_____

_____

Step 11
Students may be concerned that seeds need light to germinate. Remind them that the built-in food supply will sustain the plants until they can produce food through photosynthesis.

12. **Organize Data** Construct a data table in the space below. You will need columns for the pH values of the solutions being tested and for the number of seeds that germinate. You might want to include a third column for other observations.

13. **Disposal** After you gather your data, follow your teacher's instructions for cleanup and disposal of materials. Then wash your hands thoroughly with soap and hot water.

Sample Data

Data Table 2: Part B Results*		
pH	Number of Seeds Germinated	Observations
4.0	0	Seeds absorbed less of the solution as compared to the other trials.
4.6	2	Seeds absorbed less of the solution as compared to the other trials.
5.2	11	Most roots were > 1 cm in length.
5.8	15	
6.4	10	Most roots were < 1 cm in length.

*The sample data is from trials with Great Northern white beans. Each trial used 20 beans. The data was collected after 72 hours.

Analyze and Conclude

1. **Calculate** Use your data to calculate the percentage of seeds that germinated at each pH. Record the results in Data Table 3.

Sample Data

Data Table 3	
pH of Solution	Percentage of Seeds Germinated
4.0	0
4.6	10
5.2	55
5.8	75
6.4	50

2. **Graph** Use the results from Data Table 3 to make a graph. Plot pH on the *x*-axis and the percentage of seeds germinated on the *y*-axis. Ask your teacher whether you should use graph paper, a graphing calculator, or graphing software.

3. **Interpreting Graphs** Does the graph support the hypothesis you made in Part B of the procedure? Why or why not?

Sample answer: The percentage of seeds does initially increase as the pH increases, but at pH 6.4 the percentage starts to decrease again. So my hypothesis is only partially supported.

4. **Infer** At the time that bean plants and other seed plants evolved, what do you think the pH of rainfall was, and why?

Sample answer: I think the pH of rainfall was greater than 5.2 and less than 6.4 because the highest percentage of seeds germinated within that range of pH.

5. **Evaluate** Identify at least one way that this lab was not a perfect model for the effect of acid rain on the germination of seeds.

Sample answer: Acid rain contains acids such as nitric acid and sulfuric acid, not acetic acid. Students may also say that in nature the rain would be absorbed by soil, not by a paper towel.

6. **Relate Cause and Effect** Explain why acid rain could harm animals as well as plants. Which types of animals do you think would be most at risk from acid rain?

Students are likely to say that animals also could be harmed because water is an essential resource for animals as well as plants. Animals that live in water would be most at risk. (Animals could also be harmed if the plants they need to consume are harmed.)

Extend Your Inquiry

Is the average pH of rain the same in all parts of the United States? Look at a recent map of pH data collected from field stations across the lower 48 states. Identify any pattern in the data and try to explain this pattern.

Provide a recent national trends map from the National Atmospheric Deposition Program. Students should note that pH values for rain at field stations east of the Mississippi are lower than those for field stations west of the Mississippi. Possible reasons for this trend are the location of power plants and other industries that burn fossil fuels; the effect of population density on the number of homes heated with fossil fuels and the amount of traffic; and the fact that winds tend to move air from west to east.

Chapter 7 Lab **Detecting Diffusion**

Problem

How can you determine whether solutes are diffusing across a membrane?

Introduction

A cell membrane is a selectively permeable barrier. Some particles can pass through the cell membrane while other particles are held back. Solutes that can move across the membrane generally do so by diffusion. When solutes diffuse, they move from an area of high concentration to an area of lower concentration. Diffusion of certain solutes can be facilitated by protein channels that act like tunnels through the cell membrane.

In this lab, you will use dialysis tubing to represent the cell membrane. Dialysis tubing is a synthetic membrane used to filter wastes from the blood of a person who has experienced kidney failure. The tubing has small openings, or pores, that allow the passage of relatively small molecules. You will use indicators to determine which molecules diffuse through the pores.

Skills Focus

Use Models, Infer, Compare and Contrast

Materials

- dialysis tubing
- scissors
- metric ruler
- 250-mL beakers
- twist ties
- 10-mL graduated cylinders
- 1% starch solution
- iodine solution
- forceps
- 15% glucose solution
- glucose test strip

Safety 🧤 🦺 ✋ 🔪 ✂️ 🧹

Iodine solution can irritate the eyes and skin and can stain clothing. Wear gloves, safety goggles, and a laboratory apron while handling any solution that contains iodine. Rinse off any solution that spills on your skin or clothing. Do not direct the points of the scissors toward yourself or others. Use the scissors only as instructed.

Big Idea
The cell membrane regulates what enters and leaves the cell.

Skills Objectives
Students will be able to
- detect diffusion across a cell membrane.
- predict how the size of a molecule and concentration affect diffusion.

Preparation Time
30 minutes

Class Time
45 minutes

Group Size
Small groups

Materials
Because elemental iodine is relatively insoluble in water, you need to use Lugol's solution as your indicator. Use 1-inch diameter dialysis tubing.

Each group will need two beakers and two graduated cylinders unless you ask students to wash these items before they do Part B.

Advance Preparation
To prepare the 15 percent glucose solution, dissolve 15 g of glucose in enough water to make 100 mL of solution.

To prepare the 1 percent starch solution, dissolve 1 g of cornstarch in 99 mL of water. Bring the mixture to a boil to fully dissolve the starch. Allow time for the solution to slowly cool before class.

Safety
Read the MSDS on iodine. If you prepare the iodine solution, be sure to wear goggles, plastic gloves, and an apron. Ask if any student has a known sensitivity to iodine.

Pre-Lab Questions

1. **Draw Conclusions** How will you know whether starch has diffused across the membrane in Part A? How will you know whether iodine has diffused across the membrane?

   If the solution outside the tubing turns blue-black, then starch diffused

   out of the tubing. If the solution inside the tubing turns blue-black, then

   iodine diffused into the tubing.

   _____

2. **Draw Conclusions** How will you be able to tell whether glucose has diffused across the membrane in Part B?

   A glucose test strip will change color in the presence of glucose.

   _____

3. **Use Analogies** How is a window screen similar to a cell membrane?

   Sample answer: Like a cell membrane, a window screen prevents the

   passage of some things, such as insects, while allowing other things,

   such as air, to flow in and out of a house.

   _____

Procedure

In Part A, you will determine whether the dialysis membrane is permeable to starch or to iodine. In Part B, you will determine whether the membrane is permeable to glucose. **NOTE:** Iodine will turn blue-black when it comes into contact with starch.

Part A: Testing Permeability to Starch and Iodine

1. Put on your goggles, apron, and gloves. Cut a 15-cm length of dialysis tubing.

2. Add 50 mL of water to a 250-mL beaker.

3. Soak the tubing in the water for one minute.

4. Remove the tubing from the water. Fold up 1 cm of the tubing at one end. Use a twist tie to tightly seal off the folded end.

5. Roll the unsealed end of the tubing between your fingers until it opens.

6. Pour 3 mL of starch solution into the tubing.

7. Fold down 1 cm of the tubing at the open end. Use a second twist tie to tightly seal this end.

8. Use tap water to thoroughly rinse the outside of the tubing. Be sure to rinse the twist ties as well.

9. Place the tubing in the beaker. The tubing must be completely covered with water.

Teaching Tip
Demonstrate the reaction of iodine with starch so that your students know what to look for in Part A.

Step 1
You may want to have students wait to put on their gloves until after they have sealed the dialysis tubing. Students should put on the gloves before handling the iodine solution.

Step 3
Soaking the tubing in water will make it easier to open the tubing in Step 5. Don't let the tubing dry out once it is wet or it may develop leaks.

Step 4
Demonstrate how to fold and tie off the tubing.

10. Add 4 drops of iodine solution to the water in the beaker. Record your initial observations in Data Table 1. Wait 10 minutes, and then record your final observations.

11. Use a forceps to remove and dispose of the tubing as instructed by your teacher.

Sample Data

	Data Table 1					
	Inside Tubing			Outside Tubing		
	Color	Is starch present?	Is iodine present?	Color	Is starch present?	Is iodine present?
Initial	Clear	Yes	No	Brown	No	Yes
Final	Black	Yes	Yes	Brown	No	Yes

Part B: Permeability to Glucose

12. Repeat Steps 1–5 with a new 15-cm length of dialysis tubing and a clean beaker.

13. Use a clean graduated cylinder to pour 3 mL of glucose solution into the tubing.

14. Repeat Steps 7–9 with the new tubing.

15. After 10 minutes, use a glucose test strip to test the liquid outside the tubing. Record your results in Data Table 2.

Step 15
Demonstrate how to use the glucose test strips.

Sample Data

	Data Table 2	
	Inside Tubing	Outside Tubing
	Is glucose present?	Is glucose present?
Initial	Yes	No
Final	Yes	Yes

Analyze and Conclude

1. **Infer** In Part A, what happened to the iodine and the starch? In Part B, what happened to the glucose?

   In Part A, the iodine diffused into the tubing, but the starch did not diffuse out.

   In Part B, the glucose diffused out of the tubing.

2. **Apply Concepts** Use what you know about the structure of starch and glucose molecules to explain your results.

   The pores in dialysis tubing are relatively small. The small glucose molecules can pass

   through the pores, but starch, which is a polymer of glucose, is too large to pass

   through the pores.

3. **Infer** What substance other than iodine moved across the membrane in Part A? In which direction did this substance move, and why?

   Sample Answer: Water moved into the tubing. The concentration of water was higher

   in the beaker than it was in the starch solution inside the tubing.

4. **Predict** Red blood cells are placed in water that has been distilled so that there are no solutes dissolved in the water. Are the red blood cells likely to swell up or shrink? Why?

   Sample Answer: Water will diffuse into the cells because the initial concentration of

   water outside the cell is higher than the concentration of water in the cytoplasm. This

   movement of water will cause the cells to swell up, or even burst.

5. **Use Models** Describe two functions of a cell membrane that cannot be modeled with dialysis tubing.

   Sample answer: A cell membrane uses facilitated diffusion to speed up the movement

   of some solutes and uses active transport to move some solutes against their

   concentration gradients.

6. **Perform Error Analysis** When Alyssa did Part A of the experiment, she observed the solution outside the tubing turn black. What might have happened?

   Sample answer: There may have been starch solution on the outside of her tubing.

   The tubing might not have been tightly sealed, or there may have been a tear in the

   tubing.

Extend Your Inquiry

Different amounts of starch are dissolved in two beakers of water. How could you use dialysis tubing to determine which starch solution is more concentrated?

Place an equal volume of each solution in two lengths of dialysis tubing. Measure the mass of the tubing before and after the tubing is submerged in water. The tubing containing the more concentrated solution should show a greater increase in mass.

Chapter 8 Lab # Plant Pigments and Photosynthesis

Problem

Do red leaves have the same pigments as green leaves?

Introduction

Through the process of photosynthesis, plants convert energy from the sun into energy that is stored in food. Pigments make photosynthesis possible. Chlorophyll is the primary pigment in most plants. It is within chlorophyll molecules that light energy is converted to chemical energy. Chlorophyll also gives green plants their color. What about plants that do not have green leaves? What pigments are found in these plants?

Scientists can use a process called chromatography to determine which pigments are found in a particular plant. In one type of chromatography, a mixture of pigments is deposited on a piece of paper. A solvent, such as alcohol, is used to carry the pigments along the paper. Because each pigment moves at a different rate, the pigments become separated. The paper with the separated bands of pigments is called a chromatogram.

In this lab, you will use chromatography to determine whether a red-leafed plant has the same pigments as a green-leafed plant.

Skills Focus

Predict, Analyze Data, Draw Conclusions

Materials

- 2 paper clips
- 2 one-hole rubber stoppers
- 2 chromatography paper strips
- sheet of clean paper
- green and red leaves
- metric ruler
- quarter

- 2 large test tubes
- test-tube rack
- glass-marking pencil
- 10-mL graduated cylinder
- isopropyl alcohol
- colored pencils

Big Idea
Pigments are light-absorbing molecules that help plants capture energy from sunlight.

Skills Objectives
Students will be able to
- make a chromatogram.
- interpret chromatograms of pigments in leaves.

Preparation Time
15 minutes

Class Time
45 minutes

Group Size
Small groups

Materials
Use readily available leaves, such as red kale and spinach.

Advance Preparation
Use the annotation for Analyze and Conclude Question 2 to make a chart that correlates pigments to colors.
Prepare a stopper, clip, and strip assembly that students can use as a model.

Safety
Make sure students are
working in a well-ventilated
area.

Safety ⬡ ⬡ ⬡ ⬡

Because alcohol evaporates easily, you should work in a well-ventilated area. If you use glass test tubes or cylinders, check for cracks or chips. Alert your teacher immediately if you break a glass object. Do not pick up broken glass. Wash your hands thoroughly with soap and warm water when you have completed the lab.

Pre-Lab Questions

1. Design an Experiment What is the purpose of this lab?

The purpose is to find out whether red leaves have the same pigments

as green leaves.

_____

2. Control Variables What is the control in this lab?

Students may say that the green leaf or the chromatogram made from

the green leaf is the control.

3. Design an Experiment Why must you place a leaf about 2 cm from the bottom of the paper before rubbing the leaf with the coin?

Sample answer: When the strips are placed in the test tubes, the

pigment line must be above the surface of the alcohol.

_____

4. Predict Will red leaves contain the same amount of chlorophyll as green leaves? Why or why not?

Sample answer: Red leaves will have less chlorophyll than green leaves

because they are not green.

_____

Procedure

1. Straighten both paper clips. Bend each into a hook shape.

2. Push the straight end of each bent clip through the hole in a rubber stopper.

Step 3
Stress the importance of
having a pigment line that runs
straight across the strip. If the
line is not straight, the result
will be a blur rather than bands
of color.

3. Lay one strip of chromatography paper flat on a sheet of clean paper. Place the green leaf at one end of the strip as shown in Figure 1. Rock the edge of a quarter back and forth over the leaf at a location about 2 cm from the end of the strip. This motion will transfer leaf pigments to the chromatography paper.

Figure 1 How to transfer pigment

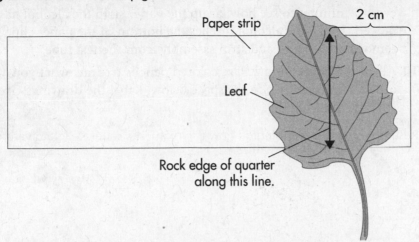

Paper strip

2 cm

Leaf

Rock edge of quarter
along this line.

4. Punch the hook end of a paper clip through the strip near the end
   without the pigments.

5. Repeat Steps 3 and 4 with the red leaf and the second strip of
   chromatography paper.

6. Place two test tubes in the test-tube rack. Insert a stopper and strip
   assembly into one test tube. Try not to let the paper touch the inside
   of the tube. Make a mark on the test tube about 1 cm below the
   pigment line. Label the test tube Red or Green, depending on which
   assembly you used. Repeat the procedure with the second stopper
   assembly and the second test tube.

7. Remove each stopper and strip assembly from its test tube. Add
   alcohol to each tube until the surface of the alcohol reaches the mark
   on the tube.

8. Reinsert each stopper and strip assembly into its test tube. Again,
   try not to let the paper touch the inside of the test tube. The alcohol
   should cover the bottom of the paper but not touch the pigment, as
   shown in Figure 2.

Step 6
Demonstrate how to insert
the paper into the test tube
without having the paper
touch the inside of the test
tube.

Step 7
Make sure students remove
any excess alcohol from the
test tube before reinserting
the strip.

Figure 2 Completed setup

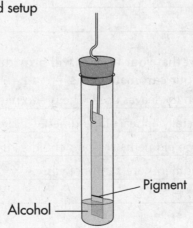

Pigment

Alcohol

Disposal
Follow local regulations for disposal of leftover isopropyl alcohol and the chromatograms.

9. Leave the test tubes undisturbed for 15–30 minutes. Check them every 5 minutes to see how far up the paper strip the alcohol has moved. When the alcohol reaches the bottom of the paper clip, remove the stopper and strip assembly from the test tube.

10. Allow the papers to dry. Use colored pencils to draw what you observe on each strip in the space below. Label the drawings Green Leaf and Red Leaf.

Results will vary depending on how the pigments separate in a given run.

Analyze and Conclude

1. **Compare and Contrast** How are the two chromatograms similar? How are they different?

Both chromatograms will show a green pigment, but the green leaf may produce a more prominent green band than the red leaf does. The red leaf will likely produce a reddish purple pigment.

2. **Analyze Data** Using the chart that your teacher will provide, identify the pigments that are visible on your chromatograms.

Answers will vary depending on the leaves used. The green pigments are chlorophyll. Chlorophyll *a* generally appears blue-green. Chlorophyll *b* appears yellow-green. The yellow-orange pigments are carotenoids. Purple-red pigments are anthocyanins. Yellow-brown pigments are xanthophylls.

3. **Apply Concepts** Based on your results, does a red-leafed plant undergo photosynthesis? Explain your answer.

Sample answer: Because a red-leafed plant contains chlorophyll, it is able to carry out photosynthesis in the same way a green leaf does.

4. **Predict** During the fall, the chlorophyll in the leaves of many plants starts to break down. The colors of other pigments present in the leaf are revealed. How do you think a chromatogram of a leaf that just turns red in the fall would compare with your chromatogram of a leaf that is red all year?

Sample answer: There will be less pigment overall in the leaf that changed colors in the fall as compared to the leaf that is red all year. In particular, there will be less chlorophyll pigment.

5. **Apply Concepts** What advantage could there be for a leaf to have pigments other than chlorophyll?

Sample answer: Each pigment absorbs some wavelengths of visible light, but not others. For example, chlorophyll does not absorb light well in the green region of the spectrum. Having many different pigments enables a plant to capture more of the energy from sunlight.

Extend Your Inquiry

If possible, repeat the experiment using a leaf that turns red only in the fall. Compare the chromatogram from that leaf with the chromatogram from the leaf that is red all year.

Students should find little or no chlorophyll in the leaf that turns red in the fall.

Chapter 9 Lab **Comparing Fermentation Rates of Sugars**

Problem

How does the type of sugar affect the rate of fermentation?

Introduction

Long ago, humans learned to harness the process of fermentation to preserve foods and to make new foods, such as cheese and bread. At an early stage in the bread-making process, yeast is added to the bread dough. Yeast are unicellular organisms that can break down carbohydrates in dough to produce carbon dioxide and ethanol. The bubbles of carbon dioxide gas that accumulate in the dough give bread its volume and texture. The alcohol evaporates as the dough rises and the bread is baked.

Sugars ferment at different rates. Commercial bakers use data on rates of fermentation to decide which sugars to use in different baked goods. In this lab, you will measure and compare rates of fermentation for five different sugars.

Skills Focus

Predict, Measure, Analyze Data, Infer

Materials

- probe interface
- gas pressure probe
- hot plate
- 400-mL beaker
- thermometer
- ring stand
- test-tube clamp
- medium test tube
- test-tube rack
- sugar solution
- yeast suspension
- 2 pipettes
- vegetable oil
- 1-hole rubber stopper
- plastic tubing with lock fitting

Big Idea
When oxygen is not available, cells can use fermentation to extract energy from food.

Skills Objectives
Students will be able to
- use a gas pressure probe to compare rates of fermentation.
- relate the results to what happens at the cellular level.

Preparation Time
30–40 minutes

Class Time
60 minutes

Group Size
Small groups

Materials
Use active dried yeast, not the faster-acting "instant" yeast. Check the expiration date on the package. Choose test tubes that will provide an airtight fit for the rubber stoppers.

Advance Preparation
To make a yeast suspension, dissolve 7 g (1 package) of dried yeast in 100 mL of lukewarm water. Incubate at 37°C–40°C for at least an hour. To make a 5% sugar solution, dissolve 5 grams of sugar in 100 mL of water.
Assemble a setup for students to use as a model.

Safety

Always wear goggles and an apron when using a water bath. If you have glass beakers or test tubes, check for cracks or chips. Alert your teacher if you break a glass object. Avoid contact with the surface of the hot plate. To avoid electric shocks, make sure cords, connections, and your hands are dry. Wash your hands thoroughly with soap and warm water at the end of the lab.

Pre-Lab Questions

1. **Infer** Why do you think you will add a layer of vegetable oil above the sugar and yeast mixture?

   Sample answer: The layer of vegetable oil will prevent oxygen from reaching the sugar and yeast mixture. In the presence of oxygen, fermentation will not take place.

2. **Relate Cause and Effect** Explain why it is possible to compare the rates of fermentation by measuring gas pressure in the test tubes.

   One of the products of fermentation is carbon dioxide, which is a gas. The faster the reaction, the greater the amount of gas in the tube and the greater the pressure will be.

3. **Predict** Which of the sugars do you think will have the highest rate of fermentation, and why?

   Students are likely to choose glucose because they know that the first step in fermentation is the conversion of glucose to pyruvic acid.

Procedure

As a class you will test glucose and fructose, which are simple sugars. You will also test sucrose, lactose, and maltose, which are disaccharides. Each group will test one sugar and share its data with the class.

Part A: Set Up the Water Bath and Probe Interface

1. Put on goggles and an apron.

2. Plug in your hot plate and use a setting that will produce a temperature between 37°C and 40°C.

Teaching Tip
If you have only 45 minutes, set up the probe interface and discuss the procedure the day before. On lab day, plug in the hot plates in advance or supply warm water.

Step 2
Adjust the procedure to reflect the settings on your hot plates.

3. Pour about 300 mL of water into a 400-mL beaker and place the beaker on the hot plate. Heat the water until it reaches a temperature between 37°C and 40°C. The yeast will need to be kept within this temperature range throughout the experiment. CAUTION: Make sure your water bath is placed away from the edge of the lab bench or table.

4. While the water is heating, follow your teacher's instructions for setting up your probe interface. Set the pressure scale on the vertical axis for 90 to 130 kPa. Set the time scale on the horizontal axis for 0 to 15 minutes. Set the data collection rate to 6 samples per minute.

Step 4
Refer to the manufacturer's instructions on how to use a gas pressure sensor probe.

Part B: Prepare the Reactants

5. Use a test-tube clamp to attach the test tube to a ring stand, as shown in Figure 1. You will need someone with a steady hand to do Steps 6–8.

6. Use a pipette to add 1 mL of the sugar solution to the test tube. CAUTION: Do not allow the solution or the pipette to touch the sides of the test tube.

Steps 6 and 7
Demonstrate how to use a pipette. Stress the importance of avoiding contamination.

7. Use a second pipette to gently stir the yeast suspension. Then use the pipette to add 1 mL of the suspension to the test tube. CAUTION: Do not allow the solution or the pipette to touch the sides of the test tube.

8. Use a dropper to carefully construct a layer of vegetable oil to completely cover the yeast and sugar mixture as shown in Figure 2. Add enough oil to make a layer that is about 0.5 cm deep.

Figure 1 Overall setup   **Figure 2** Test tube with liquids

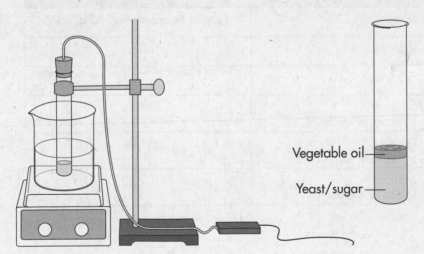

Vegetable oil

Yeast/sugar

Step 9
Make sure that there are no kinks in the tubing.

9. Insert the rubber stopper with the post for connecting tubing to the stopper. **CAUTION:** Don't connect the tubing to the stopper at this time. You don't want pressure to build up in the test tube before you are ready to measure the pressure.

10. Carefully lower the test tube into the water bath until the contents are fully submerged in the warm water.

11. You will need to incubate the test tube in the water bath until the yeast have used up all the oxygen that is dissolved in the yeast and sugar mixture. Make sure the temperature stays between 37°C and 40°C.

Part C: Collect Data

12. After 10 minutes, connect the plastic tubing to the rubber stopper. Collect data for 15 minutes. Keep monitoring the temperature during this time. **CAUTION:** If the pressure exceeds 115 kilopascals, the stopper will pop off. Disconnect the tubing if the pressure reaches 113 kilopascals.

13. After 15 minutes, find the value of the slope, *m,* for the change in pressure in the test tube. This is the rate of fermentation.

14. Record the slope in the appropriate row of the data table. Post your data on the board and record data from other groups in your table.

15. Turn off the hot plate. Follow your teacher's instructions for dismantling the setup and for cleanup. Wash your hands thoroughly with soap and warm water before leaving the lab.

Disposal
You can flush the contents of the test tubes down the drain.

Sample Data

Data Table	
Sugar	**Rate of Fermentation (kPa/min)**
Glucose	1.750
Fructose	1.311
Sucrose (glucose + fructose)	0.872
Lactose (galactose + glucose)	0.002
Maltose (glucose + glucose)	1.723

Analyze and Conclude

1. Interpret Tables Which sugar had the highest rate of fermentation? Which sugar had the lowest rate?

Either glucose or maltose will probably have the highest rate. Lactose should have the lowest rate.

2. Draw Conclusions Use what you know about the structures of the sugars to explain the results for glucose, fructose, sucrose, and maltose.

Sample answer: Simple sugars have a high rate of fermentation because they do not have to be broken down before fermentation, unlike disaccharides. (If your class data for maltose is similar to the sample data, discuss why there might be such a significant difference between the rates for sucrose and maltose.)

3. Infer Why do you think little or no fermentation occurred with lactose? *Hint:* Recall the role that enzymes play in reactions that take place in cells.

Sample answer: Yeast are unable to ferment lactose because they lack the enzyme to break down lactose into simple sugars.

4. Predict The solutions used in this lab contained only 5 percent of sugar. Would an increase in the concentration of sugar change the rate of fermentation? Explain.

Sample answer: Increasing the concentration of sugar would increase the rate of fermentation because the availability of the substrate is increased.

5. Apply Concepts Why did all of the oxygen in the mixture have to be used up before fermentation could begin?

Sample answer: Aerobic respiration is a much more efficient process for releasing the energy in food than is fermentation, and yeast are capable of both processes.

Extend Your Inquiry

Find a recipe for bread and make one or more loaves. Record your observations at each stage in the process. Use as many of your senses as possible.

Students can do this extension at home with family members or you could involve a home economics teacher. Students may want to work with a partner or in small groups.

Chapter 10 Lab **Regeneration in Planaria**

Problem

How potent are the stem cells in planaria?

Introduction

Planarians are freshwater flatworms that are able to regenerate body parts. Figure 1 shows the external anatomy of a planarian. When a planarian is cut, stem cells collect at the site of the injury. Stem cells have the ability to differentiate into other types of cells. Stem cells that can form any tissue in an organism's body are *totipotent*. Stem cells that can differentiate into some, but not all, cell types are *multipotent*.

In this lab, you will design an experiment to determine how potent planarian stem cells are. Then you will share your results with the rest of the class. From these combined results, you should be able to infer where stem cells are found in a planarian's body.

Figure 1 External anatomy of planarian

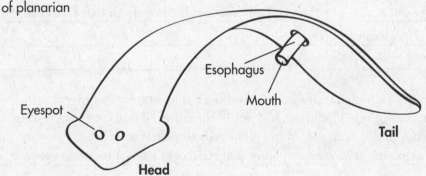

Esophagus

Mouth

Eyespot

Tail

Head

Skills Focus

Form a Hypothesis, Design an Experiment, Draw Conclusions

Materials

- fresh water or spring water
- planarians
- petri dishes
- glass-marking pencil
- forceps
- scalpel
- dissecting microscope
- glass microscope slide
- lens paper
- pipette
- small paintbrush
- clear ruler

Big Idea
During development, an organism's cells differentiate into many types of cells.

Skills Objectives
Students will be able to
• form a hypothesis about how potent planarian stem cells are.
• design an experiment to test the hypothesis.
• relate the results to the concept of cell differentiation.

Preparation Time
10 minutes every other day for 1–2 weeks; and 15 minutes the day before the lab

Class Time
45 minutes plus 10 minutes every other day for 1–2 weeks (for *Dugesia tigrina*) or longer for larger species

Group Size
Small groups

Materials
You will need 3 planarians and 4–5 petri dishes per group. Use hand lenses if you do not have dissecting microscopes.

Advance Preparation
Order planarians about 2–3 weeks in advance. They need about 1–2 weeks to acclimate to their new surroundings. Follow the care instructions provided by the supplier. Raw liver and egg yolks are possible food sources.

The day before the lab, freeze water in some petri dishes. If students are having trouble making cuts because the planarians are moving too quickly, they can use the ice to slow them down.

Safety
Demonstrate the proper way to use a scalpel so that students can avoid injuries.

Safety

A scalpel is an extremely sharp instrument. Never hold a flatworm with your fingers while making a cut. If you are using glass petri dishes or pipettes, check for cracks or chips. Alert your teacher if you break a glass object. Wash your hands thoroughly with soap and warm water before leaving the lab.

Pre-Lab Questions

1. **Apply Concepts** What would you expect to observe if the stem cells in planarians are totipotent? What would you expect to observe if the stem cells are multipotent?

   Sample answer: If the stem cells are totipotent, a cut planarian should regenerate completely. If the cells are multipotent, regeneration should be incomplete.

2. **Control Variables** What will you use as a control in your experiment? Explain why you need this control.

   Sample answer: I will use an uncut planarian. Growth that takes place in the uncut planarian can be compared with the growth that takes place during regeneration.

Teaching Tip
Some students may object to cutting a live organism. Remind students that the procedure is similar to what happens when planarians reproduce asexually.

3. **Infer** Two planarians are cut at different locations. Regeneration occurs in one planarian, but not in the other. Based on these results, what might you infer about stem cells in planarians?

   Sample answer: You might infer that stem cells are not found at every location in a planarian.

Procedure

Part A: Care and Handling of Planarians

Your teacher has been caring for the planarians while they were adjusting to their new environment. Your teacher may ask you to care for the planarians as you observe them for one or two weeks. You will also need to know the most effective way to make cuts.

Step 1
Store the pipettes that students will be using in this lab in fresh water or spring water.

1. **Water** Planarians need to be kept in fresh water or bottled spring water in a dark area at room temperature. The water should be changed every other day. Use a pipette to remove the old water from the petri dish and to add new water. **CAUTION:** Never add tap water or distilled water to the petri dish.

2. **Food** The planarians need to be fed once a week. Your teacher may assign you the task of feeding the planarians. If so, place a small piece of food in each petri dish. Do not let uneaten food sit for more than four hours. Clean the bottom of the dish with a paper towel and add a fresh supply of water.

3. **Moving Planarians** Use a pipette to move a planarian from one dish to another. Be sure to transfer the planarian quickly or it may attach itself to the inside of the pipette. **CAUTION:** If a planarian attaches itself to a petri dish, do not use a hard object to scrape it off the dish. Use a small paintbrush instead.

4. **Making Cuts** Figure 2 shows a vertical cut and a horizontal cut. It also shows the difference between a partial cut and a complete cut. A vertical cut is generally more difficult to make than a horizontal cut. Try using a glass slide with lens paper wrapped around it as a cutting surface. If you are making a partial cut, leave the scalpel in the cut for 5–10 seconds to prevent the cut from sealing back up immediately.

Step 4
Students may need to reopen partial cuts for a few days after the initial cut.

Figure 2 Examples of cuts

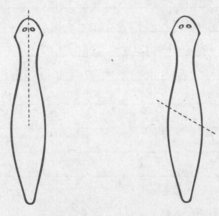

Partial Vertical Cut   **Complete Horizontal Cut**

Part B: Design an Experiment

Assume you will have three planarians to work with.

5. **Form a Hypothesis** How potent are stem cells in planaria? Record the hypothesis you will test to answer this question.

Hypothesis: *Sample answer:* Cut planarians will regenerate completely
because stem cells in planarians are totipotent.

_____

6. **Control Variables** Decide which independent variable you will investigate—the type of cut or the location of the cut. Record your independent and dependent variables.

Independent Variable: *Sample answer:* type of cut _____

Dependent Variable: *Sample answer:* amount of regeneration _____

Step 7

Encourage students to think about the different ways they could track changes including measurements, drawings, and written observations.

Expected Outcome

After a few days, students should begin to see some growth in the cut planarians. For partial cuts, planarians will regenerate two heads or two tails depending on the cut. Over a two-week period, the uncut control should also show some growth.

7. **Describe Your Plan** Record the details of your plan below, including how you will track changes in the dependent variable. Use Figure 3 to record the cuts you intend to make.

Experimental Design: _____

_____

_____

_____

_____

_____

_____

_____

_____

_____

_____

_____

_____

_____

_____

_____

_____

Figure 3 Planned cuts

8. **Organize Data** Construct a data table in the space below. Depending on the cuts you make, you may have as many as five planarians to observe. Leave room for up to two weeks of observations.

9. **Disposal** After handling the planarians, wash your hands thoroughly with soap and warm water. When the experiment is over, follow your teacher's instructions for cleanup and disposal of materials.

Sample Table

Data Table				
Day	Partial vertical cut (from head)	Complete vertical cut (right side)	Complete vertical cut (left side)	Control
3				
5				
7				
9				
12				
14				

Analyze and Conclude

1. **Infer** What evidence do you have that planarians have more than one type of tissue in their bodies?

   Sample answer: A planarian has specialized structures such as skin and eyespots.

   _____

2. **Apply Concepts** What must happen to the stem cells before the different kinds of tissues can be regenerated?

   The stem cells must differentiate.

3. **Evaluate** How complete was the regeneration process? Refer to the diagram of planarian anatomy in Figure 1 to help you evaluate the results.

   For most cuts, the planarians should have been able to completely regenerate the missing part. However, in the case of partial cuts, the planarians will no longer resemble a typical planarian.

   _____

4. **Draw Conclusions** Use your results to explain why your hypothesis was supported or why it was not supported.

Sample answer: The complete regeneration of lost body parts supports my

hypothesis that stem cells in planarians are totipotent because a number of

different tissues were regenerated.

_____

5. **Analyze Data** As a class, look at the results from all the experiments. What can you conclude about the location of stem cells in a planarian's body?

Unless students made cuts at the tip of the head or through the pharynx,

students will conclude that stem cells are located in all parts of a

planarian's body.

6. **Apply Concepts** Why can the human body heal a cut on a finger but not regenerate a finger that is cut off?

Sample answer: The multipotent stem cells in the human body can repair the

limited number of tissues in skin but cannot repair all the tissues required to

regenerate an entire finger.

_____

Extend Your Inquiry

Planarians naturally swim away from bright light. How could you demonstrate that regenerated eyespots are functional?

Students could compare the response of an uncut planarian and a planarian with
regenerated eyespots to a light.

Chapter 11 Lab   Modeling Meiosis

Problem

How does meiosis increase genetic variation?

Introduction

Most cells in organisms that reproduce sexually are diploid. They have two sets of chromosomes and two complete sets of genes. Gametes are an exception. Gametes are the cells that combine during sexual reproduction. In animals, these cells are called sperm and eggs. Gametes are haploid cells with only one set of chromosomes. Meiosis is the process in which haploid cells form from diploid cells.

   In this lab, you will model the steps in meiosis. You will make drawings of your models. You will also identify points in the process that can lead to greater genetic variation.

Skills Focus

Use Models, Sequence, Draw Conclusions

Materials

- pop beads
- magnetic centromeres
- large sheet of paper
- colored pencils
- scissors

Safety ✂

Do not direct the points of the scissors toward yourself or others. Use the scissors only as instructed.

Pre-Lab Questions

1. **Control Variables** Why must you use the same number of beads when you construct the second chromosome in Step 1?

   There must be an allele for each gene on each chromosome in the
   homologous pair.

Big Idea
Meiosis produces gametes that carry information from one generation to the next during sexual reproduction.

Skills Objectives
Students will be able to
- model the process of meiosis.
- identify ways in which genetic variation is increased.

Class Time
35 minutes

Group Size
Small groups

Materials
You could substitute beads and pipe cleaners for pop beads and magnetic centromeres. Students could use tape or rubber bands to connect chromosomes and form tetrads.

2. **Infer** Why is the longer chromosome pair used to model crossing-over?

Genes that are on the same chromosome are likely to be linked. The

chances of crossing-over are greater on the longer chromosome.

_____

3. **Calculate** A diploid cell has two pairs of homologous chromosomes. How many different combinations of chromosomes could there be in the gametes?

There could be four different combinations (ignoring any variation due

to crossing-over).

Procedure

The diploid cell in your model will have two pairs of homologous chromosomes. In order to keep track of the pairs, you will make one pair longer than the other. The beads will represent genes. Use the large sheet of paper to represent the cell.

Part A: Interphase

Just before meiosis begins, the chromosomes are replicated.

1. Use ten beads and a centromere of one color to construct the long chromosome. Use ten beads and a centromere of a second color to construct the second chromosome in the long pair. Make a drawing of the chromosomes in the space below.

2. For the second pair of chromosomes, use only five beads.

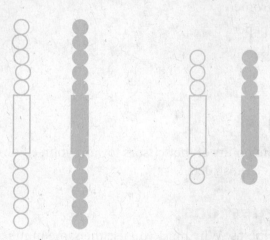

Teaching Tip
Either circulate among the groups and watch for students who are having trouble with certain steps or check students' models at agreed-upon points in the process, such as after Step 4.

Teaching Tip
Check to see if the centromeres will stick to your white board. If so, you could draw cells on the board, add structures such as spindles, and use the models to demonstrate or review meiosis.

3. Now model the replication of the chromosomes. Make a drawing of your model in the space below.

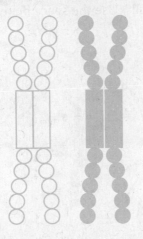 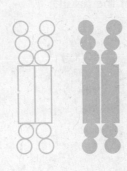

Part B: Meiosis I

During meiosis I, the cell divides into two diploid daughter cells.

4. Pair up the chromosomes to form tetrads. Use the longer tetrad to model crossing-over. Make a drawing of the tetrads in the space below.

5. Line up the tetrads across the center of your "cell." Then model what happens to the chromosomes during anaphase I.

6. Divide the cell into two daughter cells. Use the space below to make a drawing of the result.

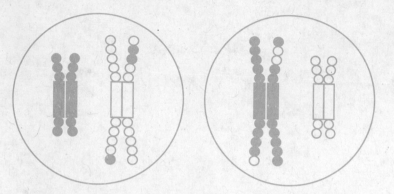

Part C: Meiosis II

During meiosis II, the daughter cells divide again.

7. Line up the chromosomes at the center of the first cell, one above the other. Separate the chromatids in each chromosome and move them to opposite sides of the cell.

8. Repeat Step 7 for the second cell.

9. Divide each cell into two daughter cells. Use the space below to make a drawing of the four haploid cells.

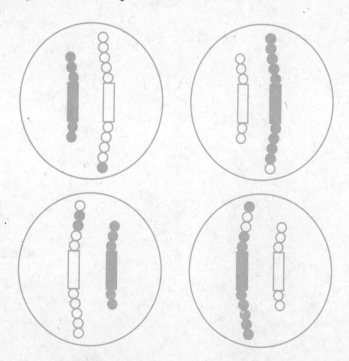

Analyze and Conclude

1. Relate Cause and Effect How does crossing-over increase variation in genes?

Crossing-over produces combinations of genes in the offspring that do not exist in

the parents' cells.

_____

2. Use Models Suppose no crossing-over takes place. Use Step 5 to explain why meiosis will still increase genetic variation.

Sample answer: In Step 5, the tetrads are independently assorted. Which chromatid

ends up in which daughter cell is random.

_____

_____

3. Compare and Contrast Compare your models of the four haploid cells with those of other groups. Describe and explain any variation that you observe.

Unless every group modeled exactly the same crossing-over in Step 4, there should

be variation among the haploid cells.

_____

_____

4. Calculate What would happen to the possible variation in gametes if the number of chromosome pairs increased from two to three? What if the number increased again from three to four?

The variation would double from 4 possible combinations to 8. It would double

again from 8 possible combinations to 16.

_____

_____

5. Apply Concepts How can independent assortment help explain genetic diversity in humans? *Hint:* How many pairs of chromosomes are in a human diploid cell?

Sample answer: Humans have 23 pairs of chromosomes. With each additional pair

of chromosomes, the number of possible variations in the gametes continues to

double. (There are 2^{23} or 8,388,608 possible different combinations.)

_____

6. **Perform Error Analysis** Suggest a way you could improve the models to better represent the process of meiosis.

Students might suggest adding something to represent the spindles or constructing

"chromosomes" with a larger number of genes.

_____

_____

7. **Draw Conclusions** In terms of adaptation, what advantage does sexual reproduction provide for a species?

Genetic diversity in a population makes it more likely that some offspring will have

traits that allow them to survive and reproduce in a changing environment.

_____

_____

_____

Extend Your Inquiry

Join with another group to model how genetic variation will increase during fertilization. Make a drawing of your model in the space below.

Due to both crossing-over and independent assortment, students in different groups should have gametes that are not identical.

Chapter 12 Lab **Extracting DNA**

Problem

What properties of DNA can you observe when you extract DNA from cells?

Introduction

A strawberry is an excellent choice for a DNA extraction. Because each strawberry cell has eight copies of its chromosomes, you will be able to collect a large amount of DNA. Ripe strawberries also contain enzymes that help break down cell walls.

In this lab, you will extract the DNA from a strawberry. You must crush the strawberry to break apart its cells, and then add a detergent to dissolve the cell membranes. You will use a filter to remove the solids from the mixture. The solution that you collect will contain DNA, proteins, sugars, and other dissolved molecules. You will use ethanol to isolate the DNA from the other dissolved molecules in the solution.

Skills Focus

Predict, Observe, Draw Conclusions

Materials

- self-sealing plastic freezer bag
- ripe strawberry
- detergent solution
- 25-mL graduated cylinder
- cheesecloth
- funnel
- test tube, medium-sized
- test-tube rack
- chilled 95% ethanol
- stirring rod

Safety 🔬 🧪 🧤 🧫 ☠ 🔥

The ethanol used in this lab could be toxic if absorbed through the skin. So rinse off any solution that spills on your skin immediately. Wash your hands thoroughly with soap and hot water at the end of the lab. Do not handle broken glassware.

Big Idea
In cells, genetic information is stored in long strands or chains of nucleotides.

Skills Objectives
Students will be able to
- extract DNA from cells.
- describe some physical properties of DNA.

Preparation Time
20 minutes

Class Time
30–40 minutes

Group Size
Small groups

Materials
Freezer bags are thick and less likely to break than other plastic bags. You can use either fresh or thawed frozen strawberries.

Advance Preparation
To prepare detergent solution for 100 extractions, mix 100 mL of liquid dishwashing detergent or shampoo (no conditioner) with 15 g of NaCl and 900 mL of water. The salt will keep the proteins in the extract from precipitating with the DNA.

Cut cheesecloth into squares that are two layers thick and will hang over the edge of the funnel.

On the day of the lab, pour the chilled ethanol into small dropper bottles. Store the bottles on ice in a central location.

Pre-Lab Questions

1. Apply Concepts Why do strawberry cells need DNA?

Sample answer: Strawberry cells need DNA to produce the proteins that

control reactions within the cells.

2. Infer If you observe a cell nucleus under a compound microscope, you will not see a molecule of DNA. Why will you be able to see the DNA you extract?

The clump of DNA will contain DNA from many cells.

3. Predict Use what you know about DNA to predict some of the physical properties of DNA.

Sample answer: The solid DNA will be made up of thin, long threads.

The solid will be flexible rather than rigid (because the DNA must be

able to fold up).

4. Design an Experiment How could you determine what percentage of a strawberry's mass is DNA?

Measure the mass of the strawberry and the mass of the extracted

DNA. Divide the mass of the DNA by the mass of the strawberry.

Procedure

1. Place your strawberry in the freezer bag. Press the bag to remove as much air as possible and then seal the bag. Crush the strawberry by mashing it with your fist for about 2 minutes.

2. Open the bag and add 10 mL of detergent solution. Carefully press out the air and reseal the bag.

3. Squeeze or mash the strawberry and detergent mixture for about 1 minute.

4. Prepare the setup shown in Figure 1. If you have a test-tube rack, secure the test tube in the rack. Make sure the cheesecloth hangs over the funnel at all points.

5. Pour the liquid from the freezer bag into the funnel. When the test tube is about one-eighth full of liquid, remove the funnel. Discard the cheesecloth and any leftover strawberry pulp.

Figure 1 Filtration setup

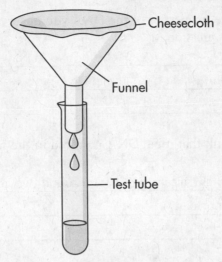

- Cheesecloth
- Funnel
- Test tube

6. You are going to use a dropper bottle to slowly add ethanol to the test tube. Position the dropper so that the drops run down the side of the test tube. Slowly add drops until the test tube is half full. The ethanol should form a separate layer above the filtered solution. Record what you observe.

   Fine white strands of DNA form at the interface between the two layers.

7. Place the tip of the stirring rod at the point where the two layers meet as shown in Figure 2. As you gently twirl the rod, bend down so you can observe what is happening at eye level. Record what you observe.

   The sticky white DNA fibers will spool around the stirring rod.

8. After you dispose of the materials as instructed by your teacher, wash your hands thoroughly with soap and warm water.

Figure 2 Placement of stirring rod

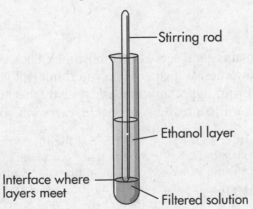

- Stirring rod
- Ethanol layer
- Interface where layers meet
- Filtered solution

Step 6
Demonstrate how to slowly add the ethanol to the test tube.

Step 8
You might want students to place some of the extracted DNA in a container with a lid such as a microcentrifuge tube. With the DNA in a container, students can more closely observe the DNA.

Disposal
You can flush the contents of the test tubes down the drain.

Analyze and Conclude

1. **Evaluate** How did the properties of the DNA you observed compare to those you predicted in Pre-Lab Question 3?

Students may say that they did not expect the DNA to be white and sticky or that

they did not expect there would be so much DNA.

2. **Infer** Why do you think that most DNA is stored in the nucleus of a cell and not in the cytoplasm?

Sample answer: Harmful chemicals must pass through two cell membranes to reach

the DNA stored in the nucleus.

3. **Use Analogies** Sewing thread is very thin and difficult to see once a length of thread is removed from its spool. How is the thread and spool an analogy for what happened to the DNA in Step 7?

The fine threads of DNA were not easy to see when they first appeared at the

interface between the layers but quite easy to see when they spooled around the

stirring rod.

4. **Draw Conclusions** Water is the main ingredient in the detergent solution. Ethanol is a type of alcohol. What can you conclude about the solubility of DNA in water and alcohol?

DNA dissolves more easily (is more soluble) in water than it does in alcohol.

5. **Predict** Do you think it would be easier or harder to extract DNA from animal cells than from plant cells? Explain your answer.

Sample answer: It would be easier to extract DNA from animal cells because animal

cells do not have cell walls.

Extend Your Inquiry

Each cell in a strawberry contains eight sets of chromosomes. Each cell in a banana contains three sets of chromosomes. Which cells do you think will yield more DNA? Design an experiment to test your hypothesis and ask your teacher to review the design. With your teacher's permission and supervision, carry out your experiment.

Students will need to use a balance to measure and control the mass of the fruits. They will also need to transfer the extracted DNA to similar small containers that can be placed on a balance. Students should be able to extract more DNA from the same mass of strawberry than from a similar mass of banana. With more-advanced students, you might want to discuss other variables that might affect the results, such as the number of cells in a given mass of each fruit or the length of the chromosomes.

Chapter 13 Lab **From DNA to Protein Synthesis**

Problem

What are the steps involved in making a protein?

Introduction

Before a protein can be built, the biochemical blueprints for its construction must be packaged and transferred out of the DNA "library." First, the specific sequence of DNA that codes for the protein is transcribed into a complementary strand of mRNA. In eukaryotic cells, the mRNA then leaves the nucleus and enters the cytoplasm. In all cells, the mRNA molecule attaches to a ribosome, where tRNA anticodons translate the mRNA into amino acids. The completed amino acid chain, or polypeptide, then folds into its final shape as a protein.

In this lab, you will model transcription of DNA and translation of mRNA while you decode secret messages.

Skills Focus

Use Models, Sequence

Pre-Lab Questions

1. **Sequence** Describe briefly the process you will use to decode the messages.

   Transcribe the DNA to mRNA, translate the mRNA to amino acids, and

   find the single-letter abbreviation for each amino acid.

2. **Compare and Contrast** What role do stop codons play in protein synthesis? What are they used for in the coded messages?

   In protein synthesis, a stop codon is used to mark the end of a protein

   synthesis. In the coded messages, stop codons are used to represent

   spaces between words.

3. **Predict** Which six letters will not appear in the coded messages? Give a reason for your answer.

   The letters B, J, O, U, X, and Z will not appear in the messages because

   they are not used as single-letter abbreviations for amino acids.

Big Idea
The central dogma of molecular biology is that information is transferred from DNA to RNA to proteins.

Skills Objectives
Students will be able to
• model the transcription of DNA to mRNA codons.
• model the translation of codons to amino acids.

Class Time
35 minutes

Group Size
Individuals

Procedure

Part A: How to Decode Messages

Teaching Tip
Make sure that the significance of the process that students are modeling does not get lost in the fun of decoding the messages.

1. Write the complementary mRNA strand for the DNA sequence given below by finding the mRNA codon that matches each DNA triplet, base for base. The mRNA strand has been started for you. Finish the transcription.

   DNA: TAC CGT TTT CTT ATT TAC ATA ACT CTG CGA ATG

   mRNA: <u>AUG GCA AAA GAA UAA</u>

   <u>AUG UAU UGA GAC GCU UAC</u>

2. Use Figure 1 to match each mRNA codon from Step 1 with its corresponding amino acid. When the codon is a "stop" codon, include "stop" in the sequence. The amino acid sequence has been started for you. Finish the translation.

   <u>methionine, alanine, lysine, glutamic acid, stop,</u>

   methionine, tyrosine, stop, aspartic acid, alanine, tyrosine
   _____

Figure 1 Map of mRNA codons to amino acids

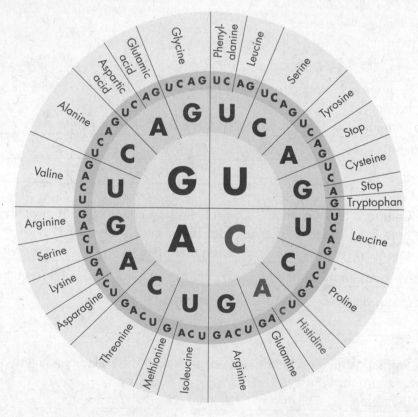

3. Use the table to find the single-letter symbol for each amino acid in the sequence from Step 2. The symbols will spell out a sentence or a familiar saying. The first word has been done for you.

MAKE MY DAY _____

Single-Letter Symbols for Amino Acids			
Amino Acid	Symbol	Amino Acid	Symbol
Alanine	A	Leucine	L
Arginine	R	Lysine	K
Asparagine	N	Methionine	M
Aspartic Acid	D	Phenylalanine	F
Cysteine	C	Proline	P
Glutamic Acid	E	Serine	S
Glutamine	Q	Threonine	T
Glycine	G	Tryptophan	W
Histadine	H	Tyrosine	Y
Isoleucine	I	Valine	V

Part B: Decoding Messages

4. Use the procedure from Part A to decode the following messages. Remember to transcribe the DNA messages into mRNA codons and then translate the codons into amino acids.

a. TGA CGA TTT CTC ACT ACA CGC GCG CTT

TAKE CARE _____

b. GTA CTT ATT TAA AGC ATC CGT ATT AGT GGC ATA

HE IS A SPY _____

c. TAC CTC CTT TGA ATT TAC CTT ACT CGT TGT ATT AAA
TAT CAG CTC

MEET ME AT FIVE _____

d. TGT GTA CTT ACT GGG GAT CGC TTG ATT GTA CGG
AGC ATC ACG GTG CGA TTG CCC CTT CTG

THE PLAN HAS CHANGED _____

e. TGT GTG CTC ACT AGA GTA TAG GGA ATT AGG CGG
TAT GAC AGC ATC CGA TGC ACT CTG CGC ACC TTA

THE SHIP SAILS AT DAWN _____

Analyze and Conclude

1. **Apply Concepts** How did you know which bases to use when you transcribed the DNA sequence to mRNA codons?

A in DNA always transcribes to U in RNA. T in DNA always transcribes to A in RNA.

C in DNA always transcribes to G in RNA. G in DNA always transcribes to C in RNA.

2. **Predict** Suppose the DNA sequence for the first message in Part B began with TGT CGA instead of TGA CGA. Would the message change? Why or why not?

The message would not change because TGT and TGA transcribe to ACA and ACU,

which both code for the same amino acid (threonine).

3. **Use Analogies** Suppose some codons mapped to two different amino acids? What would the effect be on your translation of coded messages? What would the effect be on the production of proteins?

It would be difficult to translate the messages. You would not know which amino

acid to use for some codons. (With trial and error, you might produce a logical

message.) Similarly, tRNA molecules would not "know" which amino acid to bring to

a ribosome. Thus, the structure of the polypeptide chain would not be consistent.

4. **Sequence** During the actual production of proteins in a cell, what might happen to a strand of RNA before it leaves the nucleus?

Portions of the RNA might be cut out and discarded before the mRNA molecules

leave the nucleus.

5. **Evaluate and Revise** What step could you add after you transcribe the DNA to make a more complete model of protein synthesis?

The model would be more complete if the codons were mapped to anticodons

before being translated. (To add this step would require revising Figure 1 so that it

mapped anticodons to amino acids.)

Extend Your Inquiry

Create your own secret message using DNA triplets. Exchange messages with classmates and try to solve the messages you receive. Remember that there is no triplet for the letters B, J, O, U, X, and Z. You will need to be creative to come up with messages that don't use those letters.

Remind students that messages should be in good taste and devoid of obscenities.

Name _____ Class _____ Date _____

Guided Inquiry • Forensics Lab

Chapter 14 Lab Using DNA to Identify Human Remains

Problem
How can pedigrees help scientists identify human remains?

Introduction
DNA has helped solve countless crimes and some intriguing mysteries—including the fate of the Romanovs. For 300 years the Romanov family ruled Russia. The last Romanov ruler was Tsar Nicholas II. His wife, Tsarina Alexandra, was descended from Queen Victoria of England, as shown in Figure 1.

In 1917, revolution swept through Russia. The royal family was captured and held prisoner until they were killed on July 16, 1918. The official report said that all the bodies were burned and then buried in a single grave. However, some witnesses said that one or two of the children were not buried with the others, and for many years there were rumors that Anastasia had survived.

The new government did not allow any research into the fate of the Romanovs. The house in which they were killed was destroyed, and the burial site was kept secret. In 1991, after the breakup of the Soviet Union, scientists were at last allowed to examine the burial site and remove the bones.

In this lab, you will investigate how the scientists classified the skeletons that they found. You will also figure out how pedigrees helped the scientists find living relatives whose DNA could be compared with DNA extracted from the bones.

Big Idea
Scientists use pedigrees to study human inheritance.

Skills Objectives
Students will be able to
• use data about teeth and pelvic bones to determine the age and sex of a skeleton.
• use pedigrees to draw conclusions about relationships.

Class Time
45 minutes

Group Size
Individuals

Figure 1 Simplified pedigree for Tsarina Alexandra

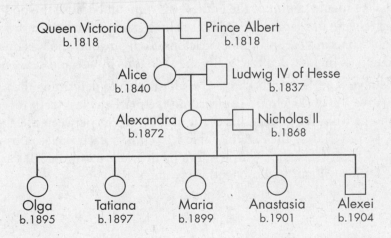

Lab Manual A • Copyright © Pearson Education, Inc., or its affiliates. All Rights Reserved.

81

Skills Focus

Analyze Data, Draw Conclusions

Pre-Lab Questions

1. **Infer** The tsar and tsarina had five children. Did all seven family members have the same mitochondrial DNA (mtDNA)? Give a reason for your answer.

   The tsarina and the children had the same mtDNA because the children inherited their mtDNA from the tsarina. The tsar had different mtDNA, which he inherited from his mother.

2. **Predict** To confirm that bones belonged to the Romanov children, which living relative would be more useful—a relative of the tsar or a relative of the tsarina? Why?

   A living relative of the tsarina would be more useful because that relative would have the same mtDNA as the children.

3. **Infer** If two people have the same mtDNA, what can you infer about their biological relationship?

   The two people have a common ancestor on the maternal side of their family trees.

Procedure

Part A: Sorting the Bones

The seven members of the Romanov family were not alone when they died. With them were a doctor, a nurse, and two servants, who were also killed. The identification of the bodies was difficult because the bodies in the grave were in a large pile. When scientists sorted the bones, they were able to reconstruct only nine skeletons. To figure out who was missing, the scientists first needed to classify the skeletons by age and sex.

Step 1
The age at which bones fuse can also be used to determine the relative age of skeletons.

1. **Relative Age** Scientists can use wisdom teeth to determine the relative age of skeletons. The wisdom teeth are the last teeth to emerge from the gums. This event usually occurs between the ages of 17 and 21. Use the data in Table 1 to classify each skeleton by age. Classify skeletons with wisdom teeth as age 22 or older. Classify skeletons without wisdom teeth as younger than age 22.

2. Sex Scientists can use the shape of the pelvis to determine the sex of a skeleton. The pelvis is a ringlike structure of bones located at the base of the spine. The pelvis of a female is wider and has a wider opening than the pelvis of a male. Use the data in Table 1 to determine each skeleton's sex.

Table 1				
Skeleton	Teeth	Pelvis	Age	Sex
1			22 or older	male
2			22 or older	male
3			under 22	female
4			22 or older	male
5			22 or older	female
6			under 22	female
7			22 or older	female
8			22 or older	male
9			22 or older	female

Part B: Finding Living Relatives of the Tsarina and Tsar

After examining the skeletons, the scientists knew which skeletons were adult males and which were adult females. However, they did not know which of the adults were the tsarina and the tsar. For this task the scientists needed to use DNA.

Recall that the bodies had been burned before they were buried. The remains had also been repeatedly frozen and thawed as the seasons changed over 75 years. Yet the scientists were still able to extract mitochondrial DNA (mtDNA) from the bones. Now they needed samples of DNA from living relatives for a comparison.

Step 3
If students are having trouble tracing the lineage in a pedigree, have them start with the latest generation and work back.

3. Tsarina Alexandra was a descendant of Queen Victoria. Both Queen Elizabeth II and her husband Prince Philip are living descendants of Queen Victoria. Use the pedigree in Figure 2 to trace the descent of Queen Elizabeth II. List the descendants in the space below.

Edward VII, George V, George VI, Elizabeth II

_____

4. Use the pedigree in Figure 2 to trace the descent of Prince Philip. List the descendants in the space below.

Alice, Victoria of Hesse, Alice of Battenberg, Prince Philip

_____

5. Based on your findings in Steps 3 and 4, whose mitochondrial DNA did scientists use to try to identify the tsarina's bones—Elizabeth or Philip? Explain your choice.

Sample answer: Elizabeth's DNA was not used because her descent from

Queen Victoria was through male ancestors. Philip's DNA was used

because his descent was through female ancestors, as was the tsarina's.

Thus, Philip and the tsarina should have the same mtDNA.

Figure 2 Simplified pedigree for Queen Elizabeth and Prince Philip

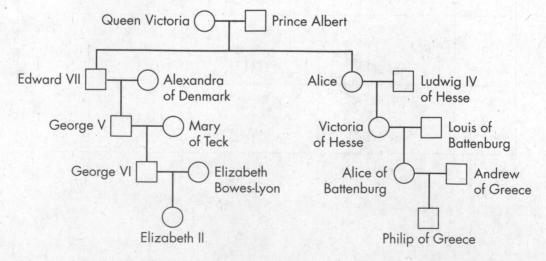

6. Scientists also needed to find living relatives of Tsar Nicholas II, who was descended from Louise of Hess-Cassel. Use the pedigree in Figure 3 to trace the tsar's descent.

Louise of Hess-Cassel, Empress Maria, Nicholas II

_____

7. Scientists identified two living descendants of Louise of Hess-Cassel who might be candidates for a DNA comparison—James Carnegie and Countess Xenia. Use Figure 3 to trace the descent of James Carnegie from Louise of Hess-Cassel.

Louise of Hess-Cassel, Alexandra, Princess Louise; Maud Carnegie, James

Carnegie _____

_____

8. Use Figure 3 to trace the descent of Countess Xenia from Louise of Hess-Cassel.

Louise of Hess-Cassel, Empress Maria, Princess Xenia; Irina Yussupov,

Irina Cheremeteff, Countess Xenia _____

_____

9. Based on your findings in Steps 5–7, what is the relationship between James Carnegie and Tsar Nicholas II? What is the relationship between Countess Xenia and Tsar Nicholas II?

James Duke of Fife's great-great-grandmother was Nicholas II's

grandmother. Countess Xenia's great-great-grandmother was Tsar

Nicholas II's mother.

Figure 3 Some descendants of Louise of Hess-Cassel

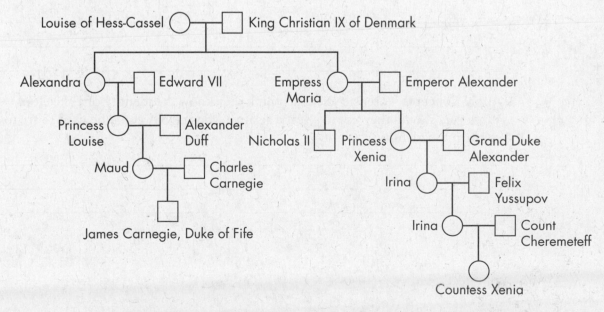

Analyze and Conclude

1. **Analyze Data** Table 2 lists the age and sex of each Romanov family member and their servants at the time of their deaths. The exact ages of the servants are not known. Compare the data in Table 2 with the data in Table 1. Who are the possible candidates for the two missing skeletons, and why?

Table 2			
Female	Age	Male	Age
Tsarina	46	Tsar	50
Olga	22	Alexei	14
Tatiana	21	Doctor	Adult
Maria	19	Servant	Adult
Anastasia	17	Servant	Adult
Nurse	Adult		

Sample answer: Prince Alexei was definitely missing because there was no skeleton of a male younger than age 22. One of the daughters was also missing (either Tatiana, Maria, or Anastasia) because there were only two skeletons of females who were younger than age 22. (Scientists were able to narrow down the identity of the missing female skeleton because other evidence was used to identify Tatiana's skeleton. In 2007, skeletons of the missing children were discovered in a grave not far from the first burial site.)

2. **Draw Conclusions** Could the mitochondrial DNA of either James Carnegie or Countess Xenia be used to try to identify the skeleton of Tsar Nicholas? Explain your answer.

James Carnegie is descended from the tsar's grandmother along the female line. Countess Xenia is descended from the tsar's mother along the female line. Either person's DNA could be used to identify the tsar's bones.

3. **Apply Concepts** Forensic scientists think they know the identity of a skeleton. What rule should they use to select a relative whose DNA could be used to try to confirm the identity?

Sample answer: They should pick a relative whose descent from a common ancestor is through the female line.

4. Infer When mitochondrial DNA from living relatives was compared with mitochondrial DNA from the skeletons, scientists determined that skeletons 3, 4, 5, 6, and 7 were members of the Romanov family. Which of these skeletons can be identified by name based on the evidence you have? Explain your answer.

Skeleton 4 must be the tsar because it is the only adult male Romanov skeleton.

Skeletons 5 and 7 are probably Tsarina Alexandra and Olga, but based on the

evidence given, it is not possible to say which is which.

5. Predict Queen Elizabeth and Prince Philip have four children. Would these offspring have been a useful source of DNA for identifying the Romanov skeletons? Why or why not?

They would not because mitochondrial DNA is inherited from the mother, and

Elizabeth does not have the same mtDNA as the Romanovs.

Extend Your Inquiry

In 1920, before the discovery of DNA, a factory worker named Anna Anderson claimed to be Anastasia Romanov. Do research to find out what evidence Anna Anderson used to back up her claim. After Anna's death, how did scientists investigate her claim?

Anna had similar hair, skin, and eye coloring as Anastasia. She was also roughly the same height and had a similarly disfigured foot. Handwriting samples, ear shape, and facial features were compared during a long court battle in Germany. The court ruled that the evidence was inconclusive. After Anna's death, mtDNA comparisons were done and scientists concluded that Anna was not a Romanov. Most scientists and historians now believe her to be a Prussian woman named Franziska Schanzkowska.

Chapter 15 Lab **Using DNA to Solve Crimes**

Problem

How can DNA samples be used to connect a suspect to a crime scene?

Introduction

When biological evidence, such as blood, is found at a crime scene, a crime scene investigator can collect a sample and send it to a crime lab. At the lab, a forensic scientist extracts and purifies the DNA. The next step takes advantage of DNA's ability to replicate itself. When thirteen selected regions in the DNA are copied, the result is a mixture of DNA fragments with varied lengths.

Gel electrophoresis is one method used to sort DNA fragments by size. An electric field pulls the fragments through a thick gel. Shorter fragments travel farther than longer fragments in a given period of time. As a result, the fragments become grouped into a pattern of bands, which forensic scientists call a profile. (Most forensic scientists use *profile* instead of *fingerprint* to avoid any confusion with other evidence collected at crime scenes.) In this lab, you will make and analyze four DNA profiles.

Skills Focus

Measure, Compare and Contrast, Draw Conclusions

Materials

- gel block
- electrophoresis chamber
- dilute buffer solution
- 250-mL beaker
- metric ruler
- 4 DNA samples
- 4 micropipettes

- five 9-volt batteries
- electric cords
- staining tray
- DNA stain
- 100-mL graduated cylinder
- clock or timer

Big Idea

The technology developed to decode the human genome has many other applications.

Skills Objectives

Students will be able to
- use electrophoresis to prepare DNA profiles.
- compare DNA profiles.

Preparation Time

60 minutes

Class Time

Part A: 20 minutes
Part B: 10 minutes for setup
Part C: 60 minutes
Part D: 10–15 minutes

Group Size

Small groups

Materials

gel casting trays, agarose gel, strapping tape, microwave, distilled water, zip-close plastic bags, Tris-Borate-EDTA, DNA stain concentrate

Advance Preparation

You can make the gel blocks up to a week in advance. Put the trays in zip-close plastic bags and add 1–2 mL of buffer solution. Store in a refrigerator.

To make 250 mL of dilute buffer solution, add 200 mL of distilled water to 50 mL of Tris-Borate-EDTA.

Prepare the stain just prior to using it. Add 5 mL of DNA stain concentrate to 95 mL of warm (50°C–55°C) distilled water.

Safety

Wear heat-protective gloves when handling the heated bottle of agarose gel.

Preparing Agarose Gel Blocks

(1) Loosen the cap and place the bottle in a microwave for 1 minute at medium heat. Remove and swirl the contents. Repeat until contents are completely liquid. (2) Tape both sides of the casting tray with strapping tape to make a tight seal. (3) Insert a well-forming comb into the grooves near one end of the tray. (4) Pour about 15 mL of liquid gel into the tray. The surface of the liquid should be just below the top of the tape. (5) Let the gel cool and solidify for 20–30 minutes. Don't disturb the tray or comb. (6) Gently pull the comb straight up and out of the gel and carefully remove the tape. **CAUTION:** Don't let the gel slip off the tray.

Safety

Wear goggles, gloves, and a lab apron to avoid staining your skin or clothing. To avoid electrical shocks, do not touch exposed metal in circuits. Alert your teacher if you break a glass object. Wash your hands thoroughly with soap and warm water before leaving the lab.

Pre-Lab Questions

1. **Control Variables** Why must you use a new pipette to load each DNA sample?

   Using the same pipette would cause all the samples to be contaminated, except the first sample.

2. **Relate Cause and Effect** Why will the DNA samples separate into bands as they move through the gel?

   The DNA samples contain fragments of different lengths. Shorter fragments will travel through the gel faster than longer fragments.

3. **Infer** Why is purple tracking dye added to the DNA samples?

   Because the DNA will not be visible until it is stained, the dye provides a visual indicator of when to stop the electrophoresis.

Procedure

Part A: Loading DNA Samples

Your teacher prepared gel blocks with depressions, or wells, to hold the DNA samples. A purple tracking dye was added to each DNA sample. The buffer solution is used to keep the pH neutral, which is necessary for the DNA fragments to remain charged.

1. Put on your goggles, lab apron, and gloves.

2. Obtain a plastic tray with a gel block. **CAUTION:** Hold the tray parallel to the floor so that the gel block does not slip off the tray. Locate the wells near one end of the block. Place the tray in the center of the electrophoresis chamber so that the wells are closest to the black (negative) electrode.

3. Add 200 mL of buffer solution to the chamber. Make sure the surface of the solution is 2–3 mm above the top of the gel block.

4. Obtain the DNA sample labeled Crime Scene. Before you open the tube, make sure the sample is at the bottom of the tube. Push the plunger all the way to the bottom of the micropipette. Insert the end of the pipette into the tube, and gently pull the plunger to draw 10 µL (microliters) of liquid into the pipette.

Teaching Tip
If you order a kit, it may include a training video that students can view before doing the lab.

Step 3
The gel tray may start to float if air is trapped under the tray. Use a micropipette to suction the trapped air through the tiny holes in the top of the tray.

Step 4
Show students how to use a quick flick of the wrist to push down a DNA sample that is not at the bottom of the tube.

5. Insert the end of the pipette into the first well in the gel block. **CAUTION:** Do not puncture the bottom of the well. Hold the pipette steady and gently press the plunger forward. When the pipette is empty, discard it in the trash.

6. Repeat Steps 4 and 5 for the Suspect 1, Suspect 2, and Suspect 3 samples. Be sure to use a new pipette for each sample and to place each sample in a separate well.

7. Make sure the chamber cover is dry, and then place the cover on the electrophoresis chamber.

Part B: Separating DNA Fragments

8. Connect five 9-volt batteries as shown in the diagram. Snap the positive terminal of one battery to the negative terminal of another battery. When you are done, you should have one open negative terminal and one open positive terminal.

9. Use the red cord to connect the open positive battery terminal and the red (positive) electrode on the chamber. Use the black cord to connect the open negative battery terminal and the black electrode. If you do not see bubbles form along the wires at the bottom of the chamber, recheck all the connections.

Step 5
Some students may need practice loading the samples. If so, have them practice with the buffer solution.

Step 8
With five 9-volt batteries, the DNA separation should take 2.5–3 hours. With one 9-volt battery, the separation will take about 12 hours.

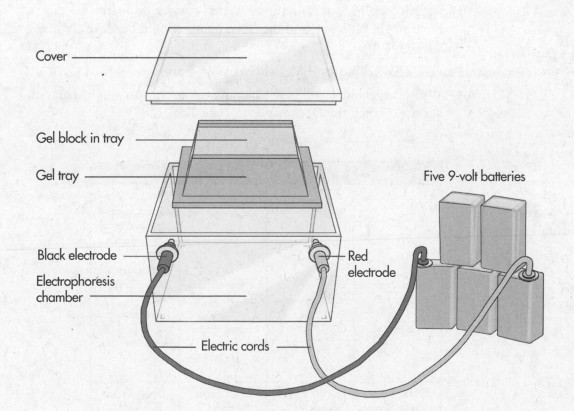

Cover

Gel block in tray

Gel tray

Five 9-volt batteries

Black electrode

Red electrode

Electrophoresis chamber

Electric cords

10. You will see the purple dye from each DNA sample slowly move through the gel. CAUTION: When the dye reaches the end of the gel block, disconnect the batteries from the chamber.

11. Remove the gel tray from the chamber and use your gloved fingers to gently push the gel block off the casting tray into a staining tray. CAUTION: The gel block is fragile and could break during the transfer.

Part C: Staining DNA Bands

12. Put on your goggles, gloves, and apron.

13. Pour 100 mL of warm DNA stain into the staining tray. Make sure the stain covers the entire gel block. Let the gel block sit in the stain for 35 minutes.

14. Gently hold the edge of the gel block as you pour the stain into the sink. Flush the sink with water.

15. Slowly pour tap water into the staining tray until the water completely covers the gel block. CAUTION: To avoid damaging the gel, do not pour water directly onto the gel. Gently rock the tray back and forth. After 5 minutes, hold the edge of the gel block as you pour the water into the sink.

16. Repeat Step 15 four more times. When you are done, the gel should have a light blue tint, and the DNA bands should be clearly visible as dark blue lines.

Part D: Sketching and Measuring DNA Bands

17. With the gel block still in the tray, place the tray on a light-colored surface. Sketch the DNA bands in Data Table 1.

Sample Data

Data Table 1			
DNA From Crime Scene	DNA From Suspect 1	DNA From Suspect 2	DNA From Suspect 3

18. For each DNA sample, measure the distance from the edge of its well to the center of each DNA band. Record the measurements in Data Table 2.

Step 18
If possible, use a digital camera to photograph the gel blocks. Print the photos and measure the distances on the photos.

Sample Data

Data Table 2				
Band	Crime Scene	Suspect 1	Suspect 2	Suspect 3
1	9 mm	10 mm	9 mm	8 mm
2	13 mm	13 mm	13 mm	12 mm
3	15 mm	18 mm	15 mm	15 mm
4	40 mm	31 mm	40 mm	21 mm
5	—	38 mm	—	31 mm
6	—	—	—	36 mm
7	—	—	—	38 mm

Analyze and Conclude

1. **Infer** Do the DNA fragments have a positive or a negative charge? Explain your answer.

    Sample answer: The fragments of DNA have a negative charge because they move toward the positive electrode when the circuit is complete.

2. **Apply Concepts** Where are the shortest fragments of DNA located? Where are the longest fragments located?

    The shortest fragments are in the band that is farthest from the well. The longest fragments are in the band that is closest to the well.

3. **Analyze Data** Based on Data Table 1, which suspect's profile most closely matches the profile of the crime scene DNA? Explain.

    Sample answer: The profile from Suspect 2 most closely matches the profile from the crime scene. Both profiles have the same number of bands, and the pattern of the bands is similar.

4. **Analyze Data** Based on Data Table 2, which suspect's profile most closely matches the profile of the crime scene DNA? Explain.

Sample answer: The DNA profile from Suspect 2 most closely matches the profile from the crime scene DNA because the measured distances of the bands from the wells is nearly the same for both profiles.

5. **Compare and Contrast** How are Data Table 1 and Data Table 2 similar? How are they different?

Sample answer: Both data tables show the location of the DNA bands for each sample. In Data Table 1, the presentation is qualitative and visual. In Data Table 2, the results are quantitative.

6. **Draw Conclusions** Based on your results, what can you conclude about the person whose profile matched the crime scene profile? What can't you conclude based on this evidence?

Sample answer: I can conclude that the person was at the crime scene, but not whether the person was at the scene when the crime occurred.

Extend Your Inquiry

Research possible errors that could occur when biological evidence is used to solve crimes. Begin at the point when investigators arrive at a crime scene. What procedures are used to avoid these errors? Choose an appropriate format for presenting your information.

Students' presentations should include information about protocols that are used to avoid contamination of evidence at every stage in the process and the requirements for detailed documentation, including a chain of custody for evidence.

Chapter 16 Lab **Amino Acid Sequences: Indicators of Evolution**

Problem

How can you use proteins to determine how closely organisms are related?

Introduction

Biologists have many ways to study evolution. They can use fossils to learn about ancient species. They can compare the anatomy of modern species. They can observe the order in which cells develop in embryos. All these clues reflect what took place over time at the molecular level. DNA and proteins, the genes and the products of genes, provide powerful evidence for descent with modification.

As DNA changes over time, the proteins that are produced by the DNA change too. The result is that many organisms have similar, but not identical, versions of a given protein. Differences among these homologous proteins provide clues to evolution.

In Part A of this lab, you will compare amino acid sequences of hemoglobin from eight mammals. In Part B, you will analyze data about sequences in a second protein—cytochrome c. In Part B, the organisms will be more diverse.

Skills Focus

Analyze Data, Graph, Draw Conclusions

Materials

- highlighter pen, light-colored
- graph paper

Big Idea
Molecular biology provides evidence for evolution.

Skills Objectives
Students will be able to
- analyze amino acid sequences of proteins.
- infer the relatedness of species from differences in proteins.

Class Time
40 minutes

Group Size
Individuals

Advance Preparation
Collect and display images of the organisms listed in Figure 1.

Pre-Lab Questions

1. Predict Based only on their anatomy, rank gorillas, bears, chimpanzees, and mice from most recent common ancestor with humans to least recent common ancestor.

Students are likely to say that chimpanzees and gorillas have a more

recent common ancestor with humans than do bears and mice. Do not

correct the rankings at this point.

2. Use Analogies You tell a story to a second person who tells it to a third person, and so on. As the story is retold, changes are introduced. Over time, the number of changes increases. How is this process an analogy for what happens to DNA over time?

Students can compare retelling the story to the replication of DNA and

the changes in the story to mutations. Despite the difference in time

frame, with both the story and the DNA the number of changes will

increase with time.

3. Infer Hemoglobin from two species is compared. On the long protein chains, there are three locations where the amino acids are different. Where would you place the common ancestor of the two species on the "tree of life," and why?

The common ancestor should be placed relatively recently along the

tree based on the limited differences between the two proteins and the

time required for mutations to occur.

Procedure

Part A: Comparing Amino Acid Sequences in Hemoglobin

Hemoglobin is the molecule in blood that carries oxygen. This complex molecule contains four protein chains. Figure 1 shows the amino acid sequence for one of those chains in eight mammals. Each letter stands for a different amino acid. Each column is a location on the protein chain. **NOTE:** Locations where the amino acids are identical in all eight mammals are not shown.

Teaching Tip
If your students have not done the Chapter 13 lab, "From DNA to Protein Synthesis," they may be curious about or confused by the symbols in Figure 1. Refer them to the table on page 79, which maps single-letter symbols to amino acids.

1. Use the row labeled Human as your control. Compare the sequence for the bear to the sequence for humans. When you find a difference in the bear sequence, highlight it.

2. Repeat Step 1 for each of the other mammals. Be sure to compare each sequence to the sequence for humans.

Step 2
The rows with the data for humans are shaded to remind students that humans are the control for this activity.

Figure 1 Comparison of amino acid sequences in hemoglobin from eight mammals

	4	5	6	9	10	12	13	20	25	33	41	43	50	51	52
Human	T	P	E	S	A	T	A	V	G	V	F	E	T	P	D
Bear	T	G	E	S	L	T	G	V	G	V	F	D	S	A	D
Chimpanzee	T	P	E	S	A	T	A	V	G	V	F	E	T	P	D
Gibbon	T	P	E	S	A	T	A	V	G	V	F	E	T	P	D
Gorilla	T	P	E	S	A	T	A	V	G	V	F	E	T	P	D
Monkey	T	P	E	N	A	T	T	V	G	L	F	E	S	P	D
Mouse	T	D	A	A	A	S	C	S	G	V	Y	D	S	A	S
Shrew	S	G	E	A	C	T	G	E	A	V	F	D	S	A	S

	54	56	58	68	69	70	71	72	73	75	76	77	80	87	104
Human	V	G	P	L	G	A	F	S	D	L	A	H	N	T	R
Bear	I	N	P	L	N	S	F	S	D	L	K	N	N	K	K
Chimpanzee	V	G	P	L	G	A	F	S	D	L	A	H	N	T	R
Gibbon	V	G	P	L	G	A	F	S	D	L	A	H	N	Q	R
Gorilla	V	G	P	L	G	A	F	S	D	L	A	H	N	T	K
Monkey	V	G	P	L	G	A	F	S	D	L	N	H	N	Q	K
Mouse	I	G	A	I	T	A	F	N	D	L	N	H	S	S	R
Shrew	V	G	P	L	H	S	L	G	E	V	A	N	N	K	R

	109	110	112	115	116	117	118	121	125	126	130	139
Human	V	L	C	A	H	H	F	E	P	V	Y	N
Bear	V	L	C	A	H	H	F	E	Q	V	Y	N
Chimpanzee	V	L	C	A	H	H	F	E	P	V	Y	N
Gibbon	V	L	C	A	H	H	F	E	Q	V	Y	N
Gorilla	V	L	C	A	H	H	F	E	P	V	Y	N
Monkey	V	L	C	A	H	H	F	E	Q	V	Y	N
Mouse	M	I	I	G	H	H	L	D	A	A	F	T
Shrew	V	L	V	A	S	K	F	E	P	V	F	N

3. In the space below, make a data table to record the number of differences you found for each mammal in comparison to humans.

Sample Data

Data Table	
Mammal	Number of Differences in Hemoglobin
Bear	15
Chimpanzee	0
Gibbon	2
Gorilla	1
Monkey	8
Mouse	29
Shrew	24

Part B: Differences in Cytochrome c

Cytochrome c takes part in electron transport during the last stage of cellular respiration. This enzyme can be found in bacteria, yeasts, fungi, plants, and animals. The human cytochrome c molecule is relatively small. Its single strand of protein has 104 amino acids.

Step 4
Labeling the axes will be easier if students use the y-axis for the species and the x-axis for the number of differences.

Teaching Tip
This lab uses limited data to demonstrate one method biologists use to study evolution. Remind students that scientists do not generally base their conclusions on such limited data.

4. In Figure 2, human cytochrome c is the standard. Column 1 lists the species that are being compared to humans. Column 2 lists the number of differences for each pairing. Use the data to make a bar graph on a separate sheet of graph paper. Select an order for the bars that will best reveal a pattern in the number of differences.

Figure 2 How human cytochrome c differs from cytochrome c found in other species

Species	Number of Differences
Chimpanzee	0
Fruit fly	29
Horse	12
Pigeon	12
Rattlesnake	14
Red bread mold	48
Rhesus monkey	1
Snapping turtle	15
Tuna	21
Wheat	43

Analyze and Conclude

1. Draw Conclusions Based on the hemoglobin data, which mammal listed is most closely related to humans? What is the evidence for your conclusion?

The chimpanzee is most closely related. There are no differences between the amino acid sequences in chimpanzees and humans.

_____

2. Analyze Data Does the cytochrome c data support your conclusion in Question 1? Explain.

Yes, because there are no differences in the amino acid sequence between chimpanzees and humans.

_____

3. Evaluate Does the data support the rankings you made as part of the pre-lab? If not, how would you explain any differences?

Analysis of biochemical differences can reveal relationships between species that are not obvious based only on anatomy.

_____

_____

4. Design an Experiment The cytochrome c in both horses and pigeons differs from the human protein at 12 locations. Based on this data, you might infer that horses and pigeons are closely related. What could you do to support or refute this hypothesis?

You would compare the amino acid sequences in the pigeon and the horse to each other rather than to the human protein.

_____

_____

5. Communicate In terms of descent, what does it mean to say that humans are more closely related to gorillas than to monkeys?

It means that the common ancestor of gorillas and humans lived more recently than the common ancestor of monkeys and humans.

_____

_____

6. Interpret Data A student used the hemoglobin data to conclude that mice and shrews are more closely related than are mice and humans or shrews and humans. Was the student correct?

No. The number of differences between the hemoglobin for mice and shrews (33) is greater than the number of differences for mice and humans (29) or shrews and humans (24).

Extend Your Inquiry

More than 100 locations were not listed in Figure 1 because the amino acid was the same in all 8 species. One possible explanation is that no mutations occurred in the codons for those locations. Suggest another possible explanation.

Sample answer: Mutations did occur, but the protein that was produced could no longer perform its function or its ability to perform the function was limited. Individuals with such a mutation would be less likely to survive and reproduce.

Chapter 17 Lab **Competing for Resources**

Problem

How can competition lead to speciation?

Introduction

At first Darwin did not pay much attention to the small brown birds he observed in the Galápagos Islands. Later, he realized that, despite their differences, all these birds were species of finches. Darwin hypothesized that the variation in beak shape and size among the species was related to the food they ate.

Because Darwin's time on the islands was limited, he was unable to gather the evidence to support his hypothesis. That task was left to Rosemary and Peter Grant, who spent years on the islands. The Grants were able to observe that finches tended to mate with finches that had similar beaks. This behavior was one of the factors leading to speciation among the Galápagos finches. Another factor was the competition for seeds.

In this lab, you will model variation in the size and shape of finch beaks. You will determine which "beaks" are better adapted to each type of food. You will also observe how competition and the abundance or scarcity of food affects survival.

Skills Focus

Use Models, Predict, Apply Concepts

Materials

- assorted tools
- seeds, large and small
- large paper plates
- small paper plates
- timer or clock with second hand

Safety ⚠

Do not direct the sharp points of any tools toward yourself or others. Do not eat any of the seeds used in this lab.

Big Idea
When populations become reproductively isolated, they can evolve into two separate species.

Skills Objectives
Students will be able to
- model how variations in phenotypes affect survival.
- draw conclusions about how adaptations lead to speciation.

Preparation Time
30 minutes

Class Time
Round 1: 25 minutes
Round 2: 20 minutes
Round 3: 20 minutes

Group Size
Small groups of equal numbers

Materials
Possible seeds include bird seed, dried beans, lentils, or seeds in the shell, such as hazelnuts and pistachios.

Supply at least as many tools as you have groups. Examples include clothes pins, tweezers, forceps, different types of pliers, kitchen tongs, and binder clips.

Choose tools your students can manipulate after minimal practice so that dexterity is not a significant factor.

Advance Preparation
Test the tools to make sure a tool can pick up at least one of the seeds you will be using and that about half the tools will work better with one type of seed and half with the other.

Safety
If students have allergies to nuts, substitute items such as plastic beads or ball bearings.

Pre-Lab Questions

1. Use Models In this lab, what do the different types of tools represent?

The tools represent different types of beaks.

2. Predict Which tools do you think will work best for picking up small seeds? Which will work best for picking up large seeds?

Answers will vary with the types of tools. Tweezers or small spoons might work well with small seeds. Pliers or ice tongs might work well with large seeds.

3. Design an Experiment Why will the time you have to collect seeds be limited?

Sample answer: Limiting the time gives an advantage to those with tools that are better adapted to pick up a certain type of seed.

Procedure

Round 1: Feeding Without Competition

In this round, you will model feeding when there is abundant food and no competition.

1. Choose a tool and obtain a large plate of small seeds and an empty small plate.

2. Each student in your group should practice using the tool to pick up seeds and transfer them to the empty plate. Pick up only one seed at a time.

3. Obtain a large plate of large seeds. Repeat Step 2. Then, decide which type of seed you can pick up more easily with your tool. Return the other plate of seeds to your teacher. Record the type of tool and the type of seeds you will use in Steps 4 and 5.

Type of Tool: tweezers

Type of Seed: small seeds

4. In this step, your goal will be to pick up as many seeds as possible in 15 seconds. Each student will do three 15-second trials. Assign each person in your group a letter code—A, B, C, and so on—to represent the order in which people will do the trials. Your teacher will tell you when to start and end each trial. Use Data Table 1 to record the number of seeds picked up and placed in the small plate for each trial. Don't count seeds that do not land in the plate.

5. After each member of your group has done three trials, calculate the average number of seeds that were picked up in 15 seconds.

Data Table 1: Seeds Picked Up in Round 1					
Trial	Number of Seeds	Trial	Number of Seeds	Trial	Number of Seeds
A1		C1		E1	
A2		C2		E2	
A3		C3		E3	
B1		D1		F1	
B2		D2		F2	
B3		D3		F3	
Average Number of Seeds Picked Up:					

Round 2: Feeding With Competition

In this round, you will model feeding when there is abundant food and competition. Use the same tool and type of seeds you used in Round 1. Your group will be paired with another group that used the same type of seeds.

6. Each student will do three 15-second trials, as in Round 1. But this time each trial will involve competition with a member of the other group. The two competitors will pick up seeds from the same large plate at the same time. Record your group's results in Data Table 2.

7. After each member of your group has done three trials, calculate the average number of seeds that were picked up in 15 seconds.

Data Table 2: Seeds Picked Up in Round 2					
Trial	Number of Seeds	Trial	Number of Seeds	Trial	Number of Seeds
A1		C1		E1	
A2		C2		E2	
A3		C3		E3	
B1		D1		F1	
B2		D2		F2	
B3		D3		F3	
Average Number of Seeds Picked Up:					

Round 3

If you have no survivors or too many survivors in Round 3, adjust the length of the trials or the number of seeds signifying survival.

Round 3: Feeding When Food Is Scarce

In this round, you will repeat the procedure from Round 2. This time, however, there will be fewer seeds on the large plate to represent a time when food is scarce, which is a true test of your tool's adaptability. You will work with the same group you worked with in Round 2.

8. Count out 30 seeds and put them on the large plate. Return the rest of the seeds to your teacher.

9. Repeat Steps 6 and 7.

Data Table 3: Seeds Picked Up in Round 3					
Trial	Number of Seeds	Trial	Number of Seeds	Trial	Number of Seeds
A1		C1		E1	
A2		C2		E2	
A3		C3		E3	
B1		D1		F1	
B2		D2		F2	
B3		D3		F3	
Average Number of Seeds Picked Up:					

Analyze and Conclude

1. **Compare and Contrast** Look at all the tools that were used to pick up seeds. Identify at least one general difference between the tools that were better at picking up small seeds and those that were better at picking up large seeds.

   Answers will vary depending on the tools. Tools, such as tweezers, that have smaller

   tips will likely be better at picking up small seeds but will not be able to grasp most

   larger seeds.

   _____

2. **Analyze Data** In nature, a seed-eating bird would need to collect a minimum number of seeds to survive. For your model, assume that the minimum for survival is 14 seeds in 15 seconds. How many individuals in your group would have survived Round 1? How did the procedure in Round 1 help their survival?

   Most individuals should have survived in Round 1 because there was no competition

   and the groups were allowed to choose the type of seed best suited for their tool.

   _____

   _____

3. **Relate Cause and Effect** When food was abundant, how did competition affect the survival rate? Why?

Survival rates will likely decrease with competition because another person trying to feed in the same space can interfere with one's ability to pick up seeds.

_____

_____

4. **Relate Cause and Effect** When food was scarce, how did competition affect the survival rate? Why?

Survival rates should decrease when food is scarce because competitors can collect seeds that an individual needs to survive. (Students also may have been more hurried in their movements, resulting in feeding errors such as dropped seeds.)

_____

5. **Use Analogies** How might scarcity of food affect the size of a finch population?

Sample answer: The size of the population would likely decrease because fewer birds would have the resources to survive and reproduce.

_____

6. **Predict** Within a gene pool, there will be alleles that result in beaks that are well adapted to the available food and beaks that are not well adapted. Use your results with the tools to predict how which birds survive can affect the alleles in the gene pool of a bird population.

Sample answer: Birds with beaks that are not well adapted will have lower survival rates, and alleles for those beaks will gradually disappear from the population. Birds with beaks that are well adapted will have more descendants, and alleles for those beaks will spread through the population.

_____

_____

7. **Apply Concepts** How might changes in the gene pool affect the ability of birds with beaks that are not well adapted to find mates?

Sample answer: Finches tend to mate with finches that have similar beaks. As the alleles for beaks that are not well adapted decrease, there will be fewer potential mates for a bird with that type of beak.

_____

Extend Your Inquiry

Design an experiment to answer one of the following questions. Or pose your own question. (1) How would varying the depth and width of a seed container affect the ability of different "beaks" to collect seeds? (2) In nature, seeds are not found piled in one location, except in a bird feeder. How would scattering seeds affect a bird's ability to survive?

Students should discover that the shape of the container will affect the adaptability of the tools. With some tools, for example, students will not be able to reach seeds stored in a narrow, deep container. Students should also discover that it takes longer to collect seeds that are scattered. They may also notice that it becomes harder to spot the seeds.

Open-Ended Inquiry • Design Your Own Lab

Chapter 18 Lab Dichotomous Keys

Problem

Can you construct a dichotomous key that could be used to identify organisms?

Introduction

In May 2007, scientists and other volunteers gathered in Rock Creek Park, Washington, D.C., to participate in a BioBlitz—a quick, 24-hour survey of species living in the park. Teams worked in 4-hour shifts throughout the park. By the time they were done, the teams had identified more than 650 species!

Teams included experts on different types of organisms such as birds, beetles, fungi, and plants. The experts used identification guides, or keys, to help them identify the organisms they found.

In this lab, you will first use a dichotomous key to identify sharks. A dichotomous key is built around pairs of statements that describe a visible trait. The reader must select the statement in each pair that best describes a specimen. By following the steps in the key, the reader narrows down the list of choices and finally names the specimen. After you have learned to use a dichotomous key, you will design your own key for a group of organisms.

Skills Focus

Observe, Classify, Compare and Contrast, Sequence

Materials

• reference materials

Pre-Lab Questions

1. **Observe** Name three different physical traits that are used in the shark dichotomous key.

   Answers may include: number of fins, body shape, mouth placement,

   and presence or absence of spines.

___

Big Idea
A dichotomous key is one way to organize and classify organisms.

Skills Objectives
Students will be able to
• identify an organism using a dichotomous key.
• design a dichotomous key.

Preparation Time
60–90 minutes if you identify the reference materials

Class Time
Part A: 15 minutes
Part B: 30 minutes; more if students must find appropriate reference materials

Group Size
Part A: Individuals
Part B: Small groups

Advance Preparation
Collect reference books and photographs that illustrate a variety of groups of living organisms or identify relevant Web sites. Avoid field guides that contain dichotomous keys.

2. Classify Do all the sharks you will try to identify belong to the same genus? Explain your answer.

No, because the first word in each of their scientific names is different.

3. Apply Concepts After you make a list of physical traits that you can use in your dichotomous key, how will you decide which trait to pick for the first step?

Sample answer: I will pick a trait that divides all the species into two smaller groups.

Procedure

Part A: Use a Dichotomous Key

1. Before you try to identify sharks, you need to understand a bit about shark anatomy. Figure 1 is a general shark drawing with labels showing the possible locations of fins. Refer to Figure 1 as you use the dichotomous key to identify the sharks in Figure 2.

2. Tear out the sheet with the shark drawings (pages 113–114). Choose one shark from Figure 2. Begin by reading statements 1a and 1b in the key. One of the statements describes the shark; the other does not. Choose the statement that describes the shark and follow the directions for that statement.

3. Continue following the steps in the key until you have identified the shark. Record the scientific and common name of the shark in the data table.

4. Repeat Steps 2 and 3 for the other sharks in Figure 2.

Figure 1 General external anatomy of shark

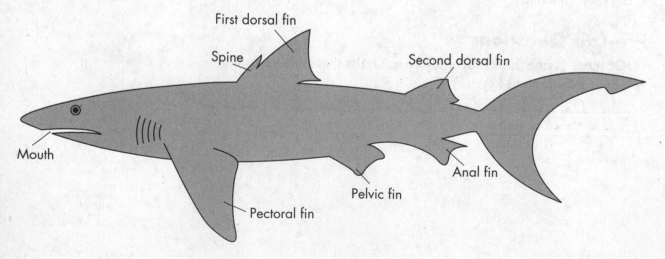

First dorsal fin

Spine

Second dorsal fin

Mouth

Pelvic fin

Anal fin

Pectoral fin

Dichotomous Key for Sharks

Step	Characteristic	Species
1a	Anal fin present . . . *Go to Step 2*	
1b	No anal fin . . . *Go to Step 6*	
2a	One dorsal fin	*Notorynchus cepedianus,* Sevengill shark
2b	Two dorsal fins . . . *Go to Step 3*	
3a	Spines on dorsal fins	*Heterodontus francisci,* Horn shark
3b	No spines on dorsal fins . . . *Go to Step 4*	
4a	Mouth at front of head	*Rhincodon typus,* Whale shark
4b	Mouth at bottom of head . . . *Go to Step 5*	
5a	Eyes on ends of hammerlike projection	*Sphyrna zygaena,* Smooth hammerhead
5b	No hammerlike head	*Carcharodon carcharias,* Great white shark
6a	Flattened body (like ray)	*Squatina squatina,* Angel shark
6b	Body not flattened . . . *Go to Step 7*	
7a	Long sawlike projection from snout	*Pristiophorus schroederi,* Bahamas sawshark
7b	No sawlike projection	*Somniosus microcephalus,* Greenland shark

Data Table

Shark	Scientific Name	Common Name
A	*Rhincodon typus*	Whale shark
B	*Carcharodon carcharias*	Great white shark
C	*Heterodontus francisci*	Horn shark
D	*Somniosus microcephalus*	Greenland shark
E	*Sphyrna zygaena*	Smooth hammerhead
F	*Squatina squatina*	Angel shark

Part B: Construct a Dichotomous Key

You will be working with a group of organisms such as snails, birds, antelopes, rodents, or aquarium fish. You will need to consult reference books or Web sites that include illustrations.

5. Choose a group of organisms. Then make a list of visible physical traits that vary among the species in the group.

_____

_____

_____

_____

_____

_____

_____

_____

_____

_____

_____

6. Choose 6 or 8 species from the group. On a separate sheet of paper make a simple drawing of each species. Use a letter to label each drawing. Record the scientific name and common name of each species next to the appropriate letter.

A: _____

B: _____

C: _____

D: _____

E: _____

F: _____

G: _____

H: _____

Step 7
Stress the need to make each pair of statements mutually exclusive descriptions of only one trait.

7. Use the space on page 111 to construct a dichotomous key for your group of organisms, using the key for sharks as a model.

8. Check the usefulness of your key by making a copy of your key and asking another student to use it to identify your drawings.

Dichotomous Key

Analyze and Conclude

1. **Predict** How would the dichotomous key for sharks need to change if you wanted to use it to identify 10 different sharks?

   Sample answer: Steps would need to be added to the key to distinguish the additional sharks from the rest of the sharks.

   _____

   _____

2. **Evaluate** What was the most challenging part of making your own dichotomous key?

   Sample answer: Figuring out the sequence of steps was the most challenging part.

   _____

   _____

3. **Infer** Suppose you had real specimens of your organisms instead of drawings. What other traits could you use to build a dichotomous key?

Answers can include any visible trait that is not captured in a line drawing, such as smell, color, or relative size of the organisms.

4. **Compare and Contrast** The shark dichotomous key groups three species that lack anal fins together. But a recent cladogram of sharks indicates that one of them (the Greenland shark) is actually most closely related to the Sevengill shark, which has an anal fin. What does this tell you about the difference between a dichotomous key and a cladogram?

Sample answer: A dichotomous key is a tool used to sort and identify organisms. The key does not sort organisms based on evolutionary relationships. In contrast, a cladogram organizes organisms into categories that reflect evolutionary descent.

5. **Draw Conclusions** In what way are the characters used to design a dichotomous key more limited than the characters that are used to build a cladogram?

Dichotomous keys use external physical characters, which can be observed easily and quickly. A cladogram can also use characters that are not easily observed, such as internal anatomy or DNA sequences.

6. **Infer** The dichotomous keys in this lab are used to trace organisms to the species level. Could keys be designed which classify unknown organisms to higher levels of the Linnaean system—to a family or order, for example? Why or why not?

Yes. Traits can be chosen to sort organisms to any of the levels of the Linnaean taxonomic system.

Extend Your Inquiry

Find a cladogram in your textbook or other reference that lists derived characters. Which of the derived characters could be used as traits in a dichotomous key? Which of the traits could not be used, and why?

Students are likely to find that some, but not all, of the traits could be used in a key. Traits that are not visible or that do not lend themselves to paired statements could not be used.

Figure 2 Shark species

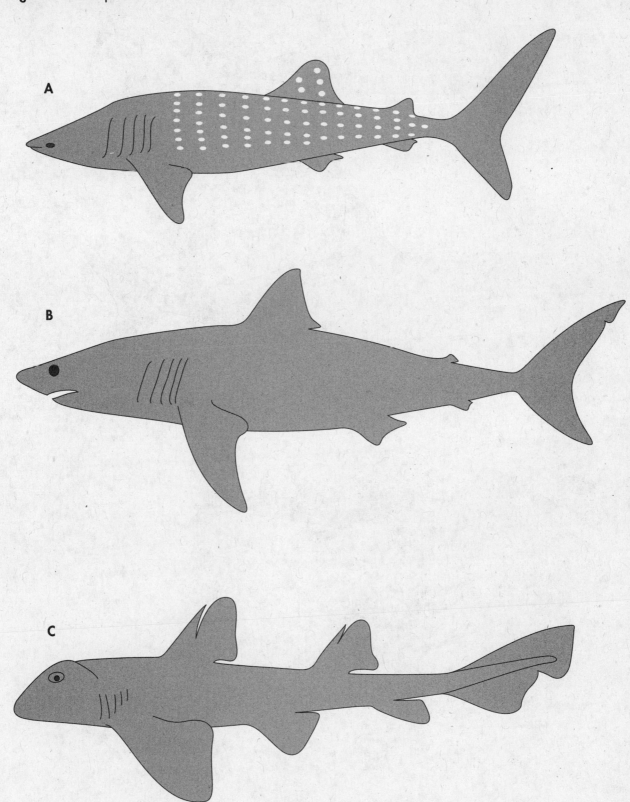

D

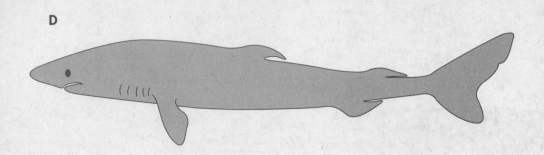

E

F

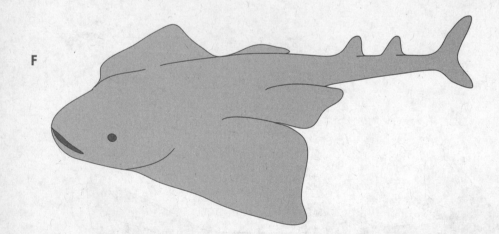

Chapter 19 Lab Using Index Fossils

Problem

How can fossils be used to determine the relative ages of rock layers?

Introduction

It is easy to compare the ages of fossils found in sedimentary rocks at one location. Fossils found in an upper rock layer will be younger than fossils found in a lower layer, unless the layers have been overturned. It is not as easy to compare the ages of fossils found in rocks at different locations. Scientists use index fossils to determine the relative ages of rock layers. Scientists use radiometric dating to find the actual age of rocks and fossils.

In this lab, you will work with drawings of rock layers from different locations. Each layer will contain at least two fossils. Using the fossils as clues, you will organize the layers from oldest to youngest.

Skills Focus

Interpret Visuals, Sequence, Draw Conclusions

Materials

• scissors

Safety ✂

Do not direct the points of the scissors toward yourself or others. Use the scissors only as instructed.

Pre-Lab Questions

1. **Organize Data** After you cut out the drawings of the rock layers, how will you begin the process of sorting the layers by age?

   Sample answer: I will use the Key to Fossils to identify the fossils in each

   layer.

2. **Infer** *Desmatosuchus* was a crocodile relative that lived only during the Triassic Period. Horsetails are plants that first appeared in the Triassic Period and still exist. Which of these organisms would be more useful as an index fossil for the Triassic Period? Why?

   The crocodile relative would be more useful as an index fossil for the

   Triassic Period because it would not occur in rock layers from other

   periods.

Big Idea
Scientists can use index fossils to determine the relative age of a rock layer or fossil.

Skills Objectives
Students will be able to
• identify fossils that might be used as index fossils.
• use fossils to determine the correct sequence of rock layers.

Class Time
35 minutes

Group Size
Individuals

Background
After students complete the lab, explain that most index fossils are tiny marine organisms that meet the general characteristics of index fossils. They need to be distinctive and geographically widespread. They need to undergo rapid evolution and, thus, exist in a geologically narrow timeframe. Only a few of the fossils in the key to fossils would qualify as index fossils.

3. Use Analogies Luke found a box of photos labeled 1970–1995. Each photo shows his entire extended family. No dates appear on the photos. Luke knows that his grandmother died in 1985 and his uncle was born in 1975. Luke's sister was born in 1990. How can Luke use this information to sort the photos into four batches? How are Luke's relatives similar to index fossils?

Sample answer: Possible batches are photos with (1) grandmother only from 1970–1975, (2) grandmother and uncle from 1975–1985, (3) uncle only from 1985–1990, and (4) uncle and sister from 1990–1995. The people are like index fossils because they exist in specific time ranges relative to the overall range of the photos.

Procedure

You will use fossils to order the rock layers pictured at the end of this lab. Nine of the layers represent periods from the Paleozoic and Mesozoic Eras. One layer represents the Cenozoic Era.

1. Tear out pages 121 and 123 at the end of this lab. Cut out each drawing of a rock layer. **NOTE:** The fossils are not drawn to scale.

2. Spread out the layers on a flat surface. Use the Key to Fossils to identify the fossils in each layer. Write the names of the fossils on the drawings. **NOTE:** Some of the drawings represent one species or one genus. Some represent a higher taxonomic level.

3. The oldest rock layer is from the Cambrian Period. Some organisms in this layer will not be found in any other layer. No organism in this layer still exists. Locate the layer that represents the Cambrian Period.

4. Look for fossils that are found in only two layers. Using this information, pair up layers that must represent consecutive periods in the geologic record.

5. Use other fossils to determine which layer in each pair is older and the order of all the layers from oldest to youngest.

6. Each drawing has a letter in the upper left corner. Use the letters to record the correct sequence of layers in the data table on page 118. Record the letter for the youngest layer in the first row and the letter for the oldest layer in the last row. Also record the names of the fossils found in each layer.

7. Use pages 560–563 in your textbook to identify the geologic period that corresponds to each rock layer.

Teaching Tip
You might want to display photographs or drawings of the organisms, especially organisms that don't have modern relatives.

Step 5
If students are having trouble with this step, ask leading questions that will draw their attention to relevant data.

Step 6
When the layers are in the right order, they spell "cretaceous."

Key to Fossils

acanthodian
(jawed fish with bony spines)

agnostid
(order of trilobites)

ammonite
(mollusk with coiled shell)

beetle
(order of insects)

Brachiosaurus
(long-necked dinosaur)

cockroach
(order of insects)

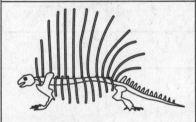

Edaphosaurus
(sail-backed herbivore)

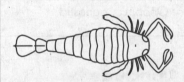

eurypterid
(large, ancient sea scorpion)

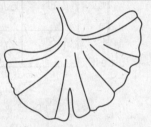

ginkgo
(tree with fan-shaped leaves)

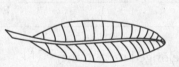

Glossopteris
(plant with veined leaves)

oak
(tree with broad leaves)

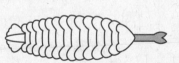

Opabinia
(small animal with five eyes)

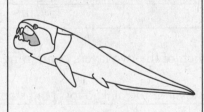

placoderm
(armored fish)

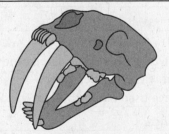

Smilodon
(saber-toothed cat)

Wiwaxia
(small, spiny bottom feeder)

Data Table		
Layer	Fossils Found	Geologic Period
C	*Smilodon*, oak, ginkgo, cockroach	Cenozoic
R	*Brachiosaurus*, oak, ginkgo, cockroach, ammonoid	Cretaceous
E	*Brachiosaurus*, ginkgo, cockroach, ammonoid	Jurassic
T	*Glossopteris*, ginkgo, cockroach, ammonoid	Triassic
A	*Glossopteris, Edaphosaurus*, cockroach, acanthodian, ammonoid, eurypterid	Permian
C	*Edaphosaurus*, cockroach, acanthodian, ammonoid, eurypterid	Carboniferous
E	ammonoid, acanthodian, placoderm, eurypterid	Devonian
O	acanthodian, placoderm, eurypterid	Silurian
U	eurypterid, agnostid	Ordovician
S	*Wiwaxia, Opabinia*, agnostid	Cambrian

youngest ↑   oldest ↓

Analyze and Conclude

1. **Analyze Data** How did you identify the layer from the Cambrian Period?
Sample Answer: Three fossils appeared in only one layer—*Smilodon, Wiwaxia,* and *Opabinia*. However, the *Smilodon* fossil was in a layer with organisms that still exist. By elimination, the layer with *Wiwaxia* and *Opabinia* had to be the Cambrian layer.

2. **Sequence** How did you identify the layer that belonged next to the Cambrian layer?
I found the only other layer that contained an agnostid fossil.

3. **Sequence** How were you able to determine which of the two layers containing a *Glossopteris* fossil was the older layer?
Students could have used either the acanthodian fossil or the ginkgo fossil to establish the correct sequence.

4. Draw Conclusions Why might a placoderm be a more useful index fossil than a cockroach?

The placoderm fossil is only found in rock layers from the Silurian and Devonian

Periods. Cockroach fossils can be found in rock layers from many different periods.

5. Infer Ammonoids are found in rock layers from six different geologic periods. Yet ammonoids are considered excellent index fossils. Explain why this is possible. *Hint:* See the note in Step 2 of the procedure.

Sample answer: If species within the order existed over a shorter time period, those

species could be used as index fossils.

6. Apply Concepts Provide two explanations for why a species might disappear from the fossil record.

Sample answer: A species might have become extinct or it might have evolved into

one or more new species.

Extend Your Inquiry

Mass extinctions occurred at the end of the Permian and Cretaceous Periods. Do research to find what scientists think may have caused these extinctions. Then decide whether any of these hypotheses could help to explain the current worldwide reduction in biodiversity.

At the end of the Permian, volcanic activity may have released large amounts of CO_2 into the atmosphere, producing global warming. Species were faced with increased levels of CO_2 and reduced levels of O_2. At the end of the Cretaceous, an asteroid impact probably led to massive fires and years of cold weather. These events were followed by a CO_2 spike and extremely warm weather. The current decline in biodiversity is probably due more to habitat destruction, but changes related to global warming could have a greater impact in the future.

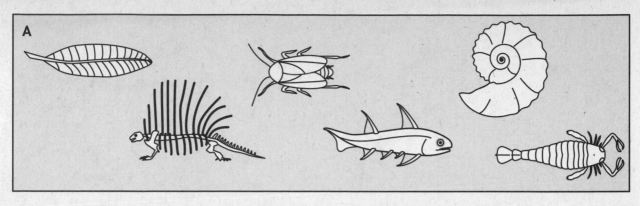

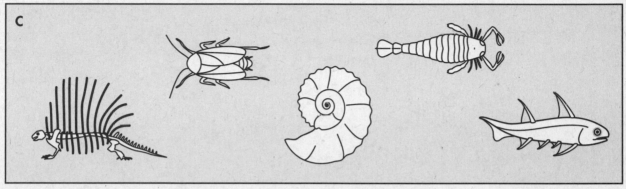

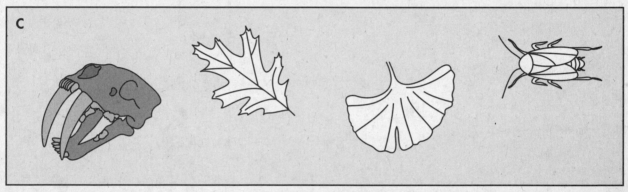

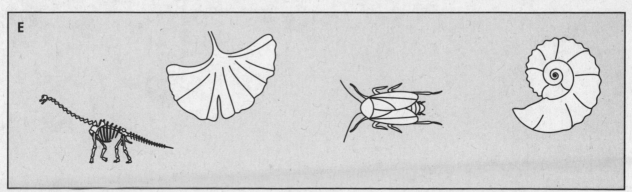

Guided Inquiry • Real-World Lab

Chapter 20 Lab Controlling Bacterial Growth

Problem
How can you determine the effectiveness of an antibiotic?

Introduction
Have you ever had an ear infection or strep throat? If you have, you likely used an antibiotic to treat the infection. Antibiotics work by blocking the growth and reproduction of bacteria. Doctors have to choose the right antibiotic for each infection because not all antibiotics work on all types of bacteria. For example, some bacteria have an outer membrane that surrounds the cell wall. Antibiotics that cannot pass through this membrane have no effect on those species of bacteria.

Bacteria that are not affected by an antibiotic are said to be resistant to that antibiotic. Over time, there has been an increase in antibiotic resistance. Bacteria that used to be killed by certain antibiotics are no longer responding to them. Some bacteria, such as MRSA, have built up many resistances. Scientists are trying to produce new drugs to kill these so-called "super bugs."

In this lab, you will test the effectiveness of antibiotics against two kinds of harmless bacteria. One of the bacteria has an outer membrane, and one does not.

Skills Focus
Observe, Measure, Draw Conclusions

Materials
- 2 agar plates
- glass-marking pencil
- 2 bacterial cultures
- 10 or more sterile glass beads
- disposal solution
- 2 sterile micropipettes
- 6 forceps
- 6 paper disks, 4 with antibiotics and 2 with distilled water
- masking tape
- metric ruler

Big Idea
Natural selection favors the emergence of bacteria that are resistant to antibiotics.

Skills Objectives
Students will be able to
- prepare bacterial cultures on agar plates.
- use sterile techniques.
- draw conclusions about the effectiveness of antibiotics.

Preparation Time
45 minutes if preparing plates; 30 minutes for other tasks

Class Time
Part A: 50 minutes
Part B: 15 minutes

Group Size
Small groups

Materials
Use penicillin and tetracycline antibiotic disks. Penicillin stops growth of the cell wall and generally affects only bacteria without an outer membrane. Tetracycline disrupts protein synthesis and will affect both types of bacteria.

Use a nonpathogenic strain of *Escherichia coli* for the bacteria with the outer membrane. Use *Bacillus subtilis* or *Staphylococcus epidermidis* for the bacteria without the outer membrane.

Advance Preparation
You can purchase prepared agar plates, or you can prepare your own plates 2 to 3 days before the lab. Use sterile bottled Luria or nutrient agar. Remove the lid and place the bottle in a boiling water bath until the agar melts.

Allow the bottle to cool until you can hold it in your hand. Pour the agar into small petri dishes. Cover and store the dishes at room temperature. Store them upside down to prevent condensation.

Advance Prep (cont.)
Either use prepared tubes of
nutrient broth or follow the
instructions on a package of
dehydrated broth. Inoculate
several cultures of the bacteria
to be used in the lab. Label the
cultures clearly.

Sterilize the micropipettes
and glass beads in containers
in an autoclave. Do not open
the containers until students
are ready to use the items in
the lab.

The day before the lab,
prepare a disposal solution of
10% bleach.

Safety
Identify students with allergies
to the antibiotics being used.
Provide an alternate activity in
a different location.

Safety 🐽 🧤 🗑 🖐

Wear goggles and gloves while working with bacterial cultures. Even
though you are working with harmless bacteria, follow your teacher's
instructions about sterile techniques. For example, any item that touches
the cultures should not touch your skin or your lab table. Follow your
teacher's instructions about safe disposal of materials. Wash your hands
thoroughly with soap and warm water before leaving the lab. Tell your
teacher before the lab if you are allergic to penicillin or tetracycline.

Pre-Lab Questions

1. Relate Cause and Effect How will you know whether an antibiotic is
able to control the growth of bacteria?

There will be a clear space on the agar plate around the antibiotic disk.

_____

2. Design an Experiment Why is it important to leave space between
the disks on the agar plates?

Sample answer: If the disks are too close together, it will be difficult to

determine which antibiotic was responsible for the results.

_____

3. Control Variables Why must you avoid direct contact between your
hands and the antibiotic disks?

Sample answer: If my hands were to touch the disks, I might transfer

bacteria from my hands, which could add an unwanted variable to the

experiment.

_____

Procedure

Part A: Setting Up the Experiment

When you add items to an agar plate, replace the lid as soon as you are
done to minimize the exposure of the plates to the air.

Step 2
Provide abbreviations for
students to use when marking
their plates.

1. Put on goggles and plastic gloves.

2. Obtain two agar plates. Use a glass-marking pencil to mark each
   lid with the name of one of the bacteria you will be testing. Use the
   pencil to divide the bottom of each plate into thirds. In two of
   the sections, write the names of the antibiotics you will use. Mark the
   third section Distilled Water.

3. Obtain a bacterial culture. Pour about five sterile glass beads into the
   agar plate labeled with the name of that bacteria.

4. Use a micropipette to transfer a few drops of the culture to the agar plate. Replace the lid and tilt the plate in different directions so that the beads spread the culture medium across the plate.

5. Remove the lid and carefully pour off the beads into the disposal solution. Replace the lid.

6. Repeat Steps 3 through 5 for the second culture.

7. Take the lid off one agar plate. Using forceps, place the first antibiotic disk on the agar in the appropriate section of the plate. Press the disk flat so it sticks to the surface of the agar. Don't move the disk once it is in place. CAUTION: Do not touch the disk or the agar with your hands.

8. Use a new forceps to place the second antibiotic disk on the agar in its section of the plate. Don't move the disk once it is in place.

9. Use a third forceps to add a disk that has been soaked in distilled water to the section marked Distilled Water. Replace the lid.

10. Tape the lid shut at two locations on opposite sides of the plate.

11. Repeat Steps 7 through 10 with the second agar plate.

12. Turn the plates upside down and incubate the cultures overnight at 37°C or for 2–3 days at room temperature.

Part B: Observing the Plates

During the incubation period, a milky film of bacteria should have formed on the agar.

13. Examine each plate. Look in particular at the areas immediately around the three disks. CAUTION: Do not uncover the plates.

14. Measure the diameter of any clear zones around the three disks. A clear zone is a zone without any noticeable bacteria. Record your data in the table below.

15. Follow your teacher's instructions for disposal of the cultures.

Step 10
Make sure the tape does not cover the viewing area.

Step 12
You can use a heating pad on its lowest setting instead of an incubator. You can prevent condensation by placing the plates under the heating pad. Once you have used a heating pad as a bacterial incubator, do not use it at home.

Step 15
To kill the bacteria before disposal, soak the plates in a 10% bleach solution for 1 hour, or autoclave them in a biohazard bag for 30 minutes.

Sample Data

Data Table		
Name of Bacteria	Material on Disk	Clear Zone Diameter (mm)
Escherichia coli	Penicillin	No
	Tetracycline	Yes
	Distilled water	No
Bacillus subtilis or Staphylococcus epidermidis	Penicillin	Yes
	Tetracycline	Yes
	Distilled water	No

Analyze and Conclude

1. Design an Experiment What is the purpose of the disk soaked in distilled water?

Sample answer: The disk soaked in distilled water acts as a control to ensure that any results are due solely to the antibiotics and not to the disk itself.

2. Infer Is there any evidence of antibiotic-resistant bacteria on your plates? Explain.

With the recommended bacteria and antibiotics, students should see clusters of bacteria growing around the penicillin disk on one agar plate.

3. Draw Conclusions Which antibiotic, or antibiotics, were effective against each type of bacteria?

Sample answer: Tetracycline was effective against both types of bacteria. Penicillin was effective only against *Bacillus subtilis*.

4. Apply Concepts Some antibiotics are less effective against a specific type of bacteria after prolonged and repeated use. What do you think is responsible for this pattern? *Hint:* Think about the principle of natural selection.

Sample answer: The antibiotic does not kill all the bacteria in the population. The surviving bacteria are resistant to the antibiotic and will produce offspring that inherit this resistance.

5. Infer Suppose you are prescribed an antibiotic to treat a bacterial infection. Your doctor tells you to take the antibiotic for 10 days even if you feel better before then. Why should you continue taking the antibiotic for the full 10 days?

Sample answer: You may feel better after the antibiotic has killed most of the bacteria causing your infection. If you stop taking the antibiotic early, any surviving bacteria will reproduce and the infection could recur.

Extend Your Inquiry

Antibiotics are not the only defense against bacteria. Household products often contain ingredients that can kill bacteria. Choose three household products and test their effectiveness against bacteria. Possible examples include alcohol, hand sanitizers, hand soap, dishwashing detergent, and mouthwash.

Students should test the products against both types of bacteria.

Chapter 21 Lab Mushroom Farming

Problem
How does the amount of available light affect mushroom growth?

Introduction
Mushrooms are probably the type of fungus most familiar to you. You can find them in lawns, on rotting logs, or as an ingredient on pizza. The "mushroom" part of a fungus is the fruiting body, which is involved in reproduction. Spores are produced in the fruiting body. The largest part of a fungus, the mycelium, actually grows underground. The mycelium is the part of the fungus that absorbs water and nutrients from the soil. Under the right conditions, fruiting bodies grow from the mycelium.

In this lab, you will design an experiment to determine the effect of light on the growth of a fruiting body. The class will be divided into groups with each group assigned to monitor one of three experimental setups. The groups will share their results and analyze the pooled data.

Skills Focus
Form a Hypothesis, Design an Experiment, Organize Data

Materials
- 3 mushroom-growing kits
- spray bottles with water
- metric rulers

Safety
Wear goggles and gloves if you are involved in the initial setup of a mushroom farm. Handle the mushrooms gently when you make measurements, and wash your hands thoroughly with soap and warm water when you are done. If you are sensitive to mold, don't handle the mushrooms. Don't eat the mushrooms grown in this lab.

Big Idea
Under the right conditions, fungi will thrive and help maintain the equilibrium in their ecosystems.

Skills Objectives
Students will be able to
- form a hypothesis about the impact of an abiotic factor on mushroom growth.
- design an experiment to test their hypothesis.
- relate the results to the concept of optimum conditions.

Preparation Time
Little time is needed if you order premade kits.

Class Time
Part A: 30 minutes
Part B: 10 minutes for setup plus 5 minutes per day for 1–2 weeks to maintain and observe

Group Size
Part A: Class
Part B: Large groups

Advance Preparation
Order kits 1–2 weeks ahead from biological supply houses or other sites on the Internet.

Safety
Students need to wear goggles while preparing the mushroom farms to avoid getting growth medium in their eyes. Check for possible allergies to fungi or the growth medium.

Pre-Lab Questions

1. Infer Where will the mushrooms get the nutrients that they need to grow and develop?

The growing medium contains food that the mushrooms can digest.

_____

_____

2. Relate Cause and Effect Why will you have to wait about 10 days to observe the mushrooms?

The mushroom spores must germinate and the mycelium form before

the fruiting bodies will appear.

_____

_____

3. Apply Concepts The mushrooms you will grow are a variety that is sold in food stores. Why do the instructions warn you not to eat the mushrooms?

Sample answer: As a general rule, food should never be consumed in the

lab. Plus, a lab is not an appropriate environment for growing food.

_____

_____

Procedure

Part A: Design Your Experiment

You need to plan the experiment as a class to ensure that all the variables are controlled in each experimental setup, except for the amount of light.

1. Form a Hypothesis How do you think the amount of light will affect mushroom growth? Record your hypothesis below.

Hypothesis: *Sample answer:* Mushrooms will grow best in the dark.

2. Control Variables Record the independent and dependent variables you will test as a class.

Independent Variable: amount of light _____

Dependent Variable: mushroom growth _____

Teaching Tip
Fruiting bodies usually will not grow without any exposure to light. However, the kit that is stored in darkness should be exposed to sufficient light while students mist and observe.

Step 2
If you can afford more than three kits, either have two groups test each condition, or have some groups design an experiment to test the effect of the amount of moisture.

3. **Design an Experiment** As a class, develop a procedure for testing how different light conditions affect the growth of mushrooms. Record the details of your plan, including how you will track changes in the dependent variable and how you will control other variables. Also record your expected outcome.

Experimental Design: <u>Students can grow one farm in darkness, a</u> <u>second in classroom light, and a third in direct light. Using the same</u> <u>type of kit for each farm should control variables such as the amount of</u> <u>nutrients. The temperature will need to be similar in all three locations.</u> <u>Students will need to follow the instructions in Step 7 to control the</u> <u>amount of moisture. Students can use variables such as number, height,</u> <u>and general appearance of fruiting bodies to track the dependent</u> <u>variable.</u>

Expected Outcome: _____

_____

_____

_____

Step 3
For the setup in direct light, fluorescent grow lights can be substituted for natural light. Do not use incandescent lights, which tend to dry out the fruiting bodies.
   For the setup in classroom light, store the setup away from the windows. For the setup in darkness, store the setup in a cabinet or in a box.

4. **Organize Data** Make a data table in the space below. Include a column for each type of observation you will make to track the dependent variable. Include enough rows to record up to two weeks of observations. In the title row of the table, include a description of the setup your group will monitor.

Step 4
Encourage students to make multiple observations, both qualitative and quantitative.

Sample Table

Observations of Mushrooms Grown in Direct Light			
Day	Number of Fruiting Bodies	Height of Tallest Fruiting Body (cm)	General Appearance

Step 5
Most kits will arrive inoculated with spores. Spraying water on the medium will cause the spores to germinate.

Step 6
Many kits come with a plastic tent to retain moisture. You can make your own tents by poking small holes in appropriately sized plastic bags.

Step 7
Have all groups spray extra water on the fungi on Friday unless someone is able to mist the setups over the weekend.

Step 8
Have volunteers do the second misting in the afternoon. Be sure students replace the tents after misting the fungi.

Step 9
Either show students a mature mushroom or display an image.

Step 10
You may want to keep the farms for the Extend Your Inquiry activity.

Disposal
Mushroom farms can be disposed of in the trash.

Part B: Observing Your Mushroom Farm

Not everyone in your group will be able to do every task, but everyone in the group should do some tasks.

5. Follow your teacher's instructions for setting up your group's farm. The kit should include a container, growth medium, and mushroom spores. The spores may come mixed with the growth medium, or you may need to add them to the medium. **CAUTION:** Those who set up the kit should wash their hands thoroughly with soap and warm water when they are done.

6. Use the spray bottle to mist the growth medium and moisten the spores. Place the farm in your group's assigned location.

7. Mist the medium once a day. To control the amount of water, spray the medium 4 times at each misting. **CAUTION:** Make sure the nozzle on the spray bottle is set to "spray."

8. In about 10 days you should see bumpy growths forming on the surface of your farm. These bumps are the fruiting bodies. Inform your teacher when you notice the growths. Your farm will need to be misted twice a day from this point on.

9. From the day you notice the first growths, the fruiting bodies will need about 4–6 days to mature. A fruiting body is mature when you can see fully formed gill ridges on the underside of the cap. Once your mushrooms have matured, begin making daily observations. Record these observations in your data table. **CAUTION:** If you need to hold the mushrooms to make measurements, handle them gently. Wash your hands thoroughly with soap and warm water when you are done.

10. Once the experiment is complete, follow your teacher's instructions for cleanup and disposal of materials.

11. Post your results on the board for the rest of the class to see.

Analyze and Conclude

1. Analyze Data Did fruiting bodies appear in all three experimental setups?

Sample answer: Yes, fruiting bodies grew under all three lighting conditions.

2. Form an Operational Definition What standard did you use to decide which lighting condition was optimum? The word *optimum* means "the best out of a number of possible options."

Answers will vary. Students are likely to choose the number of mushrooms or the size of the mushrooms as their criterion.

3. Draw Conclusions Based on your answer to Question 2, which light condition was optimum for the growth of mushrooms?

Answers will vary depending on the criterion chosen in Question 2. Moderate light tends to produce tall, well-formed club fungi.

4. Perform Error Analysis Was there a possible source of error in the design of the experiment? If so, how could you change the procedure to improve your results?

Students may say that having people take turns misting the farms made it hard to control the amount of moisture. This error could be corrected by having one person do all the misting. (Some students may say that having one farm in darkness and one in direct light made it hard to control the temperature.)

5. Infer Why might mushroom farmers be concerned about the overall appearance of their mushrooms?

Sample answer: Mushrooms that are consistent in color and well-shaped are likely to be more appealing to customers.

Extend Your Inquiry

How does the amount of moisture affect mushroom growth? Select the container that had the best growth. For three days, mist the mushrooms only once a day and observe what happens. After the third day, stop misting the mushrooms and observe what happens.

The mushrooms should be less plump with reduced misting and should dry out quickly with no misting. Mushrooms do not have a protective covering, like the cuticle on a leaf, to retain moisture.

Chapter 22 Lab Exploring Plant Diversity

Problem

How many different kinds of plants are in a small ecosystem?

Introduction

On your walk or ride to school, you may pass fields with crops, a dense forest, a city park with flowerbeds, or an overgrown vacant lot. In fields where a crop is growing, all the plants will look similar. But in most other areas, you should see a variety of plants—possibly tall shade trees, flowering shrubs, climbing vines, and grass. This variation tells you that many plant species can grow in the same area.

Ecologists often count the number of species in an ecosystem and note whether the species are native to the area. In general, a high degree of diversity is a sign of a healthy, balanced ecosystem. Sometimes nonnative plants compete so well that they crowd out native species and reduce diversity. Humans can lower natural diversity by clearing land for farms and buildings.

In this lab, you will explore a small, local ecosystem and survey its plant diversity. You will also identify as many plants as possible and infer the conditions in which these plants thrive.

Skills Focus

Observe, Measure, Classify, Infer

Materials

- notepad or notebook
- protective work gloves
- measuring tape
- tweezers
- scissors
- small plastic bags
- labels
- hand lens
- field guides for plants
- camera (optional)

Safety 🧤 🌱 ✂️ 🧤

Be aware of dangerous plants that are common in your area. To avoid possible contact with poisonous or prickly plants, wear work gloves at all times. Alert your teacher to any allergies you may have. Do not disturb the nests of any animals you may encounter. Use scissors only as instructed. When you are done, wash your hands thoroughly with soap and warm water.

Big Idea
Plants are a very diverse group of organisms with different characteristics that are adapted to a wide range of ecosystems.

Skills Objectives
Students will be able to
- observe and classify diverse plant species.
- use reference materials to identify plants based on field notes, drawings, and samples.

Preparation Time
You may need a few hours to identify possible sites and, if necessary, obtain permission to use a site.

Class Time
Part A: 1–2 class periods for field observations
Part B: 40 minutes

Group Size
Small groups

Safety
Ask students about allergies to plants. Have a first-aid kit to deal with injuries from thorns, barbs, or stinging insects.

Avoid areas with poison ivy, poison oak, or poison sumac, and make sure students can identify harmful plants.

Any area chosen should be away from traffic or other obvious dangers, such as ditches or construction debris.

Advance Preparation
Find a park, wooded area, large yard, or an overgrown vacant lot with a diversity of plant types. If necessary, get permission to visit. Ask if students may collect small samples. An ideal area would be large enough so that each group can be assigned to a different section.

If you are required to have signed permission slips for a field trip, distribute the slips a few weeks before the trip and check that all are returned.

Pre-Lab Questions

1. Design an Experiment What are some ways that you can make sure that you survey all the plants in your ecosystem?

Answers will vary, but students might suggest dividing the area into smaller sections and investigating one section at a time. Or they may suggest doing the survey by type of plants—trees, shrubs, and so on.

_____

2. Classify What should you do if you are not sure that an organism is a plant?

Sample answer: I would record my observations of the organism and use reference materials later to figure out if the organism is a plant.

_____

_____

3. Infer Why might you want to use a regional field guide rather than a national field guide when identifying plants?

Sample answer: The national field guide will include many plants that don't grow in my region. It also may exclude some plants that do grow in the region.

_____

_____

Procedure

Part A: Survey Your Ecosystem

In Part A, you will work with a group to survey a local ecosystem. It may be a self-contained ecosystem or part of a larger ecosystem. You will be using the information you gather in Part A to help you identify the plants in Part B.

Step 1
If a map exists for the chosen ecosystem, provide copies for students to consult while they decide how to survey the area.

1. Decide as a group how you will ensure that you will survey the entire assigned area.

2. Record a general description of your site. Include information such as its location, whether it is sunny or shady, whether it is flat or sloped, and whether it is sheltered or windy.

3. Make a sketch of the area. Note the location of any fences, paths, nearby buildings, or sources of water. **CAUTION:** Always wear protective work gloves when handling plants outdoors.

4. Following the plan you agreed on, document the plants you observe. Assign a number to each species. Use the number to record the location of the plant on your sketch of the ecosystem. Make a drawing of each plant in your notepad. Include the assigned number with the drawing. Also include information that will help you identify the plant, such as its height, the shape and length of any leaves, and the color of any flowers.

5. If you have permission, collect pieces of plants in plastic bags. Label each bag with the plant's assigned number. Do not put samples from more than one plant in the same bag.

Part B: Classify the Plants

6. Use the data table to summarize your observations. For plant type, use the following categories: woody plant (trees, shrubs, and vines), herbaceous plant (grasses, weeds, small flowering plants), fern, or groundcover (mosses, lichens). If you found more species than will fit in the table, continue the table on a separate sheet of paper.

Step 4
If students use a camera in place of drawings, they need to match the order of the photos to the assigned numbers. They also need to use the notepad to record data they would have written on the drawings.

Step 5
Let students know whether they have permission to take samples and, if so, explain what they can collect and what they should not collect.

Data Table: Summary of Survey Results			
Assigned Number	Plant Type	Observations	Name

Step 7
If students are having trouble identifying some plants, have them check with a group that found and identified the same plant.

7. Use print references and Web sites to identify the plants you observed. You may not be able to identify all the plants to the species level. Record the best information you can find. For example, you might identify a maple tree as genus *Acer* but not have enough information to decide which species of maple it is. For some plants, you may not be able to get more specific than the plant's family.

8. Add a key to your sketch of the ecosystem in which you identify each numbered species. Display and compare your sketch with the sketches from other groups.

Analyze and Conclude

1. **Communicate** Describe the general nature of the area you surveyed.

Answers will vary depending on the site but should contain information that provides a clear picture of the location.

_____

_____

_____

_____

2. **Design an Experiment** How did your group ensure that you surveyed the entire area?

Look for specifics such as how students divided the work by laying out a grid system or by focusing on one category of plant at a time.

_____

_____

_____

3. **Form a Hypothesis** Why do you think your ecosystem contained as many (or as few) species as were present?

Students' hypotheses should allude to the general nature of the area and the amount of human care. A wild field, for example, will likely have more diversity than a small public park.

_____

_____

_____

4. Compare and Contrast Did other groups find plants that you did not? If so, why do you think that happened?

Sample answer: Areas may have different plants because of variation in abiotic and biotic factors. For example, one area may receive more direct sunlight or be less windy. Ground cover that requires shade can thrive in an area with large shade trees.

_____

_____

_____

5. Predict Would the survey results be different at another time of the year? Explain your answer.

The results would be different at another time of the year because some plants grow for only part of the year. Trees and bushes would be visible all year, but other plants have shorter life cycles. For example, bulb plants such as tulips grow and bloom in spring and are gone by summer. Many herbaceous plants that grow all summer die back in the fall.

_____

Extend Your Inquiry

An invasive species is one that is not native to a region and whose growth is uncontrolled. Invasive plant species generally spread easily, grow rapidly, and tolerate many different environments. Pick one local invasive plant species. Find out whether it was introduced accidentally or deliberately, what problems it has caused, and what is being done to control it. Explain why invasive species are hard to eradicate.

Most regions have a least one notable invasive plant species. Some examples are Giant Hogweed (*Heracleum mantegazzianum*), Japanese knotweed (*Polygonum cuspidatum*), cheatgrass (*Bromus tectorum*), kudzu (*Pueraria montana*), and tree of heaven (*Ailanthus altissima*). Students should conclude that invasive species are hard to eradicate because the factors that kept them in check in their native regions are missing from their current ecosystems.

Guided Inquiry • Design Your Own Lab

Chapter 23 Lab **Identifying Growth Zones in Roots**

Problem

Where does growth occur in plant roots?

Introduction

The tissues in plant roots perform many different functions. Some tissues produce food, some provide support, and others absorb water and nutrients. As the root grows, the number of cells in these tissues increases. The new cells are formed from undifferentiated cell clusters called meristems.

In this lab, you will grow bean seedlings. You will use the seedlings to determine the location of a root's apical meristem, which is where lengthwise growth occurs in roots.

Skills Focus

Design an Experiment, Measure, Organize Data, Analyze Data

Materials

- 150-mL beaker
- paper towels
- 4 large bean seeds
- petri dish
- masking tape
- metric ruler
- fine-tip permanent marker

Safety 🥽 🧤 ✋

If you have glass petri dishes or beakers, check them for cracks and chips. Alert your teacher if you break a glass object. Handle the seedlings only as instructed. If you are allergic to certain plants or seeds, tell your teacher. Wash your hands thoroughly with soap and warm water before leaving the lab.

Big Idea
Each type of plant tissue has one or more specific functions.

Skills Objectives
Students will be able to
- form a hypothesis about the growth of plant tissues.
- design an experiment to test the hypothesis.
- relate plant structure to function.

Preparation Time
15 minutes

Class Time
15 minutes for Part A setup
30 minutes for Part B setup
30 minutes to obtain final data

Group Size
Small groups

Materials
You can use corn or pea seeds instead of bean seeds.

Safety
Students can handle the seedlings with their bare hands, as long as they wash their hands thoroughly before leaving the lab.

Teaching Tip
To allow enough time for root growth, have students "plant" their seeds on a Friday and mark the roots on Monday.

Teaching Tip
To enhance the opportunity
for inquiry, consider having
students do the experiment
before you teach Lesson 23.2.

Pre-Lab Questions

1. **Predict** A root is marked at two points along its length. What will happen to the distance between these marks if the root grows longer only near the tip? What will happen if growth occurs evenly along the entire length of the root?

   The marks will stay the same distance apart if growth occurs only near the tip. If growth occurs evenly all along the root, then the distance between the marks will increase.

2. **Design an Experiment** The procedure in Part A asks you to use four seeds. Why not use two seeds instead?

   Sample answer: One seed might not germinate, or one seedling might die before the experiment is done. Having a larger sample makes it more likely that the gathered data is typical (not the result of abnormal growth).

3. **Design an Experiment** How will you keep track of which seedling is which?

   Sample answer: Use a small piece of tape on the outside of the beaker to label the location of each seedling. Remove only one seedling at a time from the beaker when making measurements.

Procedure

In Part A, you will grow plants from bean seeds. In Part B, you will design an experiment to determine where growth occurs along the roots of these plants.

Part A: Seed Germination

Step 2
The paper towels in the
beaker must be kept damp
throughout the experiment.

Step 3
Students should keep seeds
away from the bottom of the
beaker not only to avoid the
standing water but also to
provide room for growth.

1. Fill the 150-mL beaker with loosely crumpled paper towels.

2. Dampen the towels with water, leaving standing water 1 cm deep in the bottom of the beaker.

3. Place four seeds between the damp towels and the sides of the beaker. Distribute the seeds evenly around the beaker. **CAUTION:** Do not allow any of the seeds to touch the water in the bottom of the beaker. Cover the beaker with a petri dish.

4. After three days, water your seeds again.

Part B: Design an Experiment

Wait until the roots are at least 20 mm long to do Part B. While you are waiting, plan your procedure. To mark the roots, you will need to remove the seedlings from the beaker. CAUTION: You will need to handle the seedlings gently to avoid breaking the roots or separating them from either half of the bean.

5. **Form a Hypothesis** Where does the growth occur that causes a root to increase in length? Record the hypothesis you will test to answer this question.

   Hypothesis: *Sample answer:* The growth that causes a root to increase in length will occur only near the tip of the root.

   _____

6. **Describe Your Plan** Describe the procedure you will use to test your hypothesis. As you develop your plan, consider the following questions. How many marks will you make on each root? How will you distribute the marks along the root? What measurements will you make initially? Should you wait a few days before measuring the roots again?

   Experimental Plan: If students make fewer than three or four marks, they will have trouble pinpointing the location of the apical meristem. Ideally, the marks should be placed so that they divide the root into roughly equal sections. However, the marks do not have to be in exactly the same location on each root. Students should measure the initial distance from the tip of the root to each mark. Given the rate of growth, encourage students to make only one additional set of measurements about three days after the initial set.

   _____

   _____

   _____

   _____

   _____

   _____

   _____

7. **Control Variables** What will your independent variable be? What will your dependent variable be?

   Independent Variable: initial distance from root tip to marks

   Dependent Variable: change in distance from root tip to marks

Step 8
Make sure that students plan to place one mark close to the tip of the root.

8. Construct a data table in the space below to record your measurements of the distance from the root tip to each mark. Leave space to record both the initial and final measurements. Include a column for observations. Review your procedure with your teacher before you do the experiment.

9. If you plan to do the Extend Your Inquiry experiment, keep growing your seedlings. Otherwise, follow your teacher's instructions for cleanup and disposal of materials.

Sample Table With Data

Data Table 1: Distance From Root Tip (mm)		Mark 1	Mark 2	Mark 3	Mark 4	Observations
Seedling 1	Initial	3	10	15	20	Straight root
	Final	3	33	39	45	
Seedling 2	Initial	3	10	15	20	Curled root
	Final	3	32	38	43	
Seedling 3	Initial	3	10	15	20	Leaves forming
	Final	3	33	38	42	
Seedling 4	Initial	—	—	—	—	Failed to germinate
	Final	—	—	—	—	

Analyze and Conclude

1. **Calculate** Use the data you collected to calculate the distances between marks for both the initial and final measurements. Record your results in Data Table 2.

Sample Data

Data Table 2: Distance Between Marks (mm)		Tip to Mark 1	Mark 1 to Mark 2	Mark 2 to Mark 3	Mark 3 to Mark 4
Seedling 1	Initial	3	7	5	5
	Final	25	8	5	6
Seedling 2	Initial	3	7	5	5
	Final	26	7	5	5
Seedling 3	Initial	3	7	5	5
	Final	25	7	6	6

2. **Interpret Tables** What patterns of growth are revealed by the data in Data Table 2?

Sample answer: The distance from the root tip to Mark 1 increased, while the other

distances remained constant (within the margin of error for the measurements).

_____

_____

3. **Draw Conclusions** In what region of the root is the apical meristem located? Give a reason for your answer.

The apical meristem is located within 3 mm of the root tip because that is the region

in which growth occurred.

_____

_____

4. **Infer** Do you think it would be adaptive for root growth to occur at the very tip of the root? Why or why not?

Sample answer: No, because the cells at the very tip of a root can be scraped off as

the root pushes through the soil.

_____

_____

5. **Compare and Contrast** Which cells in animals are comparable to cells in plant meristems, and why?

Undifferentiated stem cells in animals are comparable to the undifferentiated cells

produced in plant meristems.

_____

_____

Extend Your Inquiry

A driver backed a car into a young tree, which left a scar in the bark one meter from the ground. Will the scar remain at the same distance from the ground as the tree grows? Design an experiment using your bean seedlings to determine where most stem growth occurs.

Students can make marks along the stems similar to the marks they made along the roots. Students should discover that the stem also grows from its tip. Thus, the position of the scar on the bark should not change as the tree grows taller.

Chapter 24 Lab Plant Hormones and Leaves

Problem

How does a plant hormone affect leaf loss?

Introduction

Seasonal leaf loss is an adaptation of plants to cold weather. Autumn in temperate biomes is a time of decreasing temperatures and light intensity. As the ground begins to freeze, water becomes more difficult to obtain. Each of these factors contributes to a decrease in the rate of photosynthesis. Deciduous plants respond to these changes by beginning to break down chlorophyll. In some plants, the colors of accessory pigments are visible for a short time before leaves drop for the winter.

Two classes of hormones, auxins and ethylene, are involved when trees lose their leaves in autumn. Changes in hormone concentrations cause cells near the base of the leaf petiole to break down. This area, called the abscission zone, becomes a weak point, which is vulnerable to damage. A gust of wind, a heavy rain, even the weight of the leaf can cause the petiole to break off. In this lab, you will test the effect of auxins on petioles.

Skills Focus

Observe, Draw Conclusions, Apply Concepts

Materials

- leafy plant
- masking tape
- permanent marker
- scissors
- string
- toothpick
- auxin paste
- plastic container or tray

Safety 🗝 🧤 ✂️ ⚗️ 🌱

Wear goggles while you are working with the auxin paste. Wear gloves to protect your skin against a possible reaction from the paste. Wash your hands thoroughly with soap and warm water immediately after you handle the paste. Use the scissors only as instructed. Do not direct the points of the scissors toward yourself or others. Alert your teacher if you suspect you are allergic to the plant species used in the lab.

Big Idea

Hormones serve as signals that control development of cells, tissues, and organs.

Skills Objectives

Students will be able to
- test the effect of a plant hormone on leaf loss.
- infer the effect of another plant hormone on leaf loss.

Preparation Time

1 hour for transplanting seedlings; 2 hours for preparing and planting seeds

Class Time

30 minutes plus 5 minutes per class period over 2 weeks

Group Size

Small groups

Materials

Use a leafy plant, such as *Coleus* or bean plants, with strong petioles that are 1–2 cm long.

Advance Preparation

Either buy IAA paste or make your own by mixing 100 mg of IAA (indole-3-acetic acid) powder with 25 g of lanolin (from a pharmacy).

If you buy six-packs or four-packs of seedlings, transplant the plants a few days before the lab. Use 4-inch plastic pots and add extra potting soil.

If you grow your own bean plants, start at least two weeks in advance. Soak bean seeds overnight. Rinse them in a 1% bleach solution. Plant one or two seeds in 4-inch pots in sterilized potting soil.

Safety

Be aware of possible student allergies to the plants you use.

Pre-Lab Questions

1. Use Visuals Draw a simple leaf. Label the blade and the petiole.

Students should label the flat area as the blade and the thin stalk as the petiole.

2. Control Variables What is the control in this experiment?

The control is the petiole that is not treated with auxin paste.

_____

3. Infer How will auxins move from the paste to the base of the petiole?

Sample answer: Auxins will move through the layer of vascular tissue

(specifically phloem) in the petiole.

_____

_____

Procedure

1. Obtain a leafy plant from your teacher. Apply a piece of masking tape to the plant's container and use a permanent marker to label the plant with your group number or initials.

2. Use the scissors to carefully cut off *only* the leaf blade from two leaves. **CAUTION:** Do not cut off any part of the petioles.

3. Loosely tie a small piece of string to one of the petioles that is missing a blade.

4. Use a toothpick to apply a small amount of the auxin paste to the cut end of the petiole with the string.

5. Set your plant in a plastic container or tray to catch water that may overflow when you water your plant. Place the plant in a sunny location and water it for the next two weeks as directed by your teacher.

Teaching Tip
Plants must have at least two sets of true leaves so that students can remove two leaf blades.

Step 2
Stress that students need to leave the full length of the petiole intact when they remove the blade.

Step 5
Provide appropriate watering instructions for the type of plant you use.

6. Observe the petioles and the uncut leaves during each class period over the next two weeks. Make a data table in the space below to record your observations.

Data Table	
Day	Observations
1	
2	
3	
4	
7	
8	
9	
10	
11	

Step 6
The cut petiole not treated with auxin paste should drop off the plant. The other cut petiole and petioles with leaf blades still attached should not drop off.

Disposal
Auxin paste may be flushed down the drain. Plants and soil may be disposed of in the trash.

Analyze and Conclude

1. Communicate What happened to the petioles and the uncut leaves during the two weeks you observed the plant?

Sample answer: The uncut leaves and the petiole treated with the auxin paste

remained on the plant. The petiole that was not treated with auxin paste fell off.

_____

2. Infer What effect do auxins have on leaf loss in plants?

Auxins prevent leaf loss.

_____

3. Predict In what part of a leaf are auxins produced? Explain your answer.

Sample answer: Auxins are probably produced in the blades of leaves because the

untreated petiole that was missing its blade fell off.

_____

4. Draw Conclusions In autumn, the leaves of deciduous plants produce less auxin and more of another plant hormone, ethylene. What effect might ethylene have on leaf loss?

Sample answer: Ethylene might stimulate leaf loss in deciduous plants.

_____

Extend Your Inquiry

Is what happens in one leaf affected by what happens in other leaves? Design an experiment to determine whether the auxins produced by one leaf can affect other leaves. Obtain your teacher's approval for your procedure before doing your experiment.

Students could compare what happens to a plant when all the leaf blades are removed and when half the leaf blades are removed. The rate of leaf loss is likely to be faster in the plant with all the blades removed. From this data, students should conclude that the effect of auxins on leaf loss is localized.

Chapter 25 Lab Comparing Invertebrate Body Plans

Problem

What characteristics can be used to classify invertebrates?

Introduction

Biologists often consider the number of germ layers when they classify animals. Some animals have cells that are derived from only two germ layers—the endoderm and the ectoderm. Some also have cells that are derived from the mesoderm.

Most animals with cells derived from mesoderm have a fluid-filled body cavity located between the digestive tract and the body wall. In some animals, this cavity, called a coelom (SEE lum), is completely lined with cells derived from mesoderm. Some animals have a partially lined coelom, or pseudocoelom. *Pseudo* means "false." Animals that do not have a body cavity are acoelemates. The prefix *a-* means "not" or "without."

In this lab, you will compare the body plans and structures of invertebrates from three different phyla. The slides you will use will show a thin slice, or cross section, of each organism.

Skills Focus

Observe, Classify, Compare and Contrast

Materials

- compound microscope
- prepared slides with cnidarian, roundworm, and earthworm cross sections
- red, blue, and yellow colored pencils

Safety 🥽 🔪

Review the rules for handling a microscope. To avoid electrical shocks, keep water away from cords and plugs, and make sure your hands are dry. Handle slides gently to avoid breaking them and cutting yourself.

Big Idea
The body plans of animals reflect both unity and diversity among animal species.

Skills Objectives
Students will be able to
- compare the body plans of three different invertebrates.
- relate tissues in an adult organism to germ layers.

Preparation Time
15 minutes

Class Time
Part A: 15 minutes
Parts B–D: 45 minutes

Group Size
Small groups

Materials
Order cross sections of *Hydra, Ascaris lumbricoides,* and *Lumbricus terrestris.*

Advance Preparation
Cover the original descriptive labels with new labels. Keep track of whether a slide is labeled A, B, or C. If you have multiple classes, you might want to change the code between classes.

Teaching Tips
You may want to display
photos of the organisms that
the students will be observing.
If you have more microscopes
than sets of slides, let each
group use extra microscopes.

Pre-Lab Questions

1. **Compare and Contrast** Which two features of animal body plans will you be comparing in this lab?
   I will compare type of body cavity and number of germ layers.

2. **Apply Concepts** Where will you look for tissue that formed from the ectoderm layer?
   I will look for the outermost layer of each organism.

3. **Infer** Is a hydra smaller than, larger than, or about the same size as an earthworm? Base your answer on the procedure in this lab.
   Sample answer: I think a hydra is smaller than an earthworm because I
   will be able to view the earthworm under low power, but I will need to
   use high power to view the hydra.

Procedure

Part A: Identify the Invertebrates

Your teacher will give you slides labeled "A," "B," and "C." Your first task will be to identify the organism on each slide.

1. Figure 1 shows general body plans for the three organisms. Look at the plans and note ways in which they are different.

2. Observe each slide under low power. Compare what you see to the body plans in Figure 1. Use your observations to identify each organism. If you need to see more detail, switch to medium power.

   Slide A: *Sample answer:* earthworm

   Slide B: *Sample answer:* hydra

   Slide C: *Sample answer:* roundworm

3. Confirm your results with your teacher before you do Part B.

Figure 1 Body plans of cnidarian, roundworm, and earthworm

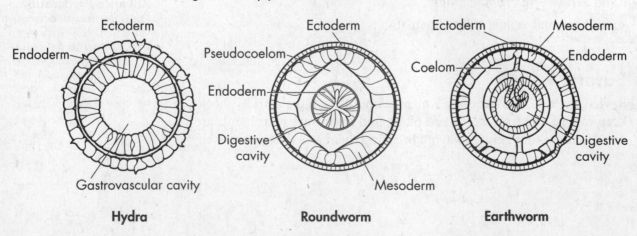

Part B: Observe the Body Plan of a Cnidarian

Organisms in the phylum Cnidaria (ny DAYR ee uh) include corals, jellyfish, sea anemones, and hydras. Your slide contains a cross section of a hydra.

4. Examine the slide under high power. Use the space below to make a labeled drawing of what you observe. Start by locating the gastrovascular cavity in the center of the cross section. The name of this cavity reflects its two functions. It is the location where both digestion and circulation occur.

5. Locate the gastroderm, or inner cell layer. You may see a whiplike structure sticking out of a cell in this layer. These whiplike structures are called flagella. They help circulate food and other materials throughout the cavity.

6. Locate the epidermis, or outer cell layer. You may see a cell that has a sharp point, or barb, on its outer surface. The barbs are called nematocysts. The barbs can sting prey that come close to the hydra and inject a poison that can stun the prey.

7. In the area between the epidermis and the gastroderm, you may be able to see a noncellular, jellylike material called mesoglea (mez uh GLEE uh).

8. Your drawing should have labels for the gastrovascular cavity, gastroderm, and epidermis. It may also have labels for flagella, nematocysts, and mesoglea if you saw those structures.

Step 7
Some students may be confused by the presence of a mesoglea in an organism that does not have a mesoderm germ layer. Explain that the mesoglea is an acellular area.

Drawing of a Hydra

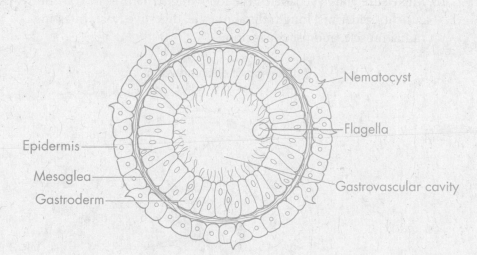

Part C: Observe the Body Plan of a Roundworm

The roundworm that you will observe is a parasite that lives in the digestive tract of animals and feeds on nutrients that flow by. Roundworms belong to the phylum Nematoda.

9. Examine the slide under medium power. Use the space below to make a labeled drawing of what you observe. First find the thin outer layer called the cuticle. This tough protective coating keeps the roundworm from being digested by its host.

10. The cuticle consists mainly of proteins that are secreted by cells in the epidermis. Find the epidermis just inside the cuticle.

11. Find the thick layer of muscle tissue just inside the epidermis. The cells in this *longitudinal* muscle tissue run lengthwise along the body. Longitudinal muscle is responsible for moving the roundworm's body.

Step 12
The tract may be folded into three parts like the leaves of a three-leaf clover.

12. Now look for a space in the center of the roundworm. This space is the roundworm's digestive tract.

13. The thin layer of cells that surrounds the digestive tract is the roundworm's intestine. Cells in the intestine absorb nutrients from the digestive tract.

14. Find the thick layer of muscle tissue that is next to the intestine. The cells in this *radial* muscle tissue are arranged in rings. As these muscle cells contract, food moves through the digestive tract.

15. The fluid-filled space between the radial muscle tissue and the longitudinal muscle tissue is the pseudocoelom.

16. Make sure you have labeled the following structures in your drawing: cuticle, epidermis, longitudinal muscle, digestive tract, intestine, radial muscle, and pseudocoelom.

Drawing of a Roundworm

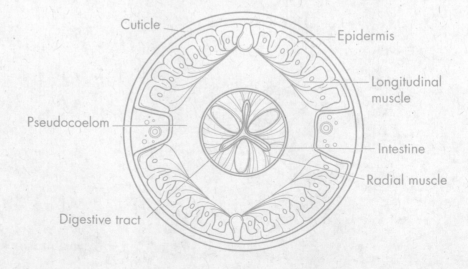

Part D: Observe the Body Plan of an Earthworm

People who garden are pleased to find earthworms in their soil. The tunnels that form as earthworms move through soil provide spaces through which air and water can circulate. Earthworms belong to the phylum Annelida.

17. Examine the slide under low power. Use the space below to make a labeled drawing of what you observe. First find the cuticle, which should be similar in appearance to the cuticle of a roundworm. Just inside the cuticle, locate the first thin layer of cells. This is the earthworm's epidermis.

18. Beneath the epidermis are two layers of muscle tissue. In the thin outer layer, the cells circle around the earthworm. In the thick inner layer, the muscle tissue is longitudinal. The cells in the inner layer should appear branched and feathery.

19. Look for a round or horseshoe-shaped space in the center of the slide. This space is the digestive tract. Three layers of cells surround the digestive tract. The innermost layer is the earthworm's intestine. The next layer is smooth muscle, which moves food along the intestine. The outermost layer is called chloragogen tissue. Cells in this tissue help remove harmful waste products.

20. The space between the chloragogen layer and the longitudinal muscle layer is the coelom.

21. Make sure you have labeled the following structures in your drawing: cuticle, epidermis, circular muscle, longitudinal muscle, digestive tract, intestine, smooth muscle, chloragogen tissue, and coelom.

Drawing of an Earthworm

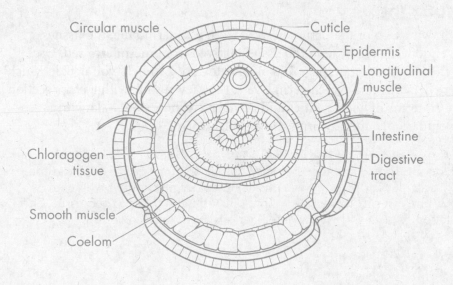

Analyze and Conclude

1. Compare and Contrast What is the main difference between the cnidarian and the other two organisms?

The cnidarian has cells derived from only two germ layers. The other two organisms

have cells derived from three germ layers.

_____

2. Infer From which germ layer was the gastroderm in a cnidarian derived? From which germ layer was the epidermis derived?

The gastroderm was derived from the endoderm layer. The epidermis was derived

from the ectoderm layer.

3. Apply Concepts Which tissue layers line the coelom in an earthworm? From which germ layer were the cells in these layers derived? How do you know?

Sample answer: The longitudinal muscle layer and the chloragogen tissue line the

coelem. The cells in these layers must be derived from mesoderm because by

definition a true coelom is completely lined with cells derived from mesoderm.

_____

4. Classify Figure 25–10 in your textbook describes features of body plans for eight phyla of invertebrates. Is it possible to use only germ layers and type of body cavity to distinguish among all eight phyla? Explain.

No. Four of the phyla have three germ layers and a true coelom.

_____

Extend Your Inquiry

(1) On your drawings, color the tissues derived from ectoderm blue, the tissues derived from endoderm yellow, and the tissues derived from mesoderm red. Use Figure 1 and the information on page 738 of your textbook to help you decide which structures were derived from which germ layers. (2) View a slide with a cross section of a flatworm. In terms of body cavities and germ layers, how does a flatworm compare to a cnidarian, a roundworm, and an earthworm?

(1) Hydra: The gastroderm should be yellow and the epidermis blue. Roundworm: The cuticle and epidermis should be blue, the radial muscle and intestine yellow, and the longitudinal muscle red. Earthworm: the cuticle and epidermis should be blue, the intestine yellow, and the circular muscle, longitudinal muscle, chloragogen tissue, and smooth muscle red. (2) Flatworms have three germ layers but no coelom.

Guided Inquiry • Forensics Lab

Chapter 26 Lab Investigating Hominoid Fossils

Problem

What can a comparison of skulls and hands reveal about the evolution of humans?

Introduction

Because hominoid fossils are rare, the discovery of a new one is an exciting event. A paleontologist takes photographs of a fossil while it is in the ground and after it is uncarthed. He or she also makes many measurements. These observations make it easier to compare the new discovery to fossils that have already been classified.

Using measurements to compare fossil skeletons is not easy, especially when the skeletons are incomplete. How can a scientist know whether a skeleton is typical of its species? For example, a scientist may find a wide variation in the height of two skeletons. Does this variation indicate that the individuals were members of two different species? Does it reflect a range of heights within the same species?

To deal with this problem, scientists use the measurements of certain bones to calculate indexes. An index is a ratio that compares the value of one measurement in relation to another. Indexes are useful because they are independent of overall size. Very tall and very short members of the same species should have similar indexes. With indexes, it is more likely that any variations are related to differences in species, not just differences in size.

In this lab, you will measure the skulls and hands of different hominoid species. You will use your measurements to calculate indexes that will help you compare these species.

Skills Focus

Measure, Analyze Data, Compare and Contrast

Materials

• metric ruler

Big Idea
The changes that occurred in certain bones as hominines evolved facilitated bipedal locomotion and tool use.

Skills Objectives
Students will be able to
• calculate indexes from pairs of related measurements.
• relate skeletal indexes to differences among species.

Class Time
45 minutes

Group Size
Individuals

Pre-Lab Questions

1. Use Models What will you use instead of actual skulls and hands to make your measurements?

I will be using images of skulls and hands.

2. Interpret Visuals The bony cavities in a skull that protect the eyes are called orbits, or eye sockets. On the skulls, what does line AC measure? What does line BC measure?

Line AC measures the distance from the bottom of the eye socket to the top of the skull. Line BC measures the distance from the top of the eye socket to the top of the skull.

3. Use Analogies Shoe sizes such as 9A and 11E (or 9 narrow and 11 extra-wide) are an example of an index. What two measurements are being compared in a shoe index?

Sample answer: In a shoe size, the width of the shoe is being compared to the length of the shoe.

Procedure

Part A: Supraorbital Height Index in Hominoids

Figure 1 shows side views of skulls from four hominoid species: *Pan troglodytes, Australopithecus afarensis, Homo erectus,* and *Homo sapiens.* You will use these drawings to determine distances from the top of the skull to the upper and lower edges of the eye socket. Then you will calculate the *supraorbital height index* (SHI), which indicates the proportion of the skull that is above the eyes. The prefix *supra-* means "above."

1. Measure the distances AC and BC in centimeters for each skull. Record the measurements in Data Table 1.

2. For each species, divide the value of BC by the value of AC and multiply the result by 100. The result is the supraorbital height index (SHI). Round the answers to the nearest whole number, and record them in Data Table 1.

Teaching Tip
If possible, have at least one skull available for students to observe and discuss.

Sample Data

Data Table 1: Skull Measurements			
Species	**BC (cm)**	**AC (cm)**	**SHI**
Pan troglodytes	1.6	4.1	39
Australopithecus afarensis	2.0	4.2	48
Homo erectus	2.9	4.7	62
Homo sapiens	3.4	4.7	72

Figure 1 Hominoid skulls

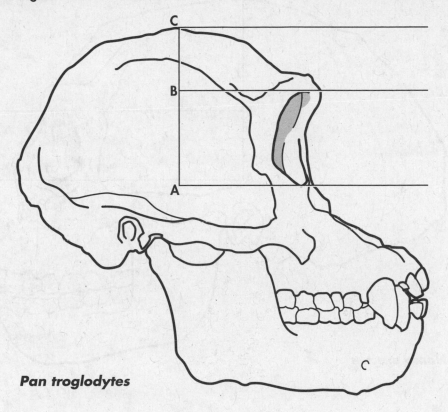

Pan troglodytes

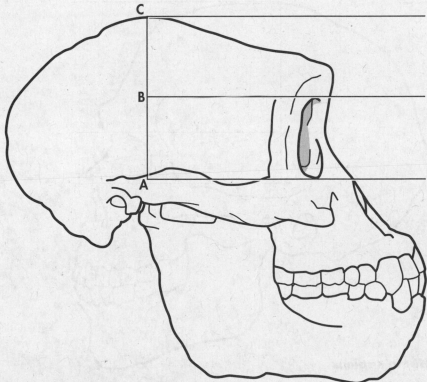

Australopithecus afarensis

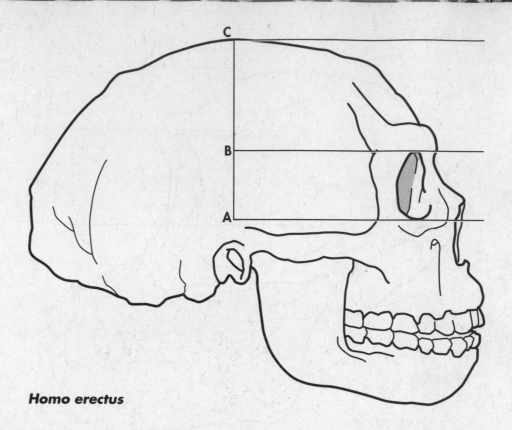

Homo erectus

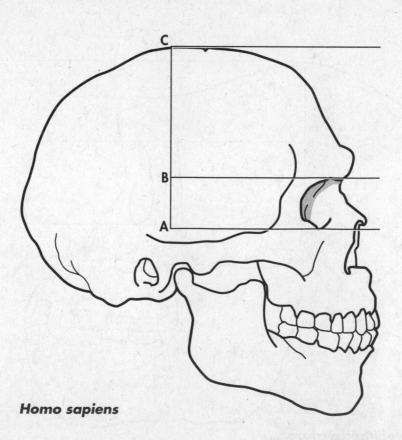

Homo sapiens

Part B: Thumb Index in Hominoids

Figure 2 depicts the thumb and index finger of *Pan troglodytes*, *Australopithecus afarensis*, and *Homo sapiens*. You will use these drawings to calculate a thumb index for each species. The thumb index compares the length of the thumb to the length of the hand.

3. For each species, measure the length of the thumb and the length of the index finger in centimeters. Make these measurements from the tip of the digit to the point where the finger and thumb meet at the wrist joint. Record your results in Data Table 2.

4. To calculate the thumb index, divide thumb length by index finger length and multiply the result by 100. Round the answer to the nearest whole number and record the result in the table.

Part B
Homo erectus is not included in Part B because there are no known thumb bone fossils for this species.

Sample Data

Data Table 2: Hand Measurements			
	Thumb Length (cm)	Index Finger Length (cm)	Thumb Index
Pan troglodytes	1.8	4.7	38
Australopithecus afarensis	2.8	4.5	62
Homo sapiens	3.0	4.7	64

Figure 2 Hand bones of three hominoids

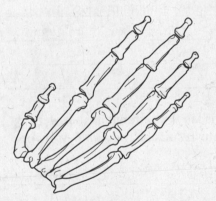 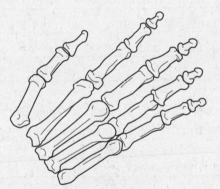 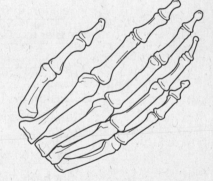

Pan troglodytes	***Australopithecus afarensis***	***Homo sapiens***

Analyze and Conclude

1. **Analyze Data** Of the species you investigated, which had the smallest SHI and which had the largest? What is the relationship between the SHI value and the shape of the skull?

   Sample answer: Pan had the smallest SHI and *Homo sapiens* had the largest. In skulls with a higher SHI value, a larger proportion of the skull is above the eye.

2. **Infer** How might an increase in a hominoid's SHI value affect the size of its brain?

   Sample answer: When the proportion of the skull above the eyes increases, there is more room for the brain. Thus, the size of the brain could increase relative to the overall size of the skull.

3. **Analyze Data** Does the data support the hypothesis that the thumb index increased as the opposable thumb hand evolved? Explain.

   Sample answer: The data (although limited) seems to support this hypothesis because *Pan,* which does not have an opposable thumb, has a smaller thumb index than *H. sapiens,* which has an opposable thumb.

4. **Relate Cause and Effect** How could an increase in the thumb index affect a hominoid's ability to use its hands?

   Sample answer: As the thumb index increases, the length of the thumb increases in relation to the rest of the hand. Longer thumbs can touch the fingertips, making it easier to grasp objects and use them as tools.

5. **Design an Experiment** Suppose you repeated this lab with drawings that were half the size of the drawings you used. Would your results be the same? Why or why not?

   Sample answer: The measurements would have been different, but the indexes would not have changed because the drawings would have the same proportions.

Extend Your Inquiry

A skeleton retains clues about the life of its owner. How can fossils be used to determine a hominid skeleton's age, sex, or diet? How can fossils be used to tell how heavy or muscular an individual was?

Students may know about wisdom teeth and pelvic shape (from a previous lab). Bone fusing is another clue to age. Teeth wear provides clues to diet. Bone mass and surface texture are clues to musculature.

Chapter 27 Lab **Anatomy of a Squid**

Problem

What structures does a squid use to obtain nutrients and eliminate wastes?

Introduction

A squid is an unusual mollusk. It doesn't have an external shell. Nor does it use a muscular foot to crawl, as snails do, or dig into the ocean bottom, as clams do. Instead, a squid uses a form of "jet propulsion." The squid expels water through an opening called the siphon, which pushes the squid through the water. By changing the siphon's position, the squid can swim forward or backward.

Unlike clams and oysters, which are filter feeders, squids are predators. They use their long tentacles to catch fish, crustaceans, and other mollusks. A squid uses its short arms to help hold the prey near its mouth and its beak to bite off pieces of the prey.

In this lab, you will dissect a squid. You will identify important structures and relate the structures to their functions.

Skills Focus

Observe, Infer, Sequence, Draw Conclusions

Materials

- squid
- dissecting tray
- hand lens
- forceps
- dissecting scissors
- dissecting pins
- dissecting probe

Safety 🫁 🧥 🧤 ✂️ 🔬

Wear your goggles, apron, and gloves while handling the squid. Use the dissecting tools only as instructed. Wash your hands thoroughly with soap and warm water before you leave the lab. Alert your teacher if you suspect you are allergic to squid.

Big Idea
Animals have specific structures that perform basic functions such as digestion, respiration, circulation, and excretion.

Skills Objectives
Students will be able to
• demonstrate proper dissection techniques.
• relate an organ's structure to its function.

Preparation Time
20 minutes to collect and prepare materials; 30 minutes to do the dissection in advance

Class Time
50 minutes

Group Size
Small groups

Materials
Buy whole squid at a local bait shop or specialty food market or make arrangements with a restaurant that serves squid.

Advance Preparation
The day before the lab, defrost frozen squid overnight in a refrigerator.

Teaching Tips
If you do the dissection prior to the lab, you can anticipate problems and questions that students might have.
Discuss with students ways to divide up the work in Part B so that all students do part of the dissection.

Pre-Lab Questions

1. **Interpret Visuals** What structure can you use to distinguish the ventral side of a squid from the dorsal side?

   The siphon is located on the ventral side.

2. **Infer** Why is it important to lift the mantle while cutting it?

   Sample answer: If the mantle is not lifted, the scissors may cut through

   the organs that lie beneath the mantle.

3. **Predict** What do you expect the gills to look like, and why?

   Sample answer: Because gas exchange takes place in the gills, I expect

   the gills to have a large surface area.

Procedure

Part A: Observe the External Structure of a Squid

1. Put on goggles, a lab apron, and plastic gloves.

2. Obtain a squid specimen in a dissecting tray. Examine both surfaces of the body thoroughly. Find the eyes and the lateral fins, which are located on the sides of the body.

3. Count the number of short arms and long tentacles. Use a hand lens to examine the suckers on the arms and tentacles.

   Number of arms: 8 _____

   Number of tentacles: 2 _____

Figure 1 External anatomy of a squid

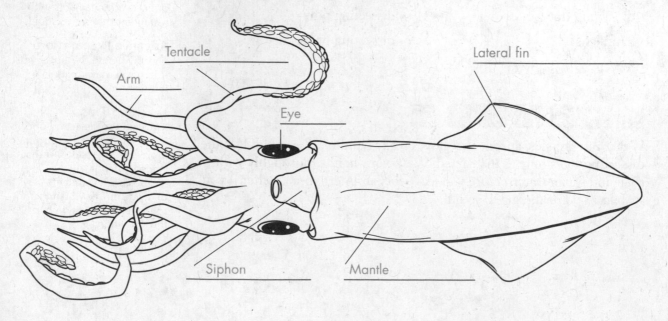

4. Most of a squid's body has a fleshy covering called the mantle. Find the tubelike structure that extends from the mantle near the head of the squid. This structure is the siphon.

5. Use the write-on lines provided on Figure 1 to label the mantle, siphon, lateral fin, eye, tentacle, and arm.

Part B: Observe the Internal Structure of a Squid

6. Position the squid with the ventral surface (the side with the siphon) facing up and the arms and tentacles facing you. Use forceps to lift the free end of the mantle just above the siphon. Using the scissors, cut the mantle in a straight line to the tail end.

7. Spread the mantle and attach it to the tray with dissecting pins. Use the probe to move aside the muscles that are attached to the siphon so that you can observe the entire length of the siphon.

8. What you see next will depend on the sex of your squid. Female squids have a two large white glands, which are attached to the ovary. Use the dissecting scissors to remove these glands so you can view the cone-shaped ovary near the tail of the squid. Note the jellylike eggs with a slight yellow color in the ovary.

9. If you don't see the large white glands, you have a male squid. Look for a white, water-filled sac near the tail. This is the male's reproductive organ, or testis.

10. Locate the gills, which look like curved feathers. Look for a small heart along the tail end of each gill and a larger systemic heart between the two small gill hearts.

Step 4
Unlike siphons that people use to transfer liquids between containers, a squid's siphon is not an intake device. In a squid, water flows in through an opening along the mantle. When that opening is sealed off, water can be pumped out through the siphon.

Step 6
Make sure students understand the difference between the ventral and dorsal surfaces.

Step 10
If time permits, have students make a wet mount of a piece of gill to view under high power.

Figure 2 Internal anatomy of a squid, Part 1

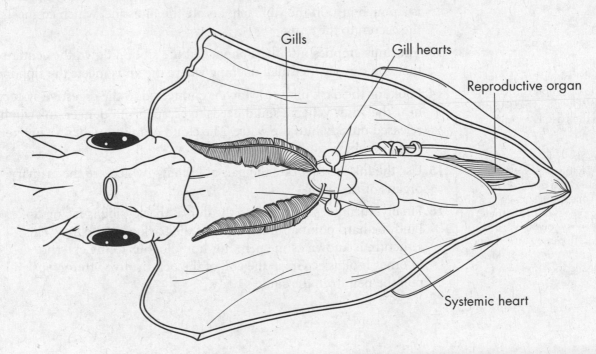

Gills

Gill hearts

Reproductive organ

Systemic heart

Figure 3 Internal anatomy of a squid, Part 2

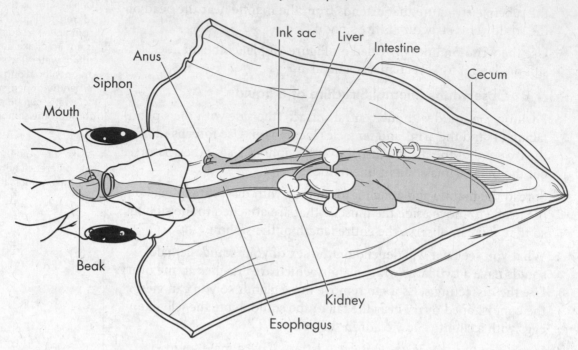

11. Turn the dissecting tray so the head is facing away from you. Make a vertical cut through the head from the neck to just past the eyes. Stop when you reach the rough, muscular organ that surrounds the beak.

12. Use the probe to open the beak and locate the mouth. From that point, locate the esophagus and trace it to the stomach. Look for the liver, which is a relatively large organ near the stomach. The liver secretes digestive enzymes into the stomach. Find the cecum, which is a pouch just off the stomach. Locate the intestine, which connects the cecum to the anus.

13. The anus empties into the siphon. Cut the siphon down the center so that you can see the small opening where the anus meets the siphon.

14. Look for the dark ink sac, which is connected to the digestive system near the anus. When a squid needs to escape from danger, ink can be released quickly into the water. The cloud of ink provides a "smoke screen," which confuses predators.

15. Use the ink sac to locate the pair of kidneys, which are the primary organs of excretion.

16. Finally, turn the squid over so the dorsal (back) side is facing up. Find the hard point at the midline of the back near the fins. This structure is known as the pen. It is homologous to the external shell in other mollusks. Grasp the end of the pen firmly with forceps and pull the pen from the squid's body.

Step 14
Squid ink is similar to the ink from the common cuttlefish (*Sepia officinalis*), which artists used in the past as a brown dye.

Disposal
Squid may be disposed of in the trash. Use a doubled trash bag to collect the specimens and any pieces of tissue that have been removed. Ask a custodian to remove the trash at the end of the school day. Wash dissecting trays and tools in soapy water.

Analyze and Conclude

1. **Sequence** Trace the path of food through the digestive system. What happens to food that is not completely digested and absorbed?

   Food passes through the mouth, to the esophagus, stomach, cecum, and intestine.

   Food that is not completely digested passes through the intestine to the anus and

   out of the squid's body through the siphon.

2. **Infer** Based on its location, what function might the cecum have in the digestive system?

   Sample answer: Digestion and absorption of food might occur in the cecum.

3. **Apply Concepts** If you viewed a piece of a gill under a microscope at high power, what would you see?

   Sample answer: I would see a network of tiny blood vessels.

4. **Infer** Why does a squid have three hearts? *Hint:* Think about where the two smaller hearts are located.

   Sample answer: The gill hearts are needed to move blood through the network of

   tiny blood vessels in the gills.

5. **Draw Conclusions** From what you observed, are you able to conclude that the squid has a closed circulatory system?

   Sample answer: No, because I did not observe the complete pathway of vessels

   through which the blood travels.

6. **Infer** How does ink get released from a squid's body?

   Sample answer: Ink passes through the anus to the siphon where it is released into

   the water.

Extend Your Inquiry

Not all of the organs you observed in this lab are involved in digestion, respiration, circulation, or excretion. In the next chapter, you will study how animals respond, move, support their bodies, and reproduce. Identify organs you observed that carry out one of these functions.

The siphon and its muscles help the squid move. The eyes help the squid respond to its environment. The ink sac is also a response organ. The pen is a support structure. The ovary and testis are reproductive organs.

Chapter 28 Lab **Comparing Bird and Mammal Bones**

Problem

Is the density of an animal's bones related to the way the animal moves?

Introduction

When you hear the word *cattle*, what image comes to mind? Do you see cows moving slowly across a pasture as they graze, or do you see an angry bull charging across a rodeo ring? Cattle are domesticated mammals that were bred to be large and muscular. The endoskeleton of cattle must be able to support a large animal standing, walking, or even running on four legs.

A duck's movement isn't restricted to walking, or waddling, from place to place. Ducks can also swim and fly. Many species of wild ducks are capable of long, sustained flights as they migrate. By contrast, chickens are domesticated birds that spend most of their time on the ground pecking for food. At most, a chicken may take flight for a few seconds.

In this lab, you will compare bones from cows, ducks, and chickens. You will observe a cross section of each type of bone and use your observations to form a hypothesis about the density of the bones. Then, you will design an experiment to test your hypothesis.

Skills Focus

Form a Hypothesis, Design an Experiment, Measure

Materials

- cross sections of chicken, duck, and cow bones
- hand lens
- small chicken, duck, and cow bones
- balance

Safety

If you use glass containers in Part B, check them for cracks or chips. Do not handle broken glassware. After you finish handling the bones, dispose of the gloves and wash your hands thoroughly with soap and warm water.

Big Idea
Different types of bone structures allow animals to respond appropriately to different environments.

Skills Objectives
Students will be able to
• devise a method for determining bone density.
• relate the structure of bones to their functions.

Preparation Time
45–60 minutes

Class Time
45 minutes

Group Size
Small groups

Terminology
Strictly speaking, *cow* should be used to refer to a subset of cattle (adult females). In everyday language, *cow* is used to refer to all cattle.

Materials
Students will need at least a 250-mL graduated cylinder, a dissecting probe to keep the less dense bones submerged, and weighing papers to protect the balance.

Pre-Lab Questions

1. **Compare and Contrast** Compare the type of data you will collect in Part A to the type of data you will collect in Part B.

   Sample answer: In Part A, the data will be qualitative. In Part B, the data will be quantitative.

   _____

2. **Predict** How might looking at cross sections of bones help you form a hypothesis about the relative density of the bones?

   Sample answer: I will be able to observe whether the bones are solid or contain air spaces.

   _____

3. **Design an Experiment** Will you need to use samples with the same mass in Part B? Why or why not?

   Sample answer: No, because density is a ratio of mass to volume

Procedure

Part A: Examine Cross Sections of Bones

By looking at cross sections cut from bones, you will be able to observe the interior of the bones.

1. Put on a pair of disposable plastic gloves. Use a hand lens to examine each cross section. Record your observations in Data Table 1. Include a drawing of each cross section.

2. **Predict** Do bird bones and mammal bones have the same density? Give a reason for your prediction.

   Prediction: *Sample answer:* Bird bones are less dense than mammal bones because there is a lot of empty space inside the bird bones.

Sample Data

Data Table 1: Observations		
Animal	**Drawing**	**Observations**
Chicken		Honeycombed interior, mostly hollow
Duck		Honeycombed interior, mostly hollow
Cow		Dense interior with some spongy material

Advance Preparation
Use a hacksaw or ask a butcher to cut cross sections of bones so that the interior structure is visible. Boil the bones to remove soft tissue and to kill bacteria. Allow the bones to dry and label the cross sections before giving them to students.

To reduce the number of cross sections needed, plan on having two groups share one set of cross sections.

Safety
Be sure to wear goggles, protective gloves, and an apron if you use a hacksaw.

Part B: Design an Experiment

In Part B, you will use small bones instead of cross sections. You will measure the mass and volume of the bones and calculate the density. The density of a sample is the ratio of the sample's mass to its volume.

$$\text{Density} = \frac{\text{Mass (g)}}{\text{Volume (mL)}}$$

3. **Describe Your Plan** You can use a balance to measure the mass of your samples. You must decide how you will measure the volume of the samples, and then gather the required materials.

Experimental Plan: Most students will know that the volume of an

irregular object can be measured by the displacement of water.

_____

_____

_____

_____

4. Make a data table in the space below to record your measurements and calculations. Have your teacher review your plan and your table before you do your procedure. Put on an apron before you begin.

Data Table 2: Measurements					
Animal	Mass (g)	Initial Volume (mL)	Final Volume (mL)	Volume Change (mL)	Density (g/mL)
Cow					1.70
Chicken					1.15
Duck					1.20

Part B:
Do not let students use the cross sections to measure the volume. Water will fill up the hollow spaces. Use wing bones for the chicken and duck. For the cow, try short ribs.

Disposal
Make sure students dispose of their gloves after completing the lab.

Analyze and Conclude

1. Analyze Data Did your results support your prediction in Step 2?

The answer will depend on the prediction. The expected outcome is that the cow

bones will be much denser than the duck and chicken bones, which should be about

equally dense.

2. Relate Cause and Effect How could the density of cow bones be adaptive for cattle?

Sample answer: Cow bones must be able to support the weight of an animal without

breaking.

3. Relate Cause and Effect How could the density of bird bones be adaptive for species, such as ducks, that fly long distances?

Sample answer: Bones that are less dense would reduce the weight of a bird and

make it easier for the bird to overcome the pull of gravity. The bird would also use

less energy while flying.

4. Draw Conclusions Is bone density the factor that prevents chickens from flying long distances? Why or why not?

Given that the chicken bones were about as dense as the duck bones, bone density

must not be the factor that prevents chickens from flying long distances.

5. Form a Hypothesis What factors other than bone density may prevent or limit the ability of chickens to fly? *Hint:* How does the ecological niche of chickens differ from that of their wild ancestors?

Some students may know that chickens are selectively bred for large amounts

of white meat (or pectoral muscles). This added mass would make it difficult for

chickens to fly. Plus chickens do not have to move (and are prevented from moving)

from place to place to find food.

Extend Your Inquiry

From your results, you might conclude that bone density is related more to the size of an animal than to its mode of movement. To test this conclusion, choose one of the following activities: do an experiment to determine the bone density of small mammals; read about a dinosaur called *Quetzalcoatlus*.

The bones of small mammals are much closer in density to cow bones than to duck bones. You may be able to obtain bones from people who hunt small mammals. Owl pellets are another source of small mammal bones. See articles on how to use road kill for scientific studies. *Quetzalcoatlus* had a wingspan of about 12 m (39 ft). Because its bones were hollow, scientists estimate that its mass was only about 100 kg (220 lb) despite its huge size.

Open-Ended Inquiry • Design Your Own Lab

Chapter 29 Lab **Termite Tracks**

Problem

How can you determine the type of stimulus that triggers a particular response?

Introduction

Termites are insects that live in large colonies, and are known for the damage they cause to trees and wooden buildings. Termites are able to eat wood because symbiotic microorganisms living in a termite's gut digest the wood. Within a colony, most termites are workers whose tasks include hunting for food and building the structures that protect the colony and queen. As the termites work, they communicate with one another.

Insects use visual cues, sound signals, and chemical signals as methods of communication. In this lab, you will observe a termite's reaction to a line drawing. You will then design an experiment to determine which type of stimulus caused the reaction.

Skills Focus

Form a Hypothesis, Design an Experiment, Draw Conclusions

Materials

- petri dishes
- paper
- scissors
- termite
- small paintbrush
- forceps
- ballpoint pens
- rollerball pens
- felt-tip pens

Safety 🐀 🧤 ✂️

To avoid injuring the termite, use a forceps and small paintbrush to gently handle the termite. If you have glass petri dishes, check for cracks or chips. Do not direct the points of the scissors toward yourself or others. Use the scissors only as directed.

Big Idea
Adaptive behaviors play a central role in the survival of populations and species.

Skills Objectives
Students will be able to
• design an experiment to identify a specific stimulus.
• explain how the response to a stimulus can be adaptive.

Preparation Time
45 minutes if you collect your own termites

Class Time
45 minutes

Group Size
Pairs

Materials
For Part A, provide Bic® or Papermate® ballpoint pens. The inks in these pens contain a chemical that is similar to a termite trail pheromone. Red inks produce the strongest response because they usually have more "pheromone" than black, blue, or green inks.

Advance Preparation
Order termites from a science supply company or collect them from decaying logs and stumps in wooded areas. The workers are milky white and have no wings. Don't collect soldiers—the ones with the large, yellow-brown heads. Store purchased termites in their shipping container— usually a plastic tank with a screen at the top to let in air. If you collect your own termites, devise a similar container. Provide moist paper or wood.

Safety
Check your state and local regulations before obtaining termites.

Pre-Lab Questions

1. **Control Variables** Why do you think the instructions ask you to draw a figure eight rather than a straight line?

   Sample answer: With the figure eight, it will be easier to tell whether the

   termite is responding to the drawn path.

   _____

2. **Draw Conclusions** How will you decide whether a termite has a positive reaction, a negative reaction, or no reaction to a stimulus?

   Sample answer: I will classify a positive reaction as movement towards the

   stimulus, a negative reaction as movement away from the stimulus, and

   no reaction as no obvious change in movement.

   _____

3. **Predict** Read pages 850–851 of your textbook. Which of the signals described could be a stimulus for the termite in this lab? Explain your answer.

   Sample answer: The termite could respond to a visual signal or a chemical

   signal.

   _____

Procedure

Part A: Observing Termite Behavior

1. You need to make a paper circle that will fit inside a petri dish. Use the dish to trace a circle on a piece of white paper. Then cut just inside the line as you cut out the circle.

2. Use the red ballpoint pen supplied by your teacher to draw a large figure eight on the paper. Retrace the figure three or four times so that the line is dark and thick. Then place the circle inside the petri dish.

3. Select a termite that seems active from the central supply. Use the forceps and small paintbrush to gently transfer the termite onto the paper in the petri dish.

Step 3
Students should select termites that are relatively active. If a selected termite stops moving during the experiment, instruct students to pick a new, more active specimen.

4. Observe the termite's behavior. Record your observations.

   Students should observe that the termite follows the drawn path.

   _____

   _____

   _____

5. Move the termite to a second petri dish where it can remain until you are ready to do Part B. **CAUTION:** Make sure the termite does not escape from the dish.

Part B: Design an Experiment

6. **Communicate** Discuss the behavior you observed in Part A with your partner. Identify two stimuli that might have caused the termite's reaction.

   Sample answer: Possible stimuli are the color of the ink and the odor of

   the ink. (Some students might suggest that the termite is following the

   groove made by the pen.)

7. **Form a Hypothesis** What stimulus caused the behavior you observed in Part A? Record the hypothesis you will test to answer this question.

   Hypothesis: *Sample answer:* A chemical in the ballpoint ink attracted the

   termite to the line.

   _____

8. **Control Variables** What will your independent variable be? What will your dependent variable be?

   Independent Variable: *Sample answer:* pen (type and brand)

   Dependent Variable: *Sample answer:* reaction of termite

9. **Describe Your Plan** Describe the procedure you will use to test your hypothesis. Focus on how your plan will vary from the experiment you did in Part A. Explain how you will ensure that the termite is responding to the selected variable and not to a different variable. Before you begin, have your teacher review your plan.

   Experimental Plan: If students are comparing different types and

   brands of pens, then they should control the color of the ink. If they

   are comparing the response to different colors of ink, then they should

   control the type and brand of pen.

   _____

   _____

   _____

   _____

   _____

10. **Organize Data** Construct a data table in the space below to record the results of your tests.

11. **Disposal** When you are done with your trials, follow your teacher's instructions for cleanup and disposal of materials.

Sample Data

Data Table				
Pen Type and Brand	Ballpoint Brand B	Ballpoint Brand B	Rollerball Brand A	Rollerball Brand A
Color	Red	Blue	Red	Blue
Reaction	Quick positive response	Slow positive response	No reaction, random movement	No reaction, random movement

Analyze and Conclude

1. **Analyze Data** Look at both your results and the results from other groups. Describe any patterns you see.

Sample answer: The termites reacted to one brand of ballpoint pens. The speed of the

reaction varied with the color of the ink. The termites had no reaction to lines drawn

with other types of pens.

_____

2. **Draw Conclusions** Termite workers are blind. Use this fact and your data to explain the behavior of the termites.

Sample answer: Termites must smell and recognize one of the chemicals in the ink

of ballpoint pens. Red ink probably has more of this chemical than the other color

inks do.

_____

3. **Perform Error Analysis** How could testing only one or two termites affect the reliability of the results? How could pooling your data with other groups affect the reliability of the results?

Sample answer: With such a small sample size, the results might not be reliable

because the behavior of the termite may not be typical. Pooling data provides a

larger, more reliable sample size.

_____

4. **Infer** How could the type of behavior you observed help a termite colony to survive? *Hint:* When might it be useful for a termite to follow the path of another termite?

Sample answer: It might be useful for a termite to follow the path of another termite to a food source.

5. **Apply Concepts** Termites can cause considerable damage to buildings that are constructed from wood. Based on your observations, how might owners protect wooden buildings without having to use insecticides?

Sample answer: Pheromones that attract termites could be used to draw the termites into traps. (Chemicals that repel termites could be used to keep the termites away from the buildings.)

Extend Your Inquiry

(1) Ink is a mixture of chemicals. Design an experiment using paper chromatography that will allow you to isolate the chemical that attracts termites. Use the pen that you used in Part A. (2) Design an experiment to determine whether the shape of the drawn path affects the behavior of the termite.

(1) Students can use alcohol to produce a chromatogram. After the paper is dry, students could cut the paper into narrow horizontal strips with only one color band on each strip and use the strips to test a termite's response to each chemical. After the experiment, discuss how the structure of the attracting chemical should be similar to a pheromone that is produced by termites. (2) The angles of the turns in the path can affect the behavior. A termite may wander off the path if the angle of a turn is too sharp.

Chapter 30 Lab **Digestion of Dairy Products**

Problem

How can an enzyme deficiency affect digestion?

Introduction

Milk is an important source of nutrients, especially calcium, which is needed for healthy bones and teeth. Suppliers of milk often add vitamin D, which helps the body absorb calcium and phosphorus. Unfortunately, some people cannot digest lactose, a sugar that is found in milk. The condition is known as lactose intolerance.

People with this condition do not produce enough of the enzyme lactase. This enzyme speeds up the breakdown of lactose, a disaccharide sugar, into the simple sugars glucose and galactose. Lactose that is not digested moves into the large intestine, where it can cause symptoms such as bloating and cramps. Thus, people who are lactose intolerant try to avoid drinking milk and eating products made from milk.

Lactose, however, can be difficult to avoid. Milk is used to make yogurt, ice cream, sour cream, and cheeses. Milk is also found in foods such as instant breakfast drinks, prepared puddings, and pancake mixes. Also, avoiding all dairy products puts people at risk of having too little calcium and vitamin D in their diets.

Is avoiding diary products the only way to solve the problem of lactose intolerance? In this lab, you will test an over-the-counter product that claims to aid in lactose digestion.

Skills Focus

Control Variables, Infer, Draw Conclusions

Materials

- spot plate
- sheet of paper
- glucose solution
- milk
- milk-digestion aid
- toothpicks
- glucose test strips
- timer or clock

Safety 🫁 🧍 🧤 🧹

If one of the dropper bottles breaks or the contents spill, follow your teacher's instructions for cleanup. Do not taste any of the materials used in the lab. Wash your hands thoroughly with soap and warm water before you leave the lab.

Big Idea
For the human body to maintain homeostasis, each enzyme must perform its function.

Skills Objectives
Students will be able to
- analyze the design of a controlled experiment.
- identify factors that can affect the digestion of dairy products.

Preparation Time
20 minutes

Class Time
25 minutes

Group Size
Small groups

Materials
Purchase liquid lactase from a pharmacy or online. Check that the product doesn't contain glucose, which may appear on the label as dextrose. You can substitute depression slides for spot plates.

Advance Preparation
To prepare the glucose solution, dissolve 2 g of glucose in 100 mL of water.
Do the lab in advance to test the time needed for digestion of the lactose and the effectiveness of the test strips. If the strips are long, you can cut them in half.

Safety
Remind students that the milk used in this lab should not be consumed.

Pre-Lab Questions

1. Design an Experiment What is the purpose of the glucose solution?

The glucose solution will show what a positive test for glucose looks like.

_____

2. Control Variables What is the control in this lab?

The sample of milk without the milk-digestion aid is the control.

3. Communicate Read the instructions on the package of glucose test strips. Then briefly describe how you will test your samples for the presence of glucose.

Depending on the type of test strips used, students will either dip a fresh

strip into each solution or use toothpicks to place a bit of each solution

on a single strip.

_____

Procedure

1. Put on your goggles and apron.
2. Place your spot plate on a sheet of paper and label four of the wells 1–4.
3. Add 2 drops of the glucose solution to Well 1.
4. Add 2 drops of milk to Well 2.
5. Add 2 drops of the milk-digestion aid to Well 3.
6. Place 2 drops of milk in Well 4. Then, add 1 drop of the milk-digestion aid.
7. After 2 minutes, test all four samples for glucose.
8. Make a data table in the space below to record your results.

Data Table: Glucose Test Results		
Well	Sample	Test Result
1	Glucose	Positive for glucose
2	Milk	Negative for glucose
3	Digestion aid	Negative for glucose
4	Milk and digestion aid	Positive for glucose

Analyze and Conclude

1. **Relate Cause and Effect** How could you tell when glucose was present in one of the wells?

   The test strip changed color in the presence of glucose. _____

   _____

2. **Draw Conclusions** What evidence do you have to support the claim that the digestion aid you used actually breaks down lactose?

   Sample answer: The sample of milk without the digestion aid tested negative for

   glucose, but the sample with the digestion aid tested positive for glucose. Thus, the

   digestion aid must have broken down the lactose in milk into glucose and galactose.

   _____

   _____

3. **Control Variables** Why was it necessary to test the digestion aid for glucose?

   Sample answer: Testing the digestion aid eliminates the possibility that the glucose

   detected in Well 4 was present in the digestion aid.

   _____

4. **Apply Concepts** Describe two different ways that the digestion aid could be used to help people that are lactose intolerant.

   Sample answer: Milk can be treated with the digestion aid before it is packaged and

   sold. A person who is lactose intolerant can ingest the aid just before eating dairy

   products that have not been treated.

   _____

5. **Predict** Would you expect milk that is labeled "lactose-free" to taste sweeter than untreated milk? Why or why not?

   Sample answer: I would expect it to taste sweeter, because the lactose has been

   converted to glucose, which has a sweet taste.

   _____

6. **Infer** Suggest a reason why people who are lactose intolerant can tolerate yogurt that contains "live cultures" or "active cultures."

   Sample answer: The bacteria in these cultures might be able to digest lactose.

   _____

   _____

7. **Infer** Scientists now think that lactose intolerance can sometimes "run in families." What does this mean, and what does it suggest about the nature of lactose intolerance?

Sample answer: The phrase "run in families" implies that lactose intolerance can be inherited. It is possible that a mutation occurred in a gene that regulates the production of lactase.

Extend Your Inquiry

Does lactase work only on lactose, or will it digest other sugars? Design an experiment to determine the effect of lactase on a disaccharide other than lactose.

Students could repeat the procedure using sucrose or maltose. Because enzymes are substrate-specific, lactase will not digest these sugars.

Chapter 31 Lab **Testing Sensory Receptors for Touch**

Problem

What factors affect a person's ability to detect gentle pressure on skin?

Introduction

Your skin is the boundary between your body and the physical world that surrounds you. So it probably is not surprising that your skin contains many different sensory receptors. Some of those receptors detect changes in temperature. Others respond to tissue injury or damage. Still others are mechanoreceptors that respond when you touch an object or when an object touches you. The receptors for touch are more concentrated in some areas of your skin than in others.

   In this lab, you will use a bent paper clip to infer the relative concentration, or density, of receptors for touch in three different areas of your skin. When the density is high, you should be able to sense two touches that are close together. When the density is low, it will be harder to distinguish two touches that are close together.

Skills Focus

Measure, Analyze Data, Draw Conclusions

Materials

- bent paper clips
- metric ruler

Safety 🔗

Use the paper clip only as instructed. The ends of the clip will be sharp. Use only gentle pressure when applying the ends to skin.

Big Idea
Sensory receptors in the peripheral nervous system collect information about the body's internal and external environments.

Skills Objectives
Students will be able to
- compare the relative density of sense receptors in different areas of the skin.
- identify factors that could affect sensitivity to touch.

Preparation Time
20 minutes

Class Time
40 minutes

Group Size
Pairs

Safety
The ends of the paper clips will be sharp. So stress that students should not press the ends into the skin. Tell students that if the paper clip does pierce the skin, the clip needs to be discarded.

Advance Preparation
To prepare the bent paper clips, unbend each clip as shown in the drawing. Then, use a wire cutter or pliers to cut the clips at the locations shown.

Prepare a few extra clips in case some need to be discarded.

cut

Pre-Lab Questions

1. **Predict** Which area will have the highest density of receptors for gentle pressure—your fingertips, the back of your hand, or your forearm?

Sample answer: Fingertips will have the highest density.

_____

2. **Control Variables** Why must you have your eyes closed while your partner touches your skin with the bent paper clip?

Sample answer: If I could see the paper clip touch my skin, I might

assume that I felt two touches when I did not.

_____

3. **Predict** Will you and your partner have the same density of touch receptors in a given area of skin? Give a reason for your prediction.

Because most physical traits vary, students may assume that the density

of receptors can vary, too.

_____

_____

Procedure

You will be working with a partner. Your partner will test your skin and record your data. You will test your partner's skin and record your partner's data. CAUTION: You and your partner should use different paper clips.

1. Practice gently touching the ends of your paper clip to your arm. Note the difference in the sensation when you use both ends of the clip and when you use only one end. CAUTION: Do not apply enough pressure to pierce the skin.

2. Squeeze your partner's paper clip until the ends are 2 cm apart. Then use Steps 3–5 to test the skin on the back of your partner's hand. Choose an area in the center of your partner's hand.

Step 3
Stress the need to use a random pattern of one-end and two-end touches. It might help if the person doing the testing fills in the Ends Used column once the partner's eyes are closed.

3. Make sure your partner's eyes are closed. Touch the paper clip to the back of your partner's hand 10 times—5 times with two ends and 5 times with one end. Mix up the two-end and one-end touches so that your partner will not recognize a pattern. After each touch, ask whether your partner felt one end or two. Record the responses in Data Table 1.

4. Decrease the distance between the ends of the paper clip to 1.5 cm and repeat Step 3. Record the responses in Data Table 1.

5. Repeat Step 4 with the distance between the ends at 1 cm, 0.5 cm, and 0.3 cm.

Data Table 1: Back of Hand										
	2 cm		1.5 cm		1.0 cm		0.5 cm		0.3 cm	
Touch	Ends Used	Ends Felt	Ends Used	Ends Felt	Ends Used	Ends Felt	Ends Used	Ends Felt	Ends Used	Ends Felt
1										
2										
3										
4										
5										
6										
7										
8										
9										
10										

6. Use the procedure in Steps 2–5 to test the skin on the tip of your partner's index finger. Record the responses in Data Table 2.

Data Table 2: Fingertip										
	2 cm		1.5 cm		1.0 cm		0.5 cm		0.3 cm	
Touch	Ends Used	Ends Felt	Ends Used	Ends Felt	Ends Used	Ends Felt	Ends Used	Ends Felt	Ends Used	Ends Felt
1										
2										
3										
4										
5										
6										
7										
8										
9										
10										

7. Repeat the procedure for your partner's forearm. Pick a location halfway between the wrist and the elbow. Record the responses in Data Table 3. Then, return the paper clip to your teacher.

	2 cm		1.5 cm		1.0 cm		0.5 cm		0.3 cm	
Data Table 3: Forearm										
Touch	Ends Used	Ends Felt	Ends Used	Ends Felt	Ends Used	Ends Felt	Ends Used	Ends Felt	Ends Used	Ends Felt
1										
2										
3										
4										
5										
6										
7										
8										
9										
10										

Step 10

If the results vary for a given area of skin, calculate the mean and the mode for that set of data. The mean is an average. The mode is the number that appears most often in the data.

You may want to use this opportunity to discuss the pros and cons of using a mean or a mode to summarize data.

Disposal

Either throw away the clips or clean the tips with alcohol and store the clips for future use.

8. What was the shortest distance at which your partner could detect two ends of the clip at least three times?

Back of hand: _____

Fingertip: _____

Forearm: _____

9. What was the shortest distance at which you could detect two ends of the clip at least three times?

Back of hand: _____

Fingertip: _____

Forearm: _____

10. Record the class results for Steps 8 and 9 on the board.

Analyze and Conclude

1. **Evaluate** Do your results support the prediction you made in Pre-Lab Question 1 about which area of skin would have the highest density of sense receptors? Explain.

   Answers will depend on the prediction that was made. Students are likely to find the

   highest density of receptors in the fingertip.

   _____

2. **Form a Hypothesis** Why do you think that humans have a higher density of receptors for touch in some areas of skin than in other areas?

   Sample answer: There are more receptors in areas that are used to grasp or

   manipulate objects.

   _____

3. **Evaluate** Do your results and those of your partner support the prediction you made in Pre-Lab Question 3? Explain.

   Answers will depend on the prediction that was made. Depending on the partners,

   students may see a lot of variation or a little.

   _____

4. **Form a Hypothesis** What factors could account for variation in sensitivity to touch from one person to another?

   Possible factors are thickness of skin, skin cells that have been damaged, and

   genetics.

   _____

5. **Form a Hypothesis** How might activities such as playing a guitar, laying bricks, preparing food, or playing video games affect a person's sensitivity to touch?

   Sample answer: Strumming a guitar, handling bricks, using knives, or even playing

   video games might cause calluses to form, which would reduce the sensitivity of the

   fingertips.

   _____

6. **Use an Analogy** The phrase *thick skinned* is used to describe people who are not easily affected by other people's criticisms. Relate this meaning of *thick skinned* to how areas of thickened skin could affect a person's sense of touch.

   Sample answer: A "thick-skinned person" is less sensitive to other people's opinions.

   Areas of thickened skin are likely to be less sensitive to touch.

   _____

   _____

7. **Apply Concepts** Automobile dashboards have many control knobs and buttons. Drivers might be involved in fewer accidents if they did not have to look at these controls to adjust the temperature or change the station on the radio. What could dashboard designers do to make it easier for drivers to keep their eyes on the road?

Sample answer: Designers could use different shapes for different controls or use

surfaces with different textures so that a driver could distinguish one control from

another by touch.

_____

_____

Extend Your Inquiry

Design an experiment to answer the following question. How does temperature affect the sensitivity to touch?

Cold temperatures should reduce the sensitivity to touch.

Chapter 32 Lab **Comparing Limbs**

Problem

How is the structure of skeletal muscles and bones related to the functions of these body parts?

Introduction

Although humans sometimes use all four limbs to move around, most of the time humans use their legs and arms for distinctly different functions. Legs support the body and carry it from place to place while arms lift and carry objects.

Despite these differences in tasks, arms and legs have similar overall structures. The upper part of each limb is supported by a single bone, and the lower part of each limb is supported by two bones. Pairs of opposing muscles move the bones around their respective joints.

Do the limbs of other vertebrates have similar arrangements of bones and muscles? For example, is the wing of a bird similar to a human arm? In this lab, you will begin by comparing the motion of arms and legs. Then, you will dissect a chicken wing and compare its internal structure to that of a human arm.

Skills Focus

Observe, Infer, Compare and Contrast

Materials

- disposable plastic gloves
- chicken wing
- disposable dissection tray
- dissecting scissors
- forceps
- colored pencils or markers

Safety 🫁 ✋ ✂️ 🗑️ 🧼

Disease-causing species of *Salmonella* bacteria may be present on raw chicken. To avoid infection, wear gloves and avoid touching your eyes, nose, and mouth. Use the dissecting scissors only as instructed to avoid injuring yourself and others. Dispose of materials only as instructed by your teacher. Wash your hands thoroughly with soap and warm water before leaving the lab.

Big Idea
Bones provide a system of levers on which muscles act to produce movement. The structures of these tissues reflect their functions.

Skills Objectives
Students will be able to
- classify arm and leg joints based on their motion.
- dissect a chicken wing.
- identify homologous structures in an arm and a chicken wing.

Preparation Time
15 minutes

Class Time
Part A: 15 minutes
Part B: 40 minutes

Group Size
Pairs

Materials
If you do not have disposable dissecting trays, use two layers of sturdy paper plates.

Advance Preparation
Keep the fresh or thawed chicken wings refrigerated. Right before the lab, wash and dry the wings to remove as many bacteria as possible.

Line a waste container with a sturdy plastic trash bag, which you will use for disposal of wings, trays, gloves, and paper towels. Arrange with the custodian to have the trash removed at the end of the day.

Safety
Use disposable gloves when you handle the wings.

Pre-Lab Questions

1. **Observe** How will you observe the structure and function of your elbow and knee joints?

   Sample answer: I will use diagrams to observe the structure of the elbow and knee joints. To observe function, I will feel each joint as I move my forearm and lower leg.

2. **Relate Cause and Effect** Why is it important to wear goggles and disposable gloves while examining the chicken wing?

   Raw chicken may contain *Salmonella* bacteria, which can cause an infection.

3. **Predict** Will the arrangement of bones and muscles in a chicken wing be similar to the arrangement in a human arm? Why or why not?

   Students may predict that the arrangement will be similar because humans and chickens share a common vertebrate ancestor. Students may predict that the arrangement will be different because wings have a different function than do arms.

Procedure

Part A: Observe the Motion of Human Limbs

1. Extend your right arm with the palm facing down and place two fingers of your left hand on the tip of your right elbow. Bend your right arm and then straighten it out. Describe any movement at the tip of your elbow.

   Sample answer: The tip of the elbow moves as the forearm moves.

2. Extend your right arm with the palm facing down and place two fingers of your left hand on the tip of your right elbow. Keep your arm straight while you rotate your hand so that your palm faces up, and then rotate your hand back to its original position. Describe any movement at the tip of your elbow.

   Sample answer: The tip of the elbow does not move.

3. Keep your right arm extended with the palm facing down. Place the fingers of your left hand under your right forearm just above the wrist. Rotate your hand so that your palm faces up, and then rotate your hand back to its original position. Describe what you feel.

Students should be able to feel one of the bones in the forearm move

over the other.

_____

4. Sit in a chair with your feet flat on the floor. Place the fingertips of your right hand on the middle of your kneecap. Raise your lower leg. Describe what happens to your kneecap.

Sample answer: The kneecap moves as the leg moves.

_____

5. Raise your lower leg again. Try to turn your foot so that the sole of the foot is facing up. Describe what happens.

Sample answer: The foot cannot be rotated to a sole-up position.

_____

6. Look at the drawings in Figure 1. Identify the muscles that bend and straighten the elbow and knee joints.

Muscles A and D bend the joints. Muscles B and C straighten the joints.

_____

Figure 1 Muscles in a human arm and leg

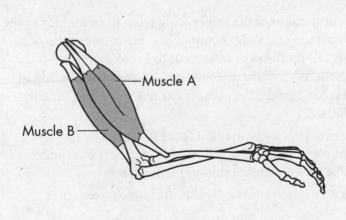
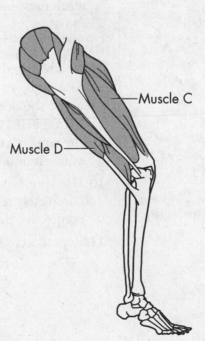

Teaching Tip Part B
To avoid contamination of notebooks and pencils, have one student in each pair start the dissection while their partner records observations.

Determine in advance when in the procedure students will switch roles. At that point, the ones who have been handling the wings should remove and discard their gloves and wash their hands before touching the notebook and pencils. Their partners need to put on gloves before handling the wings.

If students work in larger groups, you will need to further adjust the tasks.

Part B: Observe the Structure of a Chicken Wing

7. Put on goggles and gloves. Place a chicken wing in the dissecting tray and observe its structure. On the drawing in Figure 2, label the upper wing, lower wing, joints, and wing tip.

Figure 2 External Anatomy of a Chicken Wing

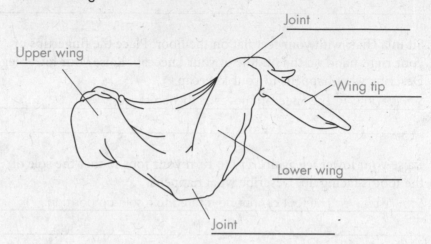

8. Bend and straighten the joint between the upper wing and the lower wing. Bend the joint between the lower wing and the wing tip. Describe the motion you observe.

Sample answer: The joint between the upper wing and lower wing can bend nearly 180°. The joint between the lower wing and wing tip has a much narrower range of motion.

_____

9. You will next cut the skin of the upper wing from the shoulder to the first joint. To start the cut, slide the tip of one blade under the skin at the shoulder. Lift up the skin as you cut to avoid damaging the tissues beneath the skin. Make a second cut on the opposite side of the wing. CAUTION: Handle the scissors carefully to avoid injuring yourself or others.

10. Use your fingers to peel away the skin from the upper wing. To completely remove the skin, you will need to carefully cut the bits of connective tissue that attach the skin to the muscles.

Step 10
Help students who are having trouble removing the skin from around the joints.

11. Repeat Steps 9 and 10 to remove the skin from the lower wing.

12. After you remove the skin, use the forceps or your fingers to gently separate the muscles from one another. Use the space below to make a sketch that shows the muscles.

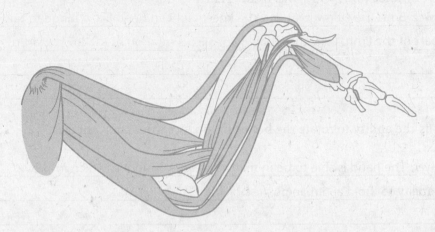

13. Pull on each muscle, one at a time, to see whether the muscle bends or straightens a joint. Identify the opposing pairs of muscles and color-code these pairs on your drawing.

14. Trace each muscle to the joint between the upper and lower wing. Cut the shiny white tendons that connect the muscles to the joint and peel back the muscles. In the space below, sketch the arrangement of the bones around the joint.

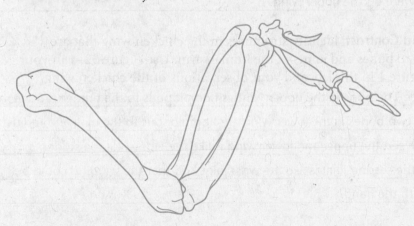

15. Follow your teacher's instructions for disposal of the chicken wings, dissecting trays, gloves, and paper towels. Wash the scissors and forceps and any surfaces you might have touched while doing the dissection. When you are done, wash your hands thoroughly with soap and warm water.

Step 15
Remind students to discard chicken wings, trays, gloves, and paper towels in the designated container.

Analyze and Conclude

1. **Compare and Contrast** How was the motion at your elbow joint similar to the motion at your knee joint? How was it different?

   Sample answer: Both the elbow joint and the knee joint can bend like a hinge to raise the lower part of the limb. Only the elbow joint allows rotation of the lower part of the limb.

2. **Infer** How is the ability to rotate the bones in the forearm an advantage for humans?

   Sample answer: The hand is able to be in many different positions, which improves the hand's ability to hold and manipulate objects.

3. **Infer** How is it an advantage for the human knee to have a smaller range of motion than the human elbow?

   Sample answer: The smaller range of motion in the knee helps keep humans steady on their feet as they stand, walk, and run.

4. **Observe** In the chicken wing, where were the muscles that bend and straighten the joint between the upper and lower wing located?

   The muscles were on the upper wing.

5. **Compare and Contrast** Identify structures in the chicken wing that are homologous to bones and joints in the human arm. Use Figure 32–1 in your textbook, Figure 1 in this lab, and your observations of the chicken wing.

   Sample answer: The bone in the upper wing is homologous to the humerus bone in the arm. The two bones in the lower wing are homologous to the ulna and radius. The joint between the upper and lower wing is like the elbow. (Some students may also say that the second joint is like the wrist joint and that the wing tip could be homologous to the hand.)

Extend Your Inquiry

View prepared slides of skeletal muscle and bone. Draw a sketch for each type of tissue. Then, write a paragraph explaining how the structure of each type of tissue is adapted to its function.

Students should note that skeletal muscle is made up of long fibers, while bone consists mostly of mineral deposits with some cells embedded within. These differences reflect the fact that muscles contract and pull on bones, while bones must be strong and rigid.

Chapter 33 Lab **Tidal Volume and Lung Capacity**

Problem

What factors can affect lung capacity?

Introduction

When you inhale, air rushes into your lungs. The amount of air that rushes in during a normal breath is called the *tidal volume*. Your lungs have the capacity to accept a much larger volume of air than you normally inhale. For example, you might be asked to take a deep breath during a medical exam. Scientists use the term *vital capacity* to describe the largest volume of air that you can exhale after you take a deep breath.

In this lab, you will measure tidal volume and vital capacity. Then you will design an experiment to investigate a factor that can affect vital capacity.

Skills Focus

Measure, Form a Hypothesis, Design an Experiment, Interpret Graphs

Materials

• round balloons

• metric ruler

• meterstick

Safety ⚠

Do not test your vital capacity if you are ill or if you have difficulty breathing. If at any point you feel faint or dizzy, stop what you are doing and sit down. Ask your partner to inform your teacher of the problem. If you have an allergy to latex, do not handle the balloons. Make sure you and your partner use different balloons.

Pre-Lab Questions

1. **Control Variables** What is the one difference between the procedures in Part A and Part B?

In Part A, the subject takes a normal breath before exhaling. In Part B,

the subject takes a deep breath before exhaling as much air as possible.

Big Idea
Lungs need sufficient capacity to replenish the oxygen in blood, which transports the oxygen to cells.

Skills Objectives
Students will be able to
• form a hypothesis about vital capacity.
• design an experiment to test the hypothesis.
• relate the results to the mechanism of breathing.

Class Time
Parts A and B: 30 minutes
Part C: 10 minutes
Part D: 25 minutes

Group Size
Pairs

Materials
To provide a sufficient volume for all students, use 9-inch round balloons.

Safety
Students with acute or chronic respiratory illnesses should not participate in the breathing activities, but they can help other students collect data. Do not let students with an allergy to latex handle the balloons.

2. **Design an Experiment** Why must you use round balloons for this experiment?

Sample answer: It would not be possible to measure the diameter of the balloons with a ruler if the balloons had a different shape.

_____

3. **Predict** Which do you think will be greater—your estimated vital capacity or your measured vital capacity? Why?

Students may say that the estimated vital capacity will be larger because they will not be able to capture all the exhaled air in the balloon. Some students may expect their measured capacity to be greater because they have done considerable aerobic training.

Procedure

Part A: Measuring Tidal Volume

1. Stretch a round balloon lengthwise several times.

2. Inhale normally, and then exhale normally into the balloon. Immediately pinch the balloon shut so that no air escapes.

3. Keep pinching the balloon as you place it on a flat surface. Have your partner measure the diameter of the balloon at its widest point as shown in Figure 1. Record the measurement in Data Table 1.

4. Allow the balloon to deflate. Repeat Steps 2 and 3 two more times.

5. Calculate the mean for the measurements from the three trials and record your answer in the data table.

Step 1
Make sure each student has his or her own balloon.

Step 2
Students may want to pinch their nostrils while exhaling to prevent air from escaping through the nose.

Figure 1 How to measure the diameter of the balloon

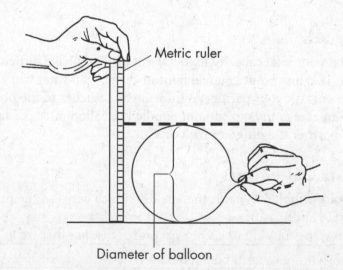

Metric ruler

Diameter of balloon

Data Table 1: Balloon Diameter (cm)		
Trial	Tidal Volume	Vital Capacity
1		
2		
3		
Mean		

Data Table 2: Volume (cm³)		
Trial	Tidal Volume	Vital Capacity
1		
2		
3		
Mean		

Part B: Measuring Vital Capacity

6. Take as deep a breath as possible. Then, exhale as much air as you can from your lungs into the balloon. Immediately pinch the balloon shut so that no air escapes.

7. Keep pinching the balloon as you place it on a flat surface. Have your partner measure the diameter of the balloon at its widest point. Record the measurement in Data Table 1.

8. Allow the balloon to deflate. Repeat Steps 6 and 7 two more times.

9. Calculate the mean for the measurements from the three trials and record your answer in the data table.

10. On the graph in Figure 2, balloon diameter in centimeters is plotted against volume in cubic centimeters (cm³). Use the graph to find the volumes that correspond to your diameter measurements. Record your results in Data Table 2.

Figure 2 Lung volume versus balloon diameter

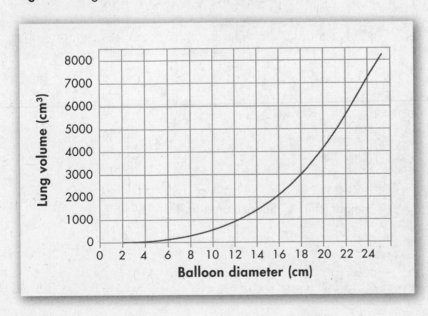

Part C: Estimating Vital Capacity

Research has shown that vital capacity is proportional to the surface area of a person's body. You can estimate your surface area if you know your height and your mass.

11. You can use the meterstick to measure your height in centimeters. Or you can convert your height in inches to centimeters by multiplying the number of inches by 2.54.

Height: *Sample answer: 5'6" = 66 in. × 2.54 = 168 cm*

Step 12
Given that some students will be sensitive about their weight, do not have students measure their mass in class. Accept students' estimates of mass.

12. To convert your mass in pounds to kilograms, multiply the number of pounds by 0.454.

Mass: *Sample answer: 130 lb × 0.454 = 59 kg*

13. Use Figure 3 to estimate the surface area of your body. Find your height on the scale on the left. Find your mass on the scale on the right. Use a ruler to draw a straight line between those points. The location where the line crosses the middle scale is your estimated surface area.

Surface area: *Sample answer: 1.68 m²*

Figure 3 Estimated surface area based on height and mass

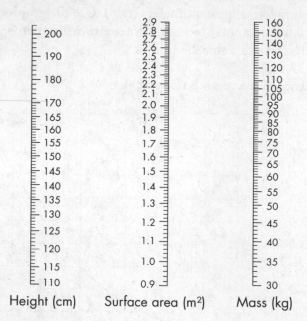

Height (cm)   Surface area (m²)   Mass (kg)

14. To calculate the estimated vital capacity of your lungs, multiply your surface area in square meters by the ratio of vital capacity to surface area. Based on research, the ratio is 2000 cubic centimeters per square meter for females. For males, the ratio is 2500 cubic centimeters per square meter. Calculate and record your answer.

Estimated vital capacity = surface area (m²) × ratio $\left(\dfrac{cm^3}{m^2}\right)$

Estimated vital capacity: *Sample answer:* 3360 cm³ or 4200 cm³

Part D: Design Your Own Lab

You were probably standing up when you measured your vital capacity. Would the results have been different if you were seated? Would your posture when seated affect the results?

15. **Form a Hypothesis** How will changing the position of your body affect your vital capacity? Record the hypothesis you will test to answer this question.

Hypothesis: *Sample answer:* The vital capacity when seated will be higher than the vital capacity when standing.

16. **Describe Your Plan** Describe the procedure you will use to test your hypothesis. How will you modify the procedure from Part B? What variables will you need to control during your trials?

Experimental Plan: If the comparison is between standing and sitting positions, students need to control their posture when seated. They could also explore vital capacity when sitting up straight, slouching, or slumped over.

17. Construct a data table in the space below. Make as many rows for recording data as the number of trials you plan to do. Include a row for recording the mean of your trials.

Data Table		
Trial	Diameter (cm)	Vital Capacity (cm³)
1		
2		
3		
Mean		

Analyze and Conclude

1. **Analyze Data** How did your estimated vital capacity compare with your measured vital capacity? Was your prediction in Pre-Lab Question 3 correct?

Answers will vary based on the student data and on the prediction.

2. **Draw Conclusions** What could have caused any difference between the estimated value and the measured value?

Sample answer: The estimated vital capacity is larger because air may escape from the nose or from the balloon before the volume is measured.

3. **Design an Experiment** Why is it important to do more than one trial when making measurements?

Sample answer: Averaging data from multiple trials provides more reliable results because slight differences between trials are erased (assuming that a major error did not occur in all trials).

4. **Infer** In Step 14, why did females and males use different ratios to calculate estimated vital capacity?

Sample answer: On average, females must have a smaller lung capacity than males with the same surface area. (Studies have shown that most of the gender difference in lung volume can be accounted for by smaller radial rib cage dimensions in females relative to height.)

5. **Analyze Data** How did your position affect the vital capacity of your lungs? Suggest an explanation for any difference you found.

The vital capacity is likely to be lower for seated positions versus standing. The vital capacity is likely to be higher for sitting with a straight back versus slumping forward. A likely explanation is that body position can affect how much air the student is able to inhale.

6. **Perform Error Analysis** In Part A, why might the volume in the first trial be smaller than in the second and third trials? How could the procedure be adjusted to avoid this result?

Sample answer: The balloon was not stretched sufficiently before the first trial.

Students could inhale into the balloon once before they begin collecting data.

7. **Predict** How would smoking affect lung capacity, and why?

Sample answer: Smoking would reduce lung capacity because smoke-laden mucus

can clog airways and smoking causes the lining of the respiratory tract to swell,

which reduces air flow.

Extend Your Inquiry

Use the class data to determine whether aerobic exercise affects vital capacity. As a class, determine which information you need about each data point to rule out the effect of other variables.

If possible, use the calculated means from one or more classes. For privacy, ask each student to supply the following information with his or her data—sex, surface area, and estimate of number of hours of aerobic exercise per week. The expected outcome is that aerobic exercise will not have a significant effect on vital capacity. However, remind students that aerobic exercise does affect the circulatory system, as in the heart's ability to pump blood and the volume of blood.

Chapter 34 Lab **Diagnosing Endocrine Disorders**

Problem

Can you diagnose an endocrine disorder based on a patient's symptoms?

Introduction

Glands in the endocrine system secrete chemical messengers called hormones. Feedback mechanisms regulate the amounts of hormones released. When the levels of hormones in the blood are normal, reactions in the body take place at a normal rate and homeostasis is maintained.

Sometimes, however, endocrine glands do not respond properly to feedback mechanisms. A gland might produce too much of a hormone, or it might produce too little. Or, a receptor might not respond to a hormone as expected. Either way, some reactions do not occur at a normal rate. As a result, a person may experience certain symptoms, which prompt a visit to a primary care doctor.

The doctor will ask the patient some questions and do a brief medical exam. If the doctor suspects an endocrine disorder, he or she will refer the patient to a specialist. A doctor who diagnoses and treats disorders of the endocrine system is an endocrinologist. In this lab, you will play the role of an endocrinologist. Based on a patient's symptoms, you will form a hypothesis about the cause and consider what should be done to confirm the diagnosis.

Skills Focus

Analyze Data, Draw Conclusions, Relate Cause and Effect

Pre-Lab Questions

1. **Interpret Tables** When patients complain of fatigue they are usually referring to a lack of energy or motivation. Which conditions listed in the table have fatigue as a symptom?

   hypothyroidism, Addison's disease, hyperparathyroidism

   _____

2. **Apply Concepts** Why do doctors typically use blood tests to diagnose endocrine disorders?

   Sample answer: They use blood tests because hormones and many of the

   substances that hormones regulate circulate in the blood.

   _____

Big Idea
The endocrine system is regulated by feedback mechanisms that help to maintain homeostasis.

Skills Objectives
Students will be able to
• identify endocrine disorders based on a patient's symptoms.
• relate the symptoms of a disorder to its cause.

Class Time
40 minutes

Group Size
Individuals

3. Infer Why is it important for doctors to consider the age and sex of a patient when diagnosing a disorder?

Sample answer: Some symptoms will occur only in women or only in men. Some disorders are more likely to occur in certain age groups.

Procedure

You will use your knowledge of hormones and the table provided to diagnose the patients described in four case studies. Column 2 in the table lists common complaints that a patient might make. Column 3 lists the results of tests that a doctor could order to confirm or rule out an initial diagnosis. Most lab tests involve chemical analysis of blood or urine samples. If you do not recall the functions of any hormones mentioned in the table, look up this information in your textbook.

Endocrine Disorders		
Disorder	**Symptoms**	**Lab Test Results**
Addison's Disease	Fatigue, muscle weakness, weight loss, increased pigment in the skin	High potassium and low sodium levels in blood; high ACTH level in blood, low cortisol level in blood
Cushing's Syndrome	Muscle weakness, backache, anxiety, depression, extra fat deposits on the back of the neck and upper back, irregular menstrual cycle in females	High levels of cortisol in blood
Diabetes Insipidus	Frequent urination, excessive thirst	No glucose in urine, normal glucose level in blood, low ADH level in blood
Hyperparathyroidism	Excessive thirst, weakened or broken bones, fatigue, nausea	High calcium levels in blood; high parathyroid hormone levels in blood
Hyperthyroidism	Nervousness, elevated body temperature, excessive sweating, rapid heart rate, weight loss, irregular menstrual cycle in females	High thyroxine level in blood, low TSH level in blood
Hypothyroidism	Muscle weakness, fatigue, weight gain, depression, slow heart rate, low body temperature and intolerance of cold	Low thyroxine level in blood, high TSH level in blood
Type I Diabetes Mellitus	Frequent urination, excessive thirst, weight loss	Glucose present in urine, elevated blood glucose, islet cell antibody in blood
Type II Diabetes Mellitus	Frequent urination, excessive thirst	Glucose present in urine, elevated blood glucose, no islet cell antibodies in blood

Case Study 1

A 35-year-old woman complains of muscle weakness, anxiety, and depression. Which disorders listed in the table could account for these symptoms? What other symptoms might you look for or ask about to distinguish between these disorders?

Sample answer: The woman might have hypothyroidism or Cushing's

syndrome. If she frequently feels cold, the condition is more likely

hypothyroidism. If her menstrual cycle is irregular, the condition is more

likely Cushing's syndrome.

_____

Case Study 2

A 42-year-old man broke a bone in his arm. The doctor who set his arm was concerned that the man's bones were unusually weak. The doctor sent the man to see an endocrinologist. The man also complained of fatigue and nausea. What disorder could this patient have? What could you do to confirm this diagnosis?

The man might have hyperparathyroidism. Its symptoms include weakened

bones, fatigue, and nausea. To confirm the diagnosis, I would have his

blood tested for elevated calcium and parathyroid hormone levels.

_____

Case Study 3

A 33-year-old man complains of fatigue. He has lost weight, although he is not trying to lose weight. A routine blood test shows that his blood glucose level is normal, but he has a low level of sodium in the blood. What test would you order next, and why?

I would determine the levels of potassium, cortisol, and ACTH in the blood

because the man might have Addison's disease. (The level of glucose in the

blood appears to rule out diabetes.)

_____

Case Study 4

Both hyperthyroidism and hypothyroidism can cause a goiter, a swelling of the thyroid gland. You notice that a patient has a swollen thyroid gland. Before you order any lab tests, you could make two measurements during a physical exam to help determine the cause of the goiter. What measurements could you make and why would they be helpful?

I would measure the patient's heart rate and temperature. A rapid heart rate

and high body temperature would point toward hyperthyroidism. A slow

heart rate and low body temperature would point toward hypothyroidism.

_____

Analyze and Conclude

1. **Draw Conclusions** Why is it important for a doctor to ask a patient questions in addition to doing a physical exam?

   Sample answer: Some symptoms of a disorder, such as frequent urination and anxiety, cannot be detected by doing a physical exam.

2. **Relate Cause and Effect** Why would a doctor expect to see low levels of TSH in the blood of a patient with hyperthyroidism?

   With hyperthyroidism, the thyroid is producing excess amounts of thyroxine. Increased levels of thyroxine cause the pituitary to stop producing TSH.

3. **Compare and Contrast** How are Type I and Type II diabetes similar? How are they different?

   With both Type I and Type II diabetes, excessive thirst, frequent urination, glucose in the urine, and elevated levels of glucose in the blood are symptoms. Islet cell antibodies are present in the blood with Type I and absent with Type II. (Students may also mention the typical age of onset for each type.)

4. **Infer** A patient is told not to eat or drink anything for 12 hours before having blood drawn to test the level of glucose. Why do you think it is necessary for the patient to fast before the test?

   Sample answer: Digestion causes changes to blood glucose levels. Fasting ensures that blood glucose levels are not influenced by a recent intake of carbohydrates.

5. **Relate Cause and Effect** One indication of diabetes insipidus is a low level of ADH in the blood. ADH is the hormone that signals the body to retain water. How could a low level of ADH lead to frequent urination and excessive thirst?

   Sample answer: Normally, as water is removed from the body and the concentration of solutes in the blood increases, ADH signals the kidneys to slow down the removal of water. Without sufficient ADH, the removal of water is not slowed, which leads to frequent urination and an increased urge to replace the lost water.

Extend Your Inquiry

Write your own case study of a patient with an endocrine disorder. Use the case studies in the lab as models. Give your description to a classmate who will try to diagnose the disorder.

Encourage students to use information in the textbook as well as the data in the table.

Chapter 35 Lab **Detecting Lyme Disease**

Problem

How can a blood test be used to detect Lyme disease?

Introduction

Lyme disease is caused by the bacterium *Borrelia burgdorferi*. The bacteria can be spread through the bite of a tiny organism called a deer tick. Campers, hikers, and gardeners all risk exposure to these disease-carrying ticks. One possible early sign of Lyme disease is a bull's-eye-shaped rash that appears around the site of the tick bite. Other possible symptoms include fever, fatigue, muscle and joint pain, sore throat, and headache. Many of these symptoms are very common and can be caused by multiple illnesses. In addition, not everyone who has Lyme disease shows all these symptoms. Thus, Lyme disease can be difficult to diagnose.

There is no direct test for the presence of the bacteria that cause Lyme disease. Instead, doctors will order a blood test to see if there are antibodies to the bacteria in a patient's blood. This test is called an Enzyme-Linked Immunosorbent Assay (ELISA). There are several steps in an ELISA. If the technician sees a color change after the final step, the test is considered positive. Once the diagnosis is confirmed, Lyme disease can be treated with antibiotics.

In this lab, you will not be doing an actual ELISA, nor will you be testing actual blood samples. Instead, you will use a procedure that simulates, or imitates, the steps in an ELISA.

Skills Focus

Control Variables, Analyze Data, Draw Conclusions

Materials

- well plate
- permanent marker
- sheet of white paper
- 400-mL beaker
- 100-mL beaker
- distilled water
- 2 micropipettes
- test solutions

Safety 🥽 🧤 🔬

Whenever you are working with unknown solutions, you should wear goggles and gloves. Wash your hands thoroughly with soap and warm water before leaving the lab.

Big Idea
The human body produces antibodies as part of the immune response to invading pathogens, which can disrupt homeostasis.

Skills Objectives
Students will be able to
• test substances in a controlled, simulated experiment.
• infer reasons for certain steps in an experimental design.

Class Time
40 minutes

Group Size
Small groups

Materials
Commercial Lyme disease test kits vary in their procedures. You may need to adjust the lab to reflect these differences.
You can use phenolphthalein in place of the positive control and infected donor solutions; a dilute (5%) NaOH solution for the substrate, and distilled water for the other solutions.

Pre-Lab Questions

1. **Sequence** Use a flowchart to show the order in which the solutions will be added to the well plate.

    The flowchart should show the solutions being added in the following order: antigen, negative and positive controls, donor samples, secondary antibody, and substrate.

2. **Infer** What is the advantage of having a control for a positive test and a control for a negative test?

    Sample answer: Seeing the expected results for both a positive test and a

    negative test will make it easier to draw conclusions about the samples.

    _____

3. **Control Variables** Why must you rinse the micropipette with distilled water before using it to add a different solution to the well plate?

    Sample answer: Rinsing keeps the contents of a well from being

    contaminated with the contents of a different well.

    _____

    _____

Procedure

The test solutions that you will use come in small bottles, which your group will need to share with other groups. Your teacher will decide the order in which groups will receive the solutions. If you are the first group to receive the test solutions, use your flowchart to line the bottles up in the order that you will use them in the procedure. As soon as you are done with a bottle, carefully pass it along to the next group. The last group to receive the bottles should return them to your teacher at the end of the lab.

Teaching Tips
Order groups based on the most efficient route for transfer of bottles from group to group. Because there are several waiting periods between steps, there should be enough time built in for the transfers.

Demonstrate how to flush out the micropipettes with distilled water. Have students practice this part of the procedure before they do Step 3.

1. Label your well plate as shown in Figure 1. S1 and S2 stand for Sample 1 and Sample 2. Place the plate on a sheet of white paper. The paper will provide a clean spot to set down a micropipette, if necessary.

Figure 1 Labeled well plate

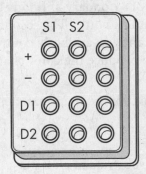

2. Put on your safety goggles and gloves. Pour about 250 mL of distilled water into a large beaker. Pour about 30 mL of water from the large beaker into a small beaker.

3. Use a micropipette to place 2 drops of antigen in all 8 marked wells. Return any unused solution to its bottle. CAUTION: Never let the micropipette touch any of the solutions in the wells.

4. Use the distilled water in the small beaker to flush the antigen solution out of the micropipette. Discard the water. Replace it with water from the large beaker.

5. Let the well plate sit for 5 minutes, which will allow time for the antigen to attach to the walls of the wells.

6. Use the micropipette to add 2 drops of the negative control to the wells next to the minus sign (−). Return any unused solution to its bottle.

7. Use the distilled water in the small beaker to flush the negative control solution out of the micropipette. Discard the water and replace it with water from the large beaker.

8. Use the micropipette to add 2 drops of the positive control to the wells next to the plus sign (+). Return any unused solution to its bottle.

9. Flush the positive control solution out of the micropipette with distilled water. Discard and replace the water.

10. Use the micropipette to add 2 drops of Donor 1 solution to the D1 wells. Return any unused solution to its bottle.

11. Flush the Donor 1 solution out of the micropipette. Discard and replace the water.

12. Use the micropipette to add 2 drops of the Donor 2 solution to the D2 wells. Return any unused solution to its bottle.

13. Discard the micropipette.

Step 3
Stress that returning unused solutions to stock bottles is usually unacceptable in a lab. However, an exception is being made in this lab because of the small amount of test solutions.
Have students alert you if they contaminate a micropipette. Provide a new micropipette and discard the contaminated one.

Step 15
Explain that this step in an ELISA is not a process that occurs in the body.

14. Let the well plate sit for 5 minutes.

15. Use a new micropipette to add 2 drops of secondary antibody to all 8 wells. Return any unused solution to its bottle. The secondary antibody is a substance that detects the antigen-antibody complex and binds to it. This step is necessary to produce the color change that indicates a positive reaction.

16. Flush the secondary antibody solution out of the micropipette. Discard and replace the water.

17. Let the well plate sit for 5 minutes.

18. Use the micropipette to add 2 drops of substrate to all 8 wells. Return any unused solution to its bottle.

19. In wells where the secondary antibody combined with an antigen-antibody complex, a reaction occurs when the substrate is added. This reaction will produce a color change. Observe the wells, and record your results in the data table.

Sample Data

Data Table: Results of ELISA Simulation		
Sample	**Column S1**	**Column S2**
Negative Control	No color change	No color change
Positive Control	Bright pink	Bright pink
Donor 1	No color change	No color change
Donor 2	Bright pink	Bright pink

Analyze and Conclude

1. Control Variables Why was it important to keep the micropipette from touching any of the solutions in the wells?

Sample answer: There could be contamination between wells and also contamination as extra solution is returned to the bottle.

2. Design an Experiment What was the purpose of having two sets of wells with exactly the same contents?

Sample answer: If a procedure produces the same results with identical samples, the results are more reliable.

3. Draw Conclusions Donor 1 and Donor 2 are patients who were bitten by deer ticks. Which patient has Lyme disease? How do you know?

One donor should test positive and one negative for Lyme disease. The color change is an indication of a positive test.

4. Infer Why did you have to wait 5 minutes after Steps 13 and 16?

Sample answer: The wait after Step 13 provides time for any antibodies that are present to bind to the antigen molecules. The wait after Step 16 provides time for the secondary antibody to bind to the antigen-antibody complex.

5. Infer A hiker removes a deer tick from his leg and develops a bull's-eye-shaped rash four days later. An ELISA run on blood drawn the next day is negative. An ELISA run on blood drawn a few weeks later is positive. The hiker was not exposed to ticks during the time between the two tests. Suggest a reason for the initial negative test.

Sample answer: It may take several weeks for the antibodies to the bacterium that causes Lyme disease to become detectable.

Extend Your Inquiry

Research whether Lyme disease is a problem in your area. If so, find out at what time of year and in what kinds of locations the risk is greatest.

Suggest students contact health departments at the local, county, or state level for information. Lyme disease is most prevalent in the Northeast and least common in the Midwest. Nebraska, Montana, New Mexico, Utah, North Dakota, South Dakota, and Hawaii have had the fewest cases of Lyme disease. Ticks are active after the last frost, with peak activity during the summer months.

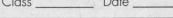

Additional Lab 1 **Making Models of Macromolecules**

Problem

How do monomers join together to form polymers?

Introduction

A small number of elements make up most of the mass of your body. Two of these elements are oxygen and hydrogen, which are the elements in water. Add carbon to hydrogen and oxygen and you have the three elements in carbohydrates. Add nitrogen and sulfur, and you have the five elements in amino acids.

Each carbon atom can form four bonds with other atoms. This property allows carbon to form the long chains or rings that are the backbone of all large biological molecules. Most of these large molecules are polymers, which are built up from smaller units called monomers.

In this lab, you will make models of three carbohydrates—glucose, maltose, and starch. Then, you will make models of two amino acid molecules. Finally, you will join the amino acid molecules together to model a peptide bond and a polypeptide chain.

Skills Focus

Use Models, Compare and Contrast, Infer

Materials

• molecular model kit

Pre-Lab Questions

1. **Review** What do the lines in a structural formula represent? What does it mean when there are two lines between atoms in a structural formula?

   The lines represent covalent bonds. Two lines represent a double bond.

2. **Use Models** In your molecular model set, what do the balls or beads represent? What do the sticks or tubes represent?

   The beads or balls represent the atoms. The sticks or tubes represent
   bonds between atoms.

Big Idea

Monomers can join together to form polymers, such as starch and polypeptides.

Skills Objectives

Students will be able to
• build models of biological molecules.
• compare the structures of macromolecules.

Class Time

45 minutes

Group Size

Pairs

3. Infer Why do you need models to visualize the structure of molecules?

Sample answer: The molecules are too small to be seen by the unaided eye (or even a light microscope).

Procedure

In most molecular model kits the "atoms" are color coded as follows: black for carbon, blue for nitrogen, red for oxygen, and white for hydrogen.

Teaching Tip, Part A
If your kits deviate from the traditional color conventions, discuss any differences with your students in advance.

Part A: Models of Carbohydrates

Most organisms rely on carbohydrates for their main source of energy. Carbohydrates include simple sugars and their polymers.

1. Glucose is a simple sugar, or monosaccharide, which means that it is a sugar with only one ring. Use the structural formula in Figure 1 to make a model of glucose. Start by joining the atoms in the ring. Then, attach the rest of the carbon and oxygen atoms.

2. Complete the model by adding a hydrogen atom to every unfilled bonding site. Check your work against the formula in Figure 1.

Figure 1 A simple sugar

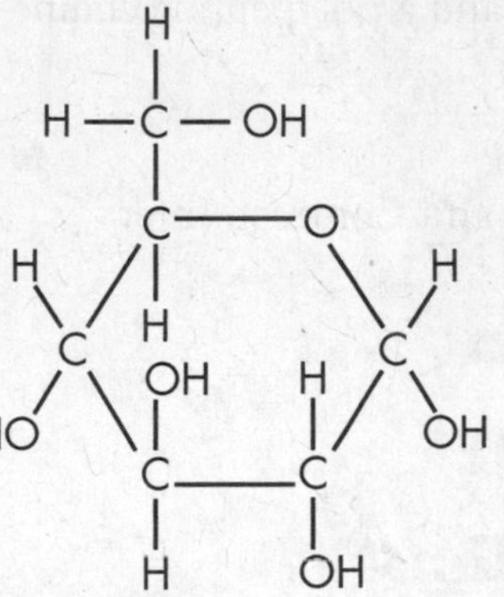

Glucose

3. Work with another group to make a model of a disaccharide, or two-ring sugar. Place your glucose models side by side as shown in Figure 2 on the next page. Remove the atoms that are circled in the formula. Use the atoms you remove to form a water molecule. A reaction in which water is removed from the reacting molecules is a *dehydration* reaction.

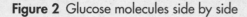

Figure 2 Glucose molecules side by side

[structural diagram of two glucose molecules side by side]

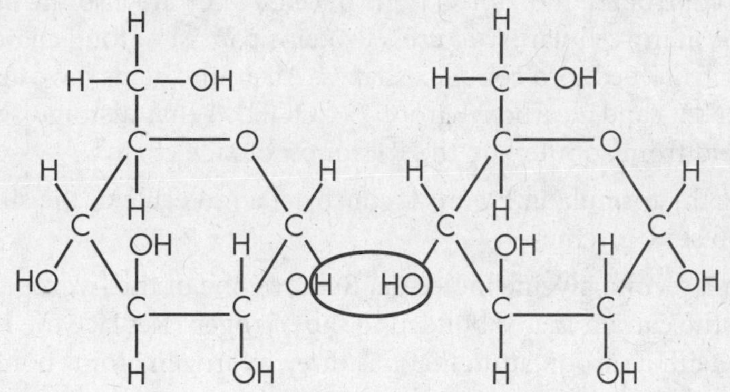

4. Join the glucose molecules by forming a bond between the oxygen atom on the left and the carbon atom on the right. You have made a model of the disaccharide maltose. Draw the structural formula for maltose in the space below.

Structural Formula for Maltose

[structural diagram of maltose]

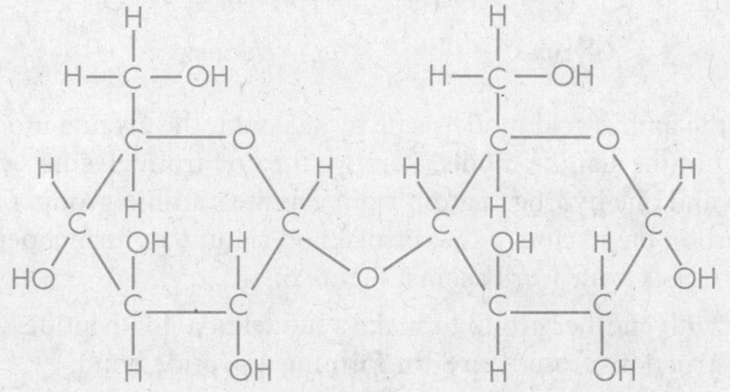

5. You will need to work with another pair of groups to make the model of starch shown in Figure 3. Combine your maltose molecules in the same way you combined the glucose molecules in Steps 3 and 4.

Figure 3 Structural formula for starch

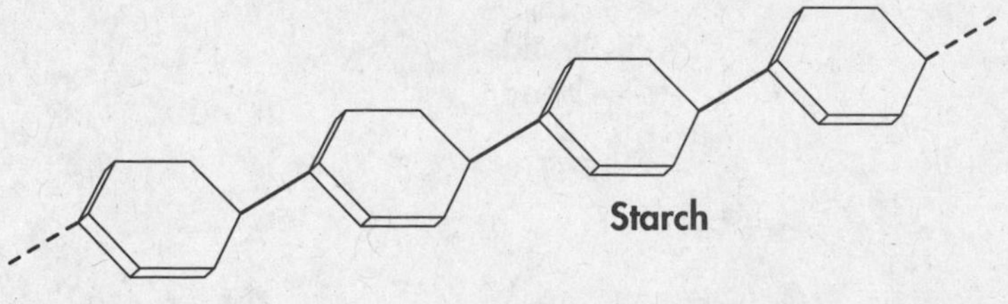

[structural diagram of starch]

Starch

Teaching Tip, Part B
Numbers of atoms and
bonds can vary between
kits. Students may need to
dismantle some models from
Part A before they can make
the models in Part B.

Step 6
Some kits will have longer,
more flexible tubes that can
be used to form the double
bond between carbon or
oxygen. Other kits may have
springs that can serve a similar
purpose.

Part B: Models of Proteins

Proteins control the rate of reactions in cells. They are also the building
blocks for many cellular structures. Proteins consist of long chains of
amino acids folded into complex shapes. All amino acids have an amino
group ($-NH_2$) and a carboxyl group ($-COOH$). What distinguishes one
amino acid from another are the R-groups, or side chains.

6. Using the formula in Figure 4, construct a molecule of the simplest
   amino acid, glycine.

7. Make a second glycine molecule. Remove one of the hydrogen atoms
   from the carbon that is bonded to the nitrogen. Replace the hydrogen
   atom with a carbon atom that has three hydrogen atoms bonded to
   it. Check your work against the formula for alanine in Figure 4.

Figure 4 Structural formulas
for two amino acids

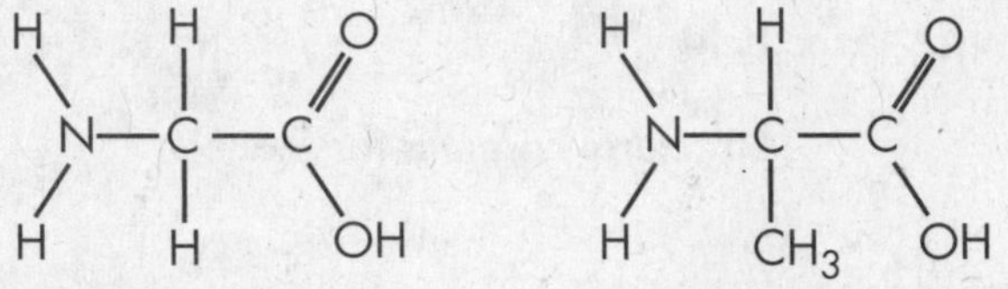

Glycine   Alanine

8. Place the amino acid models side by side with the glycine model to
   the left of the alanine model. Remove the OH from glycine's carboxyl
   group and one hydrogen atom from alanine's amino group. Connect
   the carbon on glycine to the nitrogen on alanine to form a peptide
   bond. Check your work against Figure 5.

9. Work with another group to make a model of a polypeptide. Apply
   the instructions from Step 8 for forming a peptide bond.

Figure 5 Peptide bond between glycine
and alanine

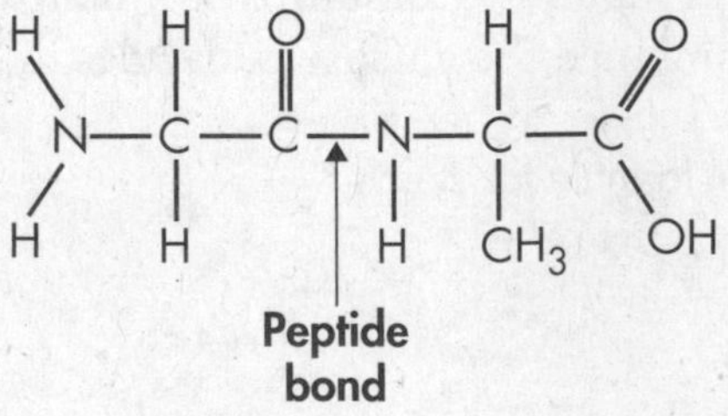

Peptide
bond

Analyze and Conclude

1. Draw Conclusions How many bonds can carbon, nitrogen, oxygen, and hydrogen atoms form?

Carbon atoms can form four bonds, nitrogen atoms can form three, oxygen atoms can form two, and hydrogen atoms can form one.

2. Compare and Contrast What can you learn from your models that you cannot learn by looking at structural formulas?

Sample answer: The three dimensional models reveal how the atoms are arranged in space. (The bond angles in 3D models are generally accurate. The bond lengths are generally not accurate.)

3. Evaluate What could you do to your models of starch and of a polypeptide chain in a protein to make them more accurate?

Students would need to join many more monomers into longer chains to represent a typical polysaccharide or polypeptide chain in a protein.

4. Infer There are thousands of proteins in a human cell, but only about 20 different amino acids. Explain how so few building blocks can be used to make so many different proteins.

Sample answer: The amino acids are similar to the letters in the alphabet. There are many possible variations in the chain depending on the amino acids used and the order of their placement in the chain.

5. Infer When starch is digested, the bonds between the monomers in the starch molecule are broken. The breakdown of starch is an example of a *hydrolysis* reaction. What is a hydrolysis reaction? *Hint:* What atoms are needed to complete each broken bond between monomers?

Sample answer: Two hydrogen atoms and one oxygen atom are needed to complete each broken bond. So a hydrolysis reaction could be defined as a reaction in which water is added to a compound.

Extend Your Inquiry

Lipids are another type of macromolecule. Lipids are used to store energy and to build cell structures, such as membranes. Use Figure 2–15 on page 47 of your textbook to make a model of a lipid. How are lipids similar to starch and to polypeptides? How are they different?

Students should note that lipids are large molecules whose backbone is made of carbon atoms. However, lipids are not polymers.

Open-Ended Inquiry • Design Your Own Lab

Additional Lab 2 Enzymes in Detergents

Problem

Are all detergents equally effective at removing protein stains?

Introduction

Every detergent maker claims that its products are the best at removing stains from clothing. Is there really that much difference among laundry detergents? All detergents have ingredients that help remove oils and grease, which do not dissolve easily in water. Detergents have other ingredients that are designed to remove stains with a high protein content, such as blood and milk. Protein stains are among the hardest stains to remove. The enzymes in detergents help break down the molecules in stains.

In this lab, you will use gelatin to compare the effectiveness of different brands of detergent. Gelatin is the main ingredient in a common fruit-flavored dessert. It is a protein that is prepared from animal tissue.

Skills Focus

Form a Hypothesis, Design an Experiment, Compare and Contrast

Materials

- containers with gelatin
- glass-marking pencil
- powder detergents
- balance
- weighing paper
- test tubes with rubber stoppers
- test-tube rack
- 10-mL graduated cylinder
- distilled water
- metric ruler

Safety

Wear safety goggles and gloves when you prepare solutions. Check glass containers for cracks and chips. Alert your teacher if you break a glass object. Do not touch broken glass. Wash your hands thoroughly with soap and warm water before leaving the lab.

Big Idea
Enzymes catalyze most biological reactions, including the breakdown of proteins.

Skills Objectives
Students will be able to
- design an experiment to compare the effectiveness of detergents.
- relate reactions that occur inside and outside the body.

Preparation Time
30 minutes

Class Time
Part A: 10 minutes
Part B: 40 minutes on Day 1 and 15–20 minutes on Day 2

Group Size
Part A: Class
Part B: Small groups

Materials
Use medium test tubes or narrow vials as containers for the gelatin. You will need 24 containers, 3 for Part A and 21 for Part B.

To avoid buying large quantities of different detergent brands, look for the small packets of detergents dispensed in laundromats.

Advance Preparation
Two days in advance, add 108 g of gelatin to 300 mL of distilled water. Bring the mixture to a boil. Place an equal amount of gelatin in each container. Place the containers in a refrigerator.

The day before the lab, use three gelatin containers for the demonstration in Part A. After adding the detergent solution and the distilled water, let the containers sit overnight at room temperature.

Pre-Lab Questions

1. **Design an Experiment** In Part A, what is the purpose of the gelatin to which no liquid has been added?

   I can see what the gelatin layer in the other test tubes looked like before

   the distilled water and the detergent solution were added.

2. **Control Variables** Why will you use distilled water to prepare your solutions?

   Using distilled water ensures that that the only substances dissolved in

   the water are substances in the detergent.

3. **Form an Operational Definition** How will you decide whether a detergent is "effective" at removing protein stains?

   Sample answer: I will consider a detergent that is able to dissolve gelatin,

   which is a protein, as effective at removing protein stains.

Procedure

In Part A, you will observe the effect of a detergent on gelatin. In Part B, you will design and perform an experiment to compare the effectiveness of three different powder detergents.

Part A: Observe the Effect of a Detergent on Gelatin

Part A
If time permits, let the class observe the preparation of the setup for Part A.

1. Yesterday, your teacher prepared the setup for Part A. He or she started with three similar containers of gelatin. Your teacher mixed 0.5 g of a detergent with 4.5 mL of distilled water. He or she added the solution to one container of gelatin, 5 mL of distilled water to the second container, and nothing to the third container. Record your observations of the three containers.

   Observations: Students should observe that some of the gelatin has

   dissolved in the container to which detergent is added, but that little or

   none has dissolved in the container with the distilled water.

Part B: Design an Experiment

2. **Form a Hypothesis** Are all powder detergents equally effective at removing protein stains? Record the hypothesis you will test to answer this question.

   Hypothesis: *Sample answer:* Some detergents will be more effective at

   dissolving gelatin than others.

3. **Control Variables** What will your independent variable be? What will your dependent variable be?

Independent Variable: detergent brand

Dependent Variable: amount of gelatin dissolved

4. **Describe Your Plan** Record the details of your plan in the space below. Assume you will have three containers of gelatin to work with. Which variables will you need to control? Before you begin, have your teacher review your plan.

Experimental Plan: Students must add the same mass of each powder to the same volume of water to control the concentration of the solutions. Students should use a different test tube to prepare each solution to avoid contamination. They should label the containers. Students could measure the initial height and the final height of the gelatin and calculate the change, or they could mark the surface of the gelatin before and after the detergent is added and measure the change.

5. **Organize Data** Construct a data table in the space below. Include a row for each detergent you plan to test.

Sample Table

Data Table			
	Height of Gelatin (mm)		
Detergent	Initial	Final	Change
Brand 1			
Brand 2			
Brand 3			

6. **Disposal** When you are done, follow your teacher's instructions for cleanup and disposal of materials. Then, wash your hands thoroughly with soap and warm water.

Analyze and Conclude

1. **Draw Conclusions** Which detergent would be most effective at dissolving protein stains, and why?

Sample answer: Brand 2 would be most effective because it dissolved more gelatin.

2. **Use Analogies** How is what happens when a person eats a gelatin dessert similar to what happens when a detergent is used to clean clothing with protein stains?

In both cases, enzymes are used to break down protein molecules.

3. **Control Variables** Why was it necessary to compare powder laundry detergents rather than liquid laundry detergents in this experiment? *Hint:* What variable were you trying to control when you made the detergent solutions.

With powder detergents, it is easier to control the concentrations of the solutions.

With liquid detergents, the actual concentration of solutes would not be known.

4. **Infer** An auto mechanic needs to remove some grease stains from clothing. Would it make sense for the mechanic to base the choice of detergent on the results of this experiment? Why or why not?

Sample answer: It would not make sense to use the results of this experiment because the results demonstrate the effectiveness of the detergents only on protein stains, not on grease stains.

5. **Predict** Would you expect the effectiveness of a detergent to increase if you increased the concentration of detergent in a solution but used the same volume of solution? Explain your answer.

I would expect a more concentrated solution to be more effective because it would contain more enzyme molecules. (At a certain point, increasing the concentration would not increase the effectiveness due to enzyme saturation.)

Extend Your Inquiry

Grocery stores must provide both the shelf price of an item—what the consumer will pay for the item—and the unit price of the item. Knowing the unit price, which is the "cost per unit," makes it easier for shoppers to compare the cost of different brands. The unit may be a mass, a volume, or the number of items in a package.

Suppose you pay $6.39 for 26 ounces of Brand A detergent and $5.29 for 33 ounces of Brand B. You know that Brand A is twice as effective as Brand B at removing protein stains. Use unit prices to determine which brand of detergent is more cost effective.

The unit price for Brand A is 25 cents per ounce. The unit price for Brand B is 16 cents per ounce. Despite having a higher unit price, Brand A is more cost effective because you would need twice of much of Brand B to be as effective at removing the stains. You may want to have students do this exercise for the brands they tested.

Additional Lab 3   **Oil-Eating Bacteria**

Problem

How can bacteria be used to help clean up an oil spill?

Introduction

What do gasoline, heating oil, jet fuel, and diesel fuel have in common? They are a few of the energy-rich materials that are produced when petroleum, or crude oil, is refined. Crude oil is usually carried from the drilling site to the refinery by a tanker or a pipeline. One risk when crude oil is transported long distances is the possibility of an oil spill.

Oil spills can harm organisms that live in aquatic ecosystems. People may use barriers to try to contain the spill, while the oil is pumped or skimmed off the surface of the water. Because this approach can be ineffective, expensive, and time-consuming, scientists have been searching for better ways to prevent and clean up oil spills.

Some species of bacteria are able to digest oil. An oil spill can cause the number of oil-eating bacteria in the area to increase rapidly. The bacteria are able to break down large molecules of oil into smaller molecules. Scientists may add other types of oil-eating bacteria or nutrients to the spill to speed up the process. This type of approach to cleaning up the environment is an example of bioremediation.

In this lab, you will compare the effect of oil-eating bacteria on different types of oil.

Materials

- plastic vials
- glass-marking pencil
- metric ruler
- disposable dropper pipettes
- small paper plates or foam trays

- test oils
- balance
- weighing paper
- oil-eating bacteria mixture
- foam stoppers or cotton balls

Safety 🥽 🧤 🦺 ☠️ 🛢️ 🧼

Wear goggles and disposable plastic gloves. Avoid getting any of the oils on your skin or on your clothing. Do not inhale any vapors. Although the bacteria used in this activity are not harmful to humans, you should still avoid getting the bacteria on your skin, clothing, or objects in the laboratory. Follow your teacher's instructions for disposal of materials. Wash your hands thoroughly with soap and warm water whenever you handle the vials.

Big Idea

Sometimes, a natural process can lessen the effect of a human activity on the environment.

Skills Objectives

Students will be able to
- model an example of bioremediation.
- infer that an organism's ability to clean up a pollutant is limited to certain types of pollutant.

Class Time

Day 1: 30 minutes
Days 2–4: 10 minutes per day
Day 5: 30 minutes

Group Size

Class

Materials

A kit you can purchase for this lab provides only 3 vials with foam stoppers and a small amount of bacterial mix. If you are conservative with the mix, you will be able to do the main lab and an extension with 2 or possibly 3 additional setups.

If there is a biotechnology company in your area that markets a similar product, perhaps you can convince them to sell you a small amount.

Choose a dense oil, such as motor oil or lubricating oil, for one of your test oils.

Safety

To avoid dissemination of the bacterial mix, do not do the experiment in an area where air is blowing. Items that come in contact with the mix should be soaked in a 10% bleach solution for 20 minutes before they are discarded in the regular trash.

Pre-Lab Questions

1. **Control Variables** Why is it important to use different pipettes when adding the oils or stirring the contents of the vials?

   Sharing pipettes between samples will contaminate the samples and

   produce unreliable results.

2. **Infer** Why is it necessary to add air to the vials each day?

   Sample answer: The bacteria will grow faster when there is a constant

   supply of oxygen to survive.

3. **Form a Hypothesis** What do you expect to happen to the level of oil in a vial if the bacteria are able to digest that oil?

   The level of the oil should decrease as the bacteria digest the oil.

Procedure

You may be working as a class to do this lab. As a class, you will need to divide up the tasks required. These tasks include setting up the experiment and making daily observations.

Part A: Setting Up the Experiment

You will use an oil that the bacteria are known to digest as a control. You will also test two additional oils.

1. Using the ruler and glass-marking pencil, measure and mark a line on each vial 5 cm from the bottom of the vial. Mark a second line 6 cm from the bottom of each vial.

2. Use the pencil to label the vials as follows: Control, Oil 1, and Oil 2.

3. Add tap water to the vials until the surface of the water is at the 5-cm mark. Use a pipette to adjust the level of water in each vial.

4. Place each vial on a small, sturdy paper plate or disposable foam tray.

5. Use a new pipette to carefully add the Control oil to the vial labeled Control. Stop when the surface of the oil is at the 6-cm mark. Store the pipette with the vial.

6. Repeat Step 5 with the other two oils and the vials marked Oil 1 and Oil 2. Store the pipettes with the vials.

Advance Preparation
As a way to ensure all students take part and that all required tasks are completed, make a sign-up sheet listing all the individual tasks for Part A and Part B.

Step 4
Try foam trays that are used to serve small quantities of food or the trays that dentists use for their instruments. Alternatively, place the vials and pipettes on a few layers of heavy paper to absorb any drips.

7. Use weighing paper to measure 0.5 g of the bacterial mix. Use the paper to sprinkle the bacterial mix on top of the oil in one of the vials. Insert a foam stopper or cotton ball into the vial.
CAUTION: Avoid getting any of the bacterial mix on the balance.

8. Repeat Step 7 with the other two vials.

Part B: Collecting Data

9. Measure the level of oil in each vial in millimeters. Record these initial measurements in the row labeled Day 1 in the data table.

10. Carefully move the plates or trays with the vials to an area where the setups will not be disturbed. Wash your hands thoroughly with soap and warm water.

11. Measure the level of oil in each vial each day for 4 more days. Record these measurements in the data table. Also record any changes in the appearance of the mixture.

12. After you make your measurements, use the stored pipettes to add air to the liquid in the vial. Your teacher will demonstrate the procedure.

13. After Day 5, follow your teacher's instructions for disposal.

Sample Data

Data Table: Observations			
	Control	Oil 1	Oil 2
Day 1	Level: 10 mm Water clear; oil clear	Level: 10 mm Water clear; oil clear	Level: 10 mm Water clear; oil clear
Day 2	Level: 8 mm Thin layer of cloudy oil at oil/water interface	Level: 10 mm	Level: 10 mm
Day 3	Level: 6 mm Most of oil layer cloudy	Level: 9 mm Thin layer of cloudy oil; most of oil layer clear	Level: 10 mm
Day 4	Level: 2 mm Thin layer of clear oil near top; pockets of digested oil in water	Level: 5 mm Much of oil layer is cloudy	Level: 10 mm
Day 5	Level: <1 mm Water very cloudy; very little clear oil visible	Level: 4 mm Third layer (of products) forms at oil/water interface	Level: 10 mm

Step 7
Demonstrate how to use the weighing paper to pour a solid into a container.
To save time and keep the bacteria away from the balances, students could add a quarter teaspoon of the mix to each vial.

Step 10
To reduce the time required to see results, use an incubator. You can build a simple incubator with a cardboard box and a light as a heat source.

Step 12
Stress that students need to measure the oil level before they aerate the mixture. Demonstrate how to aerate the mixture. Insert a pipette full of air into the vial. When the tip is near the bottom of the vial, squeeze out the air. Do not draw any liquid into the pipette as you remove it from the vial. Have students repeat this procedure three times.

Disposal
The mixtures in the vials should be disposed of in a toilet after they have been treated with a 10% bleach solution.

Analyze and Conclude

1. **Use Models** How did the setup in the vials help model an oil spill in the ocean?
   When oil spills in the ocean, a layer of oil floats on top of the water.

2. **Compare and Contrast** What happened to the oil level in the three vials?
   Sample answer: The level of the Control oil decreased steadily over five days. The level of Oil 1 also decreased, but not as rapidly. The level of Oil 2 did not decrease.

3. **Relate Cause and Effect** Explain any differences you observed in the vials in terms of the oil-eating bacteria.
   Sample answer: The bacteria were most able to digest the Control Oil, were able to digest Oil 1, and were not able to digest Oil 2.

4. **Infer** Based on your observations, would you recommend using oil-eating bacteria to clean up a large oil spill? Why or why not?
   Sample answer: I might recommend using the bacteria. However, because it takes time for the bacteria to digest the oil, I would combine the use of bacteria with other approaches.

5. **Apply Concepts** Oil leaks from a pipeline and seeps deep into the ground below the pipeline. Explain why it might take longer for oil trapped in the ground to break down than for oil on the surface of the ocean. *Hint:* Review Step 12 in the procedure.
   Oil trapped in sediments will take longer to break down because the bacteria will have less access to oxygen.

Extend Your Inquiry

Is the type of oil the only variable that could affect the rate at which oil-eating bacteria digest oil? Could changing the temperature or the pH affect the results? Could adding nutrients affect the results? Form a hypothesis and design an experiment to test one of these variables. Have your teacher review your design.

Oil-eating bacteria will survive in neutral to basic conditions and from about −2°C to 60°C. Students could add 2 drops of vinegar to make the contents of a vial acidic, or a pinch of baking soda to make the contents basic. The temperature can be altered by storing a vial in an incubator or refrigerator. Adding a bit of nitrogen fertilizer would speed up the growth of the bacteria population (and model a technique used by those who deal with oil spills). Students would need to control the type of oil.

Additional Lab 4 **Osmosis**

Problem

What effect does the concentration of solutes outside of plant cells have on the cells?

Introduction

The main ingredient in most eye drops is saline solution, which is a solution of salts dissolved in water. You might think that salt water would irritate the eyes. But saline solution and cells at the surface of your eyes are *isotonic*, which means that they have the same concentration of solutes. Because saline solution and the cells in your eyes are at "equal strength," using eye drops does not change the balance of water in the eyes. What happens when solutions are not isotonic with the cells that they bathe?

In this lab, you will make a wet mount of red onion cells and observe the cells. Then, you will compare the effect of a 10 percent salt solution and of distilled water on the onion cells.

Skills Focus

Observe, Compare and Contrast, Draw Conclusions

Materials

- red onion
- forceps
- scissors
- paper towel
- iodine solution
- microscope slide
- coverslip
- dissecting probe
- microscope
- 10% salt solution
- distilled water

Safety 🫀 ✋ 🥼 🧪 ✂ 🧤 🖐

Iodine solution can irritate the eyes and skin and can stain clothing. Wear safety goggles, gloves, and a laboratory apron while handling any solution that contains iodine. Rinse off any solution that spills on your skin or clothing. Do not direct the points of the scissors toward yourself or others. Use the scissors only as instructed. Handle slides and coverslips carefully to avoid breaking them and cutting yourself. Review the rules for handling a microscope.

Big Idea

The concentration of fluids surrounding cells can adversely affect the water balance in cells.

Skills Objectives

Students will be able to
- prepare a wet mount of plant tissues.
- identify the parts of a plant cell under a microscope.
- explain the effect of dissolved solutes on cytoplasm.

Preparation Time

15 minutes, unless you need to prepare the iodine solution

Class Time

45 minutes

Group Size

Pairs

Materials

Because elemental iodine is relatively insoluble in water, use Lugol's solution as your stain. Use sodium chloride for the salt solution.

Advance Preparation

To prepare a 10% salt solution, dissolve 10 g of sodium chloride in enough water to make 100 mL of solution.

To prepare your own stain, dissolve 3 g of potassium iodide in 25 mL of distilled water, add 0.6 g of iodine, and dilute to 200 mL.

Slice some red onions just prior to class. Red onions are easier to peel than white or yellow onions, and red onion cells are more responsive to the salt solution.

Safety

Read the MSDS on iodine. If you prepare the iodine stain, be sure to wear goggles, plastic gloves, and an apron. Ask if any student has a known sensitivity to iodine.

Pre-Lab Questions

1. Review What is osmosis?

Osmosis is the diffusion of water through a selectively permeable

membrane.

2. Apply Concepts When water is distilled, any solutes dissolved in the water are left behind. Is distilled water hypertonic or hypotonic compared to tap water? Explain.

Compared to tap water, distilled water is hypotonic because it has a

lower concentration of solutes than tap water.

3. Infer What is the purpose of the iodine solution?

Sample answer: Iodine stains the cells, making it easier to see some of the

cell structures, such as the cytoplasm.

Procedure

Step 1
Demonstrate how to remove the thin layer of onion cells.

1. Use your fingers to separate one of the curved layers from the onion. Bend the layer until the shiny surface cracks. Look for a thin, clear layer of tissue at the place where the surface cracked. Use forceps to peel away some of the tissue. Use a scissors to cut away the tissue, if necessary.

2. While your partner uses the forceps to hold the tissue sample, put on your goggles, apron, and gloves.

3. Place a drop of iodine stain in the center of a clean glass slide. Use the forceps to place the onion sample in the drop of iodine on the slide and to gently flatten the tissue so that no air bubbles are trapped underneath the tissue.

Step 4
Students can tap the coverslip gently with the end of a pencil eraser directly over an air bubble to get rid of the bubble.

4. Place a coverslip at an angle so that one edge touches the drop of iodine solution. Use a probe to slowly lower the coverslip over the onion tissue.

5. Remove your goggles. Use the low-power objective to locate some onion cells. Then, switch to high power and focus with the fine adjustment. **CAUTION:** Always view the microscope from the side when you move an objective.

6. Use the space below to draw the onion cells you see in the field of view. Choose one cell and label the cell wall, nucleus, and cytoplasm. The cytoplasm will be yellow. Note whether the cytoplasm completely fills the cell.

Step 6
Students could use colored pencils for their drawings—one color for the cells walls and another for the cytoplasm.

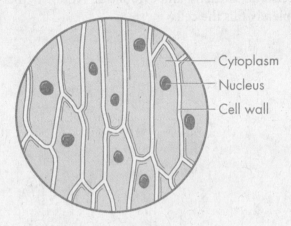

Cytoplasm
Nucleus
Cell wall

Control

7. Put a few drops of salt solution at one edge of the coverslip. Hold a small piece of paper towel at the other end of the coverslip to draw the salt solution underneath the coverslip.

8. After 3 minutes, observe the onion cells. Use the space below to draw the cells you see in the field of view. Choose one cell and label the cell wall, nucleus, and cytoplasm. Note whether there is any empty space between the cell wall and the cell membrane.

Step 7
Demonstrate how to use a paper towel to draw fluids under a coverslip.
   If students do not observe the expected plasmolysis, have them place a tiny amount of solid sodium chloride at the edge of the coverslip. Then, have them use a few drops of salt solution to wash the salt under the coverslip.

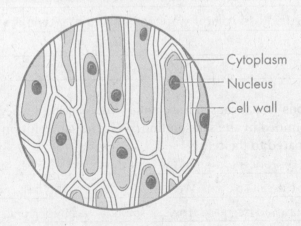

Cytoplasm
Nucleus
Cell wall

After Adding Salt Solution

Disposal
If a slide breaks, follow your school's guidelines for cleanup and disposal of broken glass.

9. Put a few drops of distilled water at one edge of the coverslip. Hold a new piece of paper towel at the other end of the coverslip to draw the distilled water underneath the coverslip.

10. After 3 minutes, observe the onion cells again. Use the space below to draw the cells you see the field of view. Choose one cell and label the cell wall, nucleus, and cytoplasm. Note whether the cytoplasm completely fills the cell.

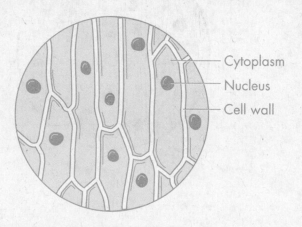

Cytoplasm

Nucleus

Cell wall

After Adding Distilled Water

Analyze and Conclude

1. **Compare and Contrast** How were the cells different after you added the salt solution? What happened after you added the distilled water?

After I added the salt solution, the cytoplasm shrank, leaving an empty space between the cell wall and the cell membrane. After I added the distilled water, the cytoplasm swelled until its volume was larger than the volume of the cytoplasm in the control.

2. **Draw Conclusions** What caused the changes you observed when the onion cells were surrounded by the salt solution? Was the salt solution hypertonic or hypotonic compared to the cells?

Sample answer: The concentration of water in the cytoplasm was higher than its concentration in the salt solution. Water diffused out of the cells, which caused the volume of cytoplasm to decrease. The salt solution was hypertonic compared to the cells.

3. **Draw Conclusions** What caused the changes you observed when the onion cells were surrounded by distilled water? Was the distilled water hypertonic or hypotonic compared to the cells?

Sample answer: The concentration of water in the distilled water was higher than its concentration in the cytoplasm. Water diffused into the cells, which caused the volume of cytoplasm to increase. The distilled water was hypotonic compared to the cells.

4. **Infer** A red blood cell can swell until it bursts. What prevented the onion cells from bursting when they swelled?

The onion cells did not burst because they are surrounded by strong, relatively rigid cell walls.

5. **Relate Cause and Effect** Some communities no longer use salt to prevent a buildup of ice on roads. Road salt can pollute water supplies and harm plants that grow along the side of roads. Explain how road salt could harm these plants.

Sample answer: Salt that dissolves in melting ice or in rainwater can flow into the soil along the edge of a road. If plant cells in the roots are surrounded by salt water, water will diffuse out of the cells and damage the roots.

Extend Your Inquiry

Design an experiment to determine what percentage of salt in a solution produces a solution that is isotonic.

Students may suggest testing a series of solutions that are progressively less concentrated than the 10% salt solution until they find one that does not cause any noticeable changes in the onion cells. (Saline solution has a 0.9% concentration of salts.)

Additional Lab 5 Photosynthesis and Cellular Respiration

Problem

How are photosynthesis and cellular respiration related?

Introduction

All organisms need energy to grow and develop. Plants are able to convert light energy into energy stored within the bonds of sugars during photosynthesis. Plants use the sugars to build complex carbohydrates. These compounds are stored until they are needed to provide energy for other reactions. The process used by both plants and animals to extract energy from compounds is cellular respiration.

In this lab, you will use closed systems to investigate reactions that take place during photosynthesis and cellular respiration. A closed system is one that keeps materials from entering or leaving. One system will have a snail, one will have an *Elodea* plant, and one will have both a snail and *Elodea*. You will observe how the amount of light affects the reactions in each system.

Skills Focus

Compare and Contrast, Relate Cause and Effect, Infer

Materials

- 8 large test tubes with rubber stoppers
- 2 test-tube racks
- glass-marking pencil
- metric ruler
- bottled spring water
- bromthymol blue solution
- 4 *Elodea* sprigs
- 4 aquatic snails

Safety 🔬 🧤 🥼 ⚗️ 🧪 🐾 🧼

Bromthymol blue solution may irritate eyes and skin and can stain clothing. Wear safety goggles, gloves, and an apron while handling this solution. Rinse off any solution that spills on your skin or clothing. Check glass containers for cracks and chips. Alert your teacher if you break a glass object. Do not touch broken glass. Always treat live organisms with respect. Wash your hands thoroughly with soap and warm water before leaving the lab.

Big Idea
The overall reaction for photosynthesis is the reverse of the overall reaction for cellular respiration.

Skills Objectives
Students will be able to
- infer whether a process is taking place in a solution.
- determine how light affects photosynthesis and cellular respiration.

Preparation Time
30 minutes

Class Time
Day 1: 25 minutes
Day 2: 15 minutes

Group Size
Small groups

Materials
Order *Elodea* and small aquatic snails online or buy them at a local pet store. Well water or aged tap water can be used instead of spring water.

If you use small glass jars instead of test tubes, adjust the placement of the marks in Step 1.

Advance Preparation
Purchase a 0.04% solution of bromthymol blue. To prepare your own solution, dissolve 0.04 g of bromthymol blue powder in 50 mL of distilled water in a 100 mL flask. Dilute to volume. Distribute the indicator in dropper bottles.

Store snails in an aquarium or glass jar containing a layer or sand of small pebbles. Add a few small aquatic plants and fill the container with spring water, well water, or aged tap water. You will need a cover to keep the snails from escaping.

Pre-Lab Questions

1. **Review** What role does carbon dioxide play in photosynthesis? What role does carbon dioxide play in cellular respiration?

   Carbon dioxide is a reactant in photosynthesis and a product of cellular respiration.

2. **Control Variables** Which test tubes are the control in this experiment and why are there two of them?

   Sample answer: The test tube with only water and bromthymol blue is the control. A control is needed for the set of test tubes that will be placed in light and the set that will be placed in the dark.

3. **Relate Cause and Effect** How will you know when carbon dioxide is added to a solution? How will you know when carbon dioxide is removed from a solution?

   The solution should turn toward yellow when carbon dioxide is added and toward blue when carbon dioxide is removed.

Procedure

When carbon dioxide dissolves in water, it reacts with the water to form a weak acid called carbonic acid. You can use bromthymol blue as an indicator to detect this change. Bromthymol blue is green in a neutral solution, yellow in an acidic solution, and blue in a basic solution.

1. Obtain 2 test-tube racks and place 4 large test tubes in each rack. Use a glass-marking pencil to label the tests tubes in the first rack 1 to 4 and the test tubes in the second rack 5 to 8. Then, make a mark on each test tube about 3 cm from the top.

2. Put on your goggles, apron, and gloves.

3. Fill each test tube with water up to the 3-cm mark.

4. Add 4 drops of bromthymol blue solution to each test tube.

5. Use Figure 1 to determine what else should be added to test tubes 1–3 and 5–7. Use forceps to gently collect the snails from their storage container.

Figure 1 Contents of test tubes

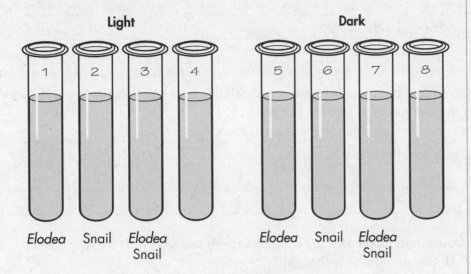

Light   Dark

1   2   3   4   5   6   7   8

Elodea Snail *Elodea*   *Elodea* Snail *Elodea*
              Snail   Snail

6. When you are done, tightly stopper each test tube.

7. Place test tubes 1–4 near a bright light source and test tubes 5–8 in total darkness. CAUTION: Do not place any of the test tubes in direct sunlight.

8. Based on your knowledge of photosynthesis and cellular respiration, predict what color the solution in each test tube will be after 24 hours. Record your predictions in the data table.

9. After 24 hours, observe each test tube and record your observations in the data table.

Step 9
Although color changes will begin within 30 minutes, have students wait 24 hours before making their observations. The test tubes can sit undisturbed for 48 hours and still produce the desired results. Color for controls will depend on content of tap water.

Disposal
You can flush the water from the test tubes down the drain. Snails bought online or at stores should not be released into local ecosystems.

Sample Data

Test Tube	Location	Contents	Predicted Color Change	Observed Color Change
1	Light	*Elodea*	Blue	Blue
2	Light	Snail	Yellow	Yellow
3	Light	*Elodea*, snail	Green	Light green
4	Light	Water only	Blue-green	None
5	Dark	*Elodea*	Yellow	Yellow
6	Dark	Snail	Yellow	Yellow
7	Dark	*Elodea*, snail	Yellow	Yellow
8	Dark	Water only	Blue-green	None

Analyze and Conclude

1. **Relate Cause and Effect** Explain the color changes you observed in test tubes 1 and 2.

In test tube 1, the indicator turned blue because *Elodea* removed carbon dioxide

from the solution during photosynthesis. In test tube 2, the indicator turned yellow

because carbon dioxide was added to the solution as a result of cellular respiration.

2. **Infer** Given that both photosynthesis and cellular respiration occur in plants, why did the indicator change color in test tube 1?

Sample answer: The amount of cellular respiration that took place in *Elodea*

was not sufficient to remove all the carbon dioxide produced by *Elodea* during

photosynthesis.

3. **Relate Cause and Effect** Did the color change in test tube 3? If so, why did it change? If not, why didn't it change?

The color probably changed a little because the amount of carbon dioxide added to

the solution by the snail and the amount removed from the solution by *Elodea* were

not the same.

4. **Infer** Identify the four test tubes in which the results were similar. What color were these solutions after 24 hours? What process must have occurred in each of the test tubes?

The results were similar in test tubes 2, 5, 6, and 7. In each test tube, the color of the

solution changed to yellow, which indicated that cellular respiration occurred in all

four test tubes.

5. **Infer** Can photosynthesis occur in the absence of light? Use your data to support your answer.

The results in test tube 5 support the inference that photosynthesis cannot occur in

the absence of light. The color would have been closer to blue had photosynthesis

taken place.

6. Predict If all the test tubes remained sealed, in which test tube would you expect life to survive longest? Why?

Life should survive longest in test tube 3 because the snail would supply carbon dioxide that *Elodea* needs for photosynthesis, and *Elodea* would produce oxygen that the snail needs for cellular respiration.

Extend Your Inquiry

A glowing ember on the end of a wooden splint will burst into flame when placed in an oxygen-rich environment. Design an experiment that includes this "splint test" to demonstrate that snails and *Elodea* cycle oxygen as well as carbon dioxide. Do not do the experiment.

Additional Lab 6 Investigating the Fermentation of Kimchi

Problem
Which type of fermentation occurs when cabbage ferments?

Introduction
In 2008, the first Korean astronaut was sent to the International Space Station. During her time in space, Yi So-yeon ate familiar foods, such as noodles, sticky rice, and kimchi. South Koreans eat about 1.6 million tons of kimchi each year. Kimchi is made by allowing vegetables, such as cabbage, to ferment.

When oxygen is not present, many cells use fermentation to extract energy from food. Organisms found on the surface of the cabbage are responsible for the fermentation of cabbage. These organisms include species of bacteria from the genus *Lactobacillus*.

In this lab, you will ferment Chinese cabbage for a month, and measure the pH of the mixture at set intervals. From the pH data and other observations, you will make inferences about the reactions that are taking place in the mixture.

Skills Focus
Measure, Interpret Graphs, Infer

Materials
- 2 resealable plastic sandwich bags
- chopped Chinese cabbage
- noniodized salt
- 1/2-teaspoon (2.5-mL) measuring spoon
- permanent marker
- pH paper
- graph paper

Safety 🗯 👁 🔥
Some of the products of fermentation can evaporate and may irritate eyes. Wear goggles whenever you open the sealed bags to measure the pH. Wash your hands thoroughly with soap and warm water after the initial setup and each time you make observations. Do not taste the kimchi.

Big Idea
The process of fermentation allows some organisms to obtain energy from food in the absence of oxygen.

Skills Objectives
Students will be able to
- measure the pH of a solution.
- use observations to infer the products of a chemical reaction

Preparation Time
30–45 minutes

Class Time
20 minutes for the initial setup, 5 minutes a day for a few days, 10–15 minutes per day once a week for 4 weeks

Group Size
Small groups

Materials
Look for Chinese (Napa) cabbage at a supermarket or Asian food store. Use regular cabbage if Chinese cabbage is unavailable.

Advance Preparation
Chop up enough cabbage in advance for all lab groups.
Figure out where you will store the setups initially. Make arrangements for access to a refrigerator for a few weeks.

Safety
To minimize the possibility of eye irritation, consider using larger lab groups or doing the lab as a class project with the tasks shared among students.

Pre-Lab Questions

1. Review What is the pH scale and how is it used?

The pH scale is a measurement system used to indicate the

concentration of H+ ions in a solution. The higher the concentration, the

lower the pH and the more acidic the solution.

2. Compare and Contrast What products form during the two types of fermentation?

Ethyl alcohol and carbon dioxide are products of alcoholic fermentation.

Lactic acid is a product of lactic acid fermentation.

3. Design an Experiment Why do you think you are asked to expel air from the plastic bags after you measure the pH in Step 6?

Accept either of these explanations. Expelling the air allows students to

tell whether one of the products of fermentation is a gas. Expelling the

air also prevents the bacteria from using the more efficient process for

extracting energy—cellular respiration.

Teaching Tip
If you begin the lab on a Monday, students should be able to make the first pH measurement by Friday.

Step 2
Demonstrate how to unseal the bags and expel any air.
   Assign numbers to the groups to provide brief identifiers for the setups.

Step 3
Choose an area where the setups will not be disturbed.

Step 5
Show students how to use pH paper or pH probes.
   Refer to the manufacturer's instructions on using a pH probe.

Procedure

1. Place one plastic bag inside the other. Half fill the inner bag with cabbage. Add half a teaspoon of salt to the inner bag. Seal both bags. Then, turn the bags upside down and right side up several times to mix the ingredients.

2. Unseal the bags, and press down on them to expel as much air as possible. Reseal the bags, and label the outer bag with your group's assigned number.

3. Place the setup in a cool area.

4. Observe the contents of the sealed bags each day for the next few days. When you see a small amount of liquid in the bottom of the inner bag, unseal the bags.

5. With your teacher's guidance, select the proper equipment to measure the pH—either pH paper or a pH probe. If you will be using a pH probe, see your teacher for instructions.

6. Measure the pH of the liquid. Record the pH and any other observations in the data table row labeled Day 1.

7. Press down on the bags to remove any excess gas before you reseal the bags. Return the setup to the cool area, and leave it undisturbed and unobserved for a week.

8. One week after your first pH measurement, observe the sealed bags. Then, open the bags and measure and record the pH.

9. Move your setup to a refrigerator. Observe the setup and measure the pH once a week for two more weeks.

10. Follow your teacher's instructions for disposal of the kimchi.

Sample Data

Data Table		
Day	pH	Observations
1	7	
8	6	
15	5	
22	4	

Analyze and Conclude

1. **Graph** Use a sheet of graph paper to make a graph that shows how the pH of the kimchi changed over time.
   Students should plot Time on the x-axis and pH on the y-axis.

2. **Interpret Graphs** What trend does the graph reveal?
   The pH drops steadily as the cabbage continues to ferment.

3. **Infer** What substance was responsible for the change in pH? What process produced this substance?
   Lactic acid caused the change in pH. It was produced by lactic acid fermentation.
   (Production of carbon dioxide also helped to acidify the mixture.)

4. Infer Describe any evidence you observed that a gas was produced? What type of fermentation would have produced a gas?

The bags inflated once fermentation began. Alcoholic fermentation would have produced carbon dioxide gas.

5. Draw Conclusions Did more than one species of bacteria help to ferment the cabbage? Give a reason for your answer.

There must be at least two species of bacteria because a single species probably would not use both lactic acid fermentation and alcoholic fermentation.

6. Infer Why was it necessary to add salt to the cabbage? *Hint:* Use what you know about diffusion.

Sample answer: The salt draws water and dissolved solutes from the cells in the cabbage, which provides a growth medium for the bacteria.

Extend Your Inquiry

During the procedure, you stored your setup initially in a cool place and then moved it to a refrigerator. Form a hypothesis about why the setup was not stored at room temperature for a month. Describe how a researcher could test this hypothesis.

Students may hypothesize that rate of fermentation would be faster at higher temperatures (which could lead to a rapid, dangerous buildup of gas in the inner plastic bag). To test this hypothesis, a researcher would need to run the procedure with the setup at different temperatures.

Additional Lab 7 # Independent Assortment and Gene Linkage

Problem
How do the positions of genes on chromosomes affect patterns of inheritance?

Introduction
Most of your cells contain 23 pairs of homologous chromosomes. The homologous chromosomes are not identical because one chromosome came from your mother and one from your father. Each may contain different versions, or alleles, of its genes. The interaction of these alleles determines your phenotype.

During mitosis, each daughter cell receives 23 pairs of chromosomes identical to the parent cell. But during meiosis, when cells form gametes, each daughter cell receives only one chromosome from each homologous pair. Thus, a gamete has just one allele for each gene. The positions of genes on chromosomes and the movements of chromosomes during meiosis affect patterns of inheritance.

In this lab, you will explore different inheritance patterns of two traits in an imaginary animal, the flightless knot-bird.

Skills Focus
Use Models, Analyze Data, Draw Conclusions

Pre-Lab Questions

1. **Infer** What are the possible genotypes for a knot-bird with straight ears? For a bird with webbed feet?

   Birds with straight ears can be either *EE* or *Ee*. Webbed feet is a recessive

   trait, that is found only in birds with the *ff* genotype.

2. **Apply Concepts** Use the Punnett square below to show how the alleles for ear shape will be inherited if a pair of heterozygous straight-eared birds mate.

		Ee	
		E	*e*
Ee	*E*	*EE*	*Ee*
	e	*Ee*	*ee*

Big Idea
The arrangement of genes on chromosomes affects whether a gene is independently assorted or is linked to other genes.

Skills Objectives
Students will be able to
• predict inheritance patterns when genes are independently assorted.
• predict inheritance patterns when genes are linked.

Class Time
40 minutes

Group Size
Individuals

Teaching Tip
This procedure in this lab assumes that students have either done the Chapter 11 lab, Modeling Meiosis, or some other activity that demonstrates the formation of haploid cells.

3. **Calculate** What fraction of the offspring from the cross in Question 2 would you expect to have straight ears?

Three-quarters of the offspring will have straight ears.

4. **Form a Hypothesis** How will the location of genes affect the inheritance patterns of genes?

Sample answer: When genes are on the same chromosome, they will tend to be inherited together. When genes are on different chromosomes, they will tend to sort independently.

Procedure

Individual knot-birds can have straight or curly ears, and feet that are webbed or have free toes. The ear and feet phenotypes are each determined by a single gene with a dominant and a recessive allele.

Alleles in Knot-Birds	
Dominant Alleles	**Recessive Alleles**
E = straight ears	*e* = curly ears
F = free toes	*f* = webbed feet

Part A: Inheritance of Genes on Different Chromosomes

A single pair of knot-birds—a male with straight ears and free toes, and a female with curly ears and webbed feet—is bred. The male is heterozygous for both traits. For Part A, assume the genes for ears and feet are on different chromosomes.

1. Identify each adult bird in Figure 1 as male or female and record its genotype for ears and feet.

Figure 1 Adult knot-birds

female: *eeff*   male: *EeFf*

2. Use the space below to show four ways the alleles for ears and feet could be combined in the male knot-bird's gametes when the genes are on different chromosomes. Draw a circle for each gamete, and use letters to represent the alleles.

EF   Ef   eF   ef

3. How will the alleles be combined in the female knot-bird's gametes? Record your answer in the first column of the Punnett square in Figure 2.

4. Transfer the data from Step 2 to the first row in Figure 2, one arrangement per column.

5. Record the genotype of each baby knot-bird on the line provided and complete the sketch of each bird's phenotype.

Figure 2 Possible offspring from knot-bird cross when genes are on different chromosomes

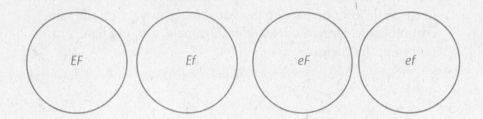

EeFf

		EF	Ef	eF	ef
eeff	ef	EeFf	Eeff	eeFf	eeff

Part B: Inheritance of Genes on the Same Chromosome

For Part B, assume that the genes for ears and feet are on the same chromosome. Also assume that on one of the male's homologous chromosomes the alleles are *Ef*, and on the other they are *eF*.

6. Use the space below to show two ways the alleles could be combined in the male knot-bird's gametes when the genes are on the same chromosome. Draw a circle for each gamete, and use letters to represent the alleles.

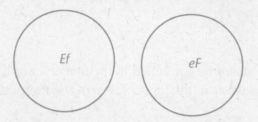

7. How will the alleles be combined in the female knot-bird's gametes? Record your answer in the first column of the Punnett Square in Figure 3.

8. Transfer the data from Step 6 to the first row in Figure 3, one arrangement per column.

9. Record the genotype of each baby knot-bird on the line provided, and complete the sketch of each bird's phenotype.

Figure 3 Possible offspring from knot-bird cross when genes are on the same chromosome

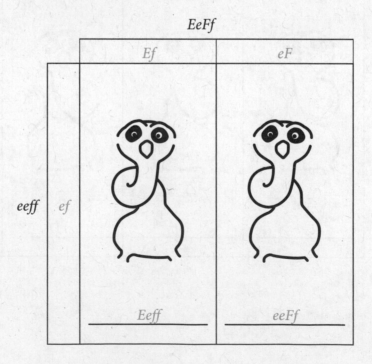

Step 6
Make sure students understand that their results will depend on the specific combinations of alleles on the chromosome. The choice of *Ef* and *eF* is arbitrary. The alleles could also be linked as *EF* and *ef*.

If students ask about the possibility of crossing-over during meiosis, ask them to assume that the genes are too close together on the chromosome to be separated during meiosis.

Analyze and Conclude

1. Use Models What principle was modeled in Part A? What principle was modeled in Part B?

Part A modeled Mendel's principle of independent assortment.

Part B modeled gene linkage.

2. Draw Conclusions What effect did moving the genes to the same chromosome have on the male bird's gametes?

Locating the genes on the same chromosome reduced the number of possible

combinations of alleles in the male's gametes.

3. Compare and Contrast Did moving the genes to the same chromosome have the same effect on the female bird's gametes? Why or why not?

Moving the genes to the same chromosome had no effect on the female's gametes

because the female is homozygous recessive for both traits. There is only one

possible combination of alleles in either case.

4. Apply Concepts Fill in the Punnett square to illustrate the cross of a pair of knot-birds who both have the genotype *EeFf*. Assume the genes are on different chromosomes. Then, describe the phenotypes that will appear in the offspring and the percentage of offspring with each phenotype.

EeFf

	EF	Ef	eF	ef
EF	EEFF	EEFf	EeFF	EeFf
Ef	EEFf	EEff	EeFf	Eeff
eF	EeFF	EeFf	eeFF	eeFf
ef	EeFf	Eeff	eeFf	eeff

EeFf

There are four possible phenotypes: straight ears and free toes (56%),

straight ears and webbed feet (19%), curly ears and free toes (19%),

curly ears and webbed feet (6%).

5. **Apply Concepts** Use the Punnett square to determine how the results change for the cross described in Question 4 when the genes are on the same chromosome. Assume that the linked combinations are *EF* and *ef* for both the mother and father. Describe the phenotypes that will appear in the offspring and the percentage of offspring that will have each phenotype.

		EeFf			
		EF	*EF*	*ef*	*ef*
EeFf	*EF*	*EEFF*	*EEFF*	*EeFf*	*EeFf*
	EF	*EEFF*	*EEFF*	*EeFf*	*EeFf*
	ef	*EeFf*	*EeFf*	*eeff*	*eeff*
	ef	*EeFf*	*EeFf*	*eeff*	*eeff*

There are only two possible phenotypes: straight ears and free toes (75%), curly ears and webbed feet (25%).

6. **Infer** The inheritance pattern you found in Question 5 persists for several generations. What does that tell you about the relative positions of the genes for ear and foot appearance on their chromosome?

The genes for ear and foot appearance must be very close together on the chromosome, minimizing the frequency of crossing-over.

Extend Your Inquiry

Suppose you cross a male with straight ears and webbed feet with a female that has curly ears and free toes. Four different phenotypes show up among their offspring: straight ears with webbed feet, straight ears with free toes, curly ears with webbed feet, and curly ears with free toes. What is the genotype of each parent? Explain your answer.

If either parent were homozygous for their dominant trait (male *EEff* or female *eeFF*), there would have been no offspring with both recessive traits. If both parents were homozygous for their dominant traits, then all of the offspring would have had the same phenotype. The genotype of the female must be *eeFf*. The genotype of the male must be *Eeff*. (Because there were only two genotype possibilities for the egg and sperm cells—*Ef* and *ef* for the male, and *eF* and *ef* for the female—it didn't matter if the genes were linked or not. The results would have been the same.)

Additional Lab 8 **Ecosystems and Speciation**

Problem

How does a founding population adapt to new environmental conditions?

Introduction

When the hurricane's winds died down, a small lizard crawled out of her hiding place in the branches of a mangrove tree. Her home was now part of a tangled mat of vegetation floating on the surface of the ocean. She shared the mat with insects and slugs, as well as other lizards from her own species. After a week, ocean currents pushed the mat onto the shore of a small, isolated island. The hungry lizards crept ashore in search of food.

In this lab, your teacher will give you a description of the island on which the lizards landed. You will be asked to suggest how the descendants of the founding population may adapt over time to their new environment.

Skills Focus

Infer, Predict, Apply Concepts

Materials

• colored pencils

Pre-Lab Questions

1. **Review** What is an adaptation?

An adaptation is any heritable trait that increase's an organism's fitness

for its environment.

_____

2. **Infer** What are the most likely sources of new genetic variation in the descendants of the founding population of lizards?

The most likely sources of new genetic variation in the descendants are

genetic recombination during sexual reproduction and mutations that

arise within the population.

Big Idea
Natural selection within an isolated population can produce phenotypic change and speciation.

Skills Objectives
Students will be able to
• demonstrate how natural selection can act on the genetic variation in a population.
• explain how an isolated population can form a new species.

Class Time
45 minutes

Preparation Time
15 minutes

Group Size
Pairs

Advance Preparation
Prepare copies of the island descriptions for students.

Island A
The island is dry, sandy, and hilly, with several species of shrubs growing on the hills. There is one species of seed-eating birds and one species of insect-eating birds. The only mammals on the island are rats. The rats are omnivores.

Island B
The island is low and rocky, with large expanses of seaweed exposed at low tide. The rocks provide many places to hide from the large population of predatory birds. The center of the island is covered with grasses.

Island C

The island is a large mountain surrounded by a sandy beach. The mountain is densely covered by large trees, which give way to smaller tropical shrubs and herbs near its peak. There are many small birds, large, flightless birds, and frogs. All the birds are omnivores. The frogs eat insects.

Island D

The island is relatively flat and covered with large trees and bushes. The island has an existing lizard species. The native lizard is yellow and slightly larger than the colonizing lizards. It hunts insects that hide on tree trunks.

3. Compare and Contrast Explain the difference between genetic drift and natural selection.

Sample answer: Genetic drift is a random change in allele frequency due to a sudden population decrease, such as when a small population colonizes a new habitat (the founder effect). Natural selection involves changes to allele frequency in response to factors in the environment.

Procedure

1. Examine the drawing of a lizard from the founding population. This small lizard feeds on insects. In the founding population, skin color varies from yellow to green to brown. Some lizards have longer bodies than others, and some have limbs that are slightly longer in proportion to their bodies. All the lizards have the same size feet, but some individuals have larger toe pads. The toe pads help the lizard stick to narrow and vertical surfaces. The flap of skin on the lizard's throat (a dewlap) is extended during social interactions with other members of the species.

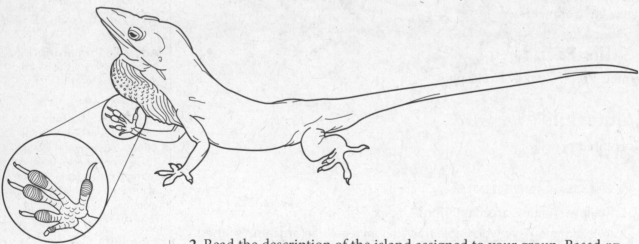

Step 2

Assign each group one of the island descriptions. Tell students to assume that insect prey and fresh water are available on each island.

2. Read the description of the island assigned to your group. Based on the characteristics of the island, identify existing phenotypes in the founding population that may be adaptive. These traits will tend to increase the fitness of the lizards who have them.

Adaptive phenotypes: Yellow skin, smaller toe pads, and larger body size might be adaptive on Island A. Green skin, longer legs, or smaller body size might be adaptive on Island B. Large toe pads might be adaptive on Island C. Green skin and smaller bodies might be adaptive on Island D. Also see answer to Analyze and Conclude Question 1.

3. Make a drawing of a descendant lizard. Your drawing should reflect how your lizard population has changed over time in response to its new environment. Label specific traits on the drawing and note how they have changed.

Drawing of Descendant Lizard

Step 3
Make sure students understand that structures don't evolve for a predetermined purpose. Instead, structures that are already present in the population are preferentially selected for by the new environment.

4. Describe a new trait, introduced through mutation, which might be adaptive for your population of lizards.

Accept any trait that makes sense given the environment. For example, thorny skin or skin that secretes a poison could be an advantage on an island with predators. On Island A, an organ that could store water for long periods of time might be advantageous.

Step 4
If time permits, have each group present their lizard description to the entire class along with the reasons for their choices.

Analyze and Conclude

1. **Relate Cause and Effect** How were the traits you described for your descendant lizard related to the conditions on your assigned island?

   Sample answers: Island A: Yellow skin could act as camouflage against sand. With

   smaller toe pads, lizards wouldn't collect as much sand on their feet. Larger lizards

   might be better able to defend themselves against rats. Island B: Green skin could act

   as camouflage against grass. Lizards with longer legs could move faster while trying

   to elude predatory birds. Smaller lizards could hide in small spaces among rocks.

   Island C: With larger toe pads, lizards would be better able to climb trees where they

   would be safe from flightless birds. The lizards could hunt for insects in the trees to

   avoid competition with the frogs, which hunt at ground level. Island D: More lizards

   may survive if they are higher up in the trees than their larger competitors. Green

   skin could act as camouflage against leaves. Lizards with smaller bodies might be

   able to climb on small branches without breaking them.

2. **Apply Concepts** Use what you know about natural selection to explain how the relocation of the lizards to a new ecosystem could affect the frequency of phenotypes in the population.

   Sample answer: Factors in the new environment may confer reproductive advantages

   (or disadvantages) for some existing phenotypes. Individuals with adaptive

   phenotypes will have more offspring than others. Over time, the frequency of the

   more adaptive phenotypes will increase. (Similar reasoning would apply to a new

   trait that arises through mutation.)

3. **Design an Experiment** How might you test whether the lizards on your island have evolved into a new species distinct from the mainland species that first colonized the island?

   Answers should focus on whether the island lizards have become reproductively

   isolated from the members of the mainland population. For example, can the island

   lizards produce fertile offspring with members of the mainland species?

4. Predict Suppose 10 percent of the mainland population of lizards are yellow. The other 90 percent are green or brown. Of 10 lizards that colonize an island, 6 of them are yellow. Will the frequency of yellow skin among the descendants of these lizards be the same as the frequency in the mainland population? Explain your answer.

Sample answer: No. The frequency of yellow-skinned lizards will be much higher in the descendants (probably closer to 60%). This situation is an example of the founder effect, which can occur when a small subgroup of a population migrates to a new habitat.

5. Predict Suppose that lizard-eating birds live on the island colonized by the lizards described in Question 4. Because the island is covered with trees and bushes, yellow lizards are easier to spot than green or brown lizards. What will happen to the frequency of yellow skin in this population of lizards, and why?

Sample answer: Predation will select against alleles for yellow skin color, and the frequency of yellow lizards should decrease over time.

6. Form a Hypothesis Lizards from the family Iguanidae are found only in North and South America, except for two species that live on the Polynesian islands of Fiji and Tonga. The Polynesian species are not found anywhere else in the world. How might their ancestors have migrated across the Pacific Ocean?

Answers will vary, but the most likely hypothesis is that the ancestors of the Polynesian species rafted to the islands on floating vegetation blown from North or South America by a storm.

Extend Your Inquiry

The most famous example of rapid speciation following colonization of a new environment is the finches on the Galápagos Islands. Research another example of rapid speciation following colonization of a new environment. Possible examples include tortoises on the Galápagos, fruit flies and honeycreepers on Hawaii, or anolis lizards in the Lesser Antilles chain of the Caribbean. As part of your response, include an explanation for why rapid speciation often occurs on volcanic islands.

Volcanic islands that emerge from the ocean are brand new environments awaiting the arrival of colonizers.

Additional Lab 9 Comparing Adaptations of Ferns and Mosses

Problem
How are mosses and ferns able to survive on land?

Introduction
Plants that live in the water and plants that live on land have the same basic needs. All plants must absorb sunlight, water, and minerals from their environment. They also must have structures that allow for the exchange of oxygen and carbon dioxide. But as land-dwelling plants evolved they faced a challenge that was not shared by their water-dwelling ancestors—how to obtain and retain water. The method a plant uses to obtain water is one of the features botanists use to divide plants into five major groups.

Two of those major groups are bryophytes, which include mosses, and vascular plants, which include ferns. Mosses and ferns are commonly found in wet areas. In this lab, you will compare a moss and a fern to determine which plant is better adapted to grow when conditions become dry.

Skills Focus
Observe, Compare and Contrast, Infer

Materials
- clump of moss
- fern frond
- forceps
- hand lens
- microscope slides
- dropper pipette
- coverslips
- dissecting probe
- compound microscope
- scissors

Safety
Handle slides gently to avoid breaking them and cutting yourself. Alert your teacher if a slide breaks. Recall the rules for handling a microscope. To avoid electrical shocks, make sure the cords, plugs, and your hands are dry when using the light source. Do not direct the points of the scissors toward yourself or others. Use the scissors only as instructed. Wash your hands thoroughly with soap and warm water after handling the plants.

Big Idea
The demands of life on land favored the evolution of plants that were capable of conserving water.

Skills Objectives
Students will be able to
- compare structures in different types of plants.
- infer which structures help land plants obtain and conserve water.

Preparation Time
15 minutes

Class Time
45 minutes

Group Size
Pairs

Advance Preparation
Obtain fern plants from a garden store or florist, and moss plants from a garden store or biological supply house. You may be able to collect samples from damp, wooded areas.

Pre-Lab Questions

1. Review Describe the structure of cells called tracheids, which are found in vascular tissue.

Tracheids are hollow, tubular cells with thick cell walls, which are

strengthened by lignin.

2. Use Analogies Veins in a plant are bundles of vascular tissue. Use the role of veins in the human body to infer the role of veins in a plant.

Sample answer: The veins in the body are part of a system that transports

blood (which in turn carries gases and nutrients) to cells throughout the

body. The veins in a plant also transport materials (in this case, water

and nutrients) to plant cells.

3. Predict Which will be harder to bend without breaking—the moss plant or the fern frond, and why?

Sample answer: The fern frond will be harder to bend because the

vascular tissue will make the cells in a frond less flexible.

Procedure

Your teacher will provide you with a clump of moss and a fern frond.

Step 1
Show students how to remove a single moss plant from a clump of moss.

Background
Both plants have a wax coating. However, the thin coating on a moss plant is usually only on the upper surface. The thick coating on the fern extends to both sides of the frond.

The scientific term for a moss "leaf" is a *phyllid.* The phyllid serves the same function as a true leaf.

1. Use your forceps to remove a single moss plant from the clump of moss. Examine the plant with a hand lens. Is its surface dull or shiny? Does it feel moist or dry?

The surface is dull and moist.

2. Examine the surface of the fern frond. Is the surface dull or shiny? Does it feel moist or dry?

The surface is shiny and dry.

3. Gently bend the moss plant and the fern back and forth. Compare the flexibility, or ability to bend, of the moss plant and the fern frond.

The moss plant is more flexible than the fern frond.

4. Use a forceps to gently remove and transfer one moss "leaf" to the center of a clean microscope slide. Use the dropper pipette, a coverslip, and the dissecting probe to complete your wet mount.

5. Use the low-power objective to examine the slide. In the space below, make a drawing of what you observe.

Step 4
Review the steps in preparing a wet-mount slide.

Step 5
Remind students to use only the low-power objective while examining their slides.

Drawing of Moss

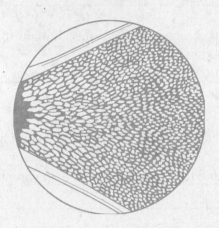

6. Use the scissors to cut a thin slice from the fern frond. Use the slice to make a wet mount.

7. Use the low-power objective to examine the slide. In the space below, make a drawing of what you observe.

Drawing of Fern

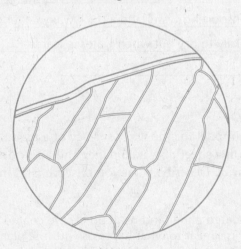

Analyze and Conclude

1. **Classify** What evidence did you see to support the classification of ferns as vascular plants?

Sample answer: Because the fern frond was difficult to bend, I inferred the presence of hardened vascular tissue. When I observed the fern under low power, I saw veins, which are bundles of vascular tissue.

2. **Infer** Use what you observed about the surface of each plant to infer which plant has a thick wax coating on its surface.

The fern, which has a shiny, dry surface, has a thick wax coating.

3. **Apply Concepts** How could the presence of a thick wax coating help a plant to survive during dry spells?

Sample answer: The coating could serve as a barrier to help conserve water in the cells beneath the surface.

4. **Infer** Why do you think moss plants are not as tall as ferns? *Hint:* How do moss cells obtain the water they need?

Sample answers: Because mosses do not have vascular tissue to transport water, each moss cell must absorb water from its environment through osmosis.

5. **Draw Conclusions** Which type of plant has structural adaptations that allow it to better grow under dry conditions? Explain.

Sample answer: Ferns are better adapted to grow under dry conditions because they have vascular tissues for transporting water and a thick waxy coating to help retain water. Thus, ferns are less likely to dry out when water is scarce.

Extend Your Inquiry

You can use waxed paper as a model for the waxy surface of a plant. Use a pipette to place a few drops of water on a sheet of waxed paper and a few drops of water on paper that is not coated with wax. Describe what you observe, and infer the purpose of the wax on the waxed paper.

Water should soak into the uncoated paper and bead up on the coated paper. (What happens with the waxed paper is similar to what happens with the plant, except that with the plant the barrier reduces evaporation of water from the cells beneath the waxy layer.)

Additional Lab 10 **Using Pollen to Solve Crimes**

Problem

How can pollen help solve crimes?

Introduction

You probably know that forensic scientists use fingerprints and DNA to help detectives solve crimes. But you might not know that pollen grains can also provide valuable evidence. Pollen grains carry the male gametes of seed plants to female gametophytes. Because the grains are dispersed by wind, water, or animals, they can be found on or in almost any object. For example, they could be on a suspect's clothing or in a soil sample from a crime scene.

Each type of pollen has a distinctive set of features, which are visible when the grains are magnified. Scientists can use these features to identify the species of plant that released a given pollen grain. The information can be used, along with other evidence, to connect a suspect to a known crime scene or to locate a crime scene.

In this lab, you will observe the structure of different pollen grains and infer how the grains are dispersed. You will also gather data about four plant species to determine how their pollen might be of use to forensic scientists.

Skills Focus

Compare and Contrast, Infer, Draw Conclusions

Materials

- compound microscope
- prepared slide of pollen
- pollen key
- computer

Safety 🔬 🧤

Review the rules for handling a microscope. To avoid electric shocks, make sure cords, connections, and your hands are dry when using the light source. Handle slides gently to avoid breaking them and cutting yourself. Alert your teacher if you break a glass object.

Big Idea
Knowledge of biology is crucial for many professions.

Skills Objectives
Students will be able to
- infer how a pollen grain is dispersed from its external structure.
- determine which types of pollen would be most useful to forensic scientists.

Preparation Time
5 minutes

Class Time
Part A: 20 minutes
Part B: 30 minutes

Group Size
Pairs

Materials
When you order prepared slides of pollen grains, you should receive a key to the pollen species on the slide.

Advance Preparation
If necessary, make copies of the pollen key.

Pre-Lab Questions

1. Explain How will you use the prepared slide of pollen?

I will use the slide to identify and draw a wind-dispersed pollen grain

and an animal-dispersed pollen grain.

2. Compare and Contrast List one feature you will use when you try to identify a wind-dispersed pollen grain. List one feature you will use for an animal-dispersed grain.

For a wind-dispersed grain, students may list a small size or a smooth

surface. For an animal-dispersed grain, students may list a larger size or a

rough surface.

3. Infer Pollen can sometimes be seen on the surface of cars in the summer. Is this pollen wind dispersed or animal dispersed? Give a reason for your answer.

Sample answer: The pollen is likely wind dispersed because the location

and amount of the pollen does not match the typical movement of

an animal.

Procedure

Part A: Surface Features of Pollen

Wind-dispersed pollen grains are often relatively small and light. They may have a smooth surface. Some wind-dispersed grains have winglike structures. Pollen grains that are dispersed by animals are often relatively large with a rough surface.

1. View your prepared pollen slide under low power. Look closely at each pollen grain.

2. Identify a pollen grain that you think is dispersed by wind. Use the space below to make a drawing of the pollen grain.

3. Identify a pollen grain that you think is dispersed by animals. Use the space below to make a drawing of the pollen grain.

Grain Dispersed by Wind   **Grain Dispersed by Animals**

  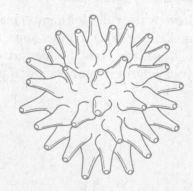

4. Obtain a pollen key from your teacher. Use the key to identify the species of the pollen grains that you selected in Steps 2 and 3.

Wind dispersed: _____

Animal dispersed: _____

Part B: Research Four Plant Species

A soil sample can contain pollen from many different plant species. Which species will be most useful in an investigation? To answer this question, forensic scientists need to know more than how a plant's pollen is typically dispersed. They also need to know where the plant typically grows and when it releases its pollen.

5. Research each species listed in the data table. Find out how its pollen is typically dispersed, when its pollen is released, and where the plant grows in the United States. Assume that pollen is released when a plant flowers. Use the information already entered in the table as a model.

Part B
Before students begin, discuss how to judge whether a Web site is authoritative.

If students are having trouble completing the table, suggest some useful searches. For example, if students enter a species name and reproduction, they should locate sites with data on type of pollination and time of pollination.

Data Table			
Species	**Dispersal Mode**	**Pollen Release Times**	**Geographic Range**
Eastern white pine (*Pinus strobes*)	Wind	April–June	Eastern United States (mainly Northeast)
Coyote bush (*Baccharis pilularis*)	Insects	July–October	California and Oregon grasslands, scrublands, and chaparrals
Annual ragweed (*Ambrosia artemisiifolia*)	Wind	August–October	All of continental United States
Green pitcher plant (*Saracenia oreophila*)	Insects	April–June	Wetlands in Georgia, Alabama, Tennessee, and South Carolina.

Analyze and Conclude

1. **Infer** Why might pollen that is wind dispersed be relatively small with a smooth surface? Why might pollen that is dispersed by animals have a rough, spiny surface?

Wind-dispersed pollen must be light enough to be carried by air currents. A smooth

surface produces less air resistance as the pollen moves through the air. Spines can

help attach pollen to an animal and keep the pollen attached as the animal moves.

_____

2. **Relate Cause and Effect** Why would a wind-pollinated plant produce more pollen than a plant that is pollinated by animals?

Sample answer: Animals can carry pollen directly into contact with a flower of the

same species. The dispersal of pollen by wind is less deliberate. Thus, the odds of any

single pollen grain reaching an appropriate flower are much lower. Increasing the

amount of pollen increases the odds.

_____

3. **Predict** Would investigators be more likely to find animal-dispersed or wind-dispersed pollen at a crime scene? Why?

They are more likely to find wind-dispersed pollen because the pollen is produced in

great quantities and spread randomly.

_____

4. **Infer** A forensic scientist identifies ragweed pollen on a suspect's jacket. What could the scientist conclude about when and where the pollen was transferred to the jacket?

The scientist could conclude that the pollen was transferred somewhere in the

continental United States between August and October.

_____

5. **Draw Conclusions** A forensic scientist compares soil taken from a suspect's shoe with soil collected at a crime scene. The scientist finds pollen from annual ragweed and green pitcher plants in both samples. Which pollen would be more useful for establishing that the suspect had been at the crime scene, and why?

Sample answer: The pollen from the pitcher plant would be more useful because its

geographic range and habitat is more limited than the range and habitat of annual

ragweed. The suspect would be more likely to contact pollen that is dispersed by

animals.

_____

6. Draw Conclusions A man is a suspect in a crime that took place in Maryland in May. In July, investigators in Oregon search the man's car and find that the air filter is full of ragweed and eastern white pine pollen. The man claims that the pollen got into the filter when he bought the car in Maine in September and drove it to Oregon. He also claims that neither he nor the car has left Oregon since September. Is the suspect telling the truth? Why or why not?

The suspect is not telling the truth. Eastern white pines were not producing pollen

in September. The car must have been on the East Coast during April, May, or June

when eastern white pines release their pollen.

_____

_____

Extend Your Inquiry

Select a local plant and research its geographic range, typical habitat, method of pollination, and time of pollination. Summarize what you learn on a separate piece of paper. Include a photograph or drawing of the plant and, if possible, a sketch of its pollen grain. As a class, make a classroom display of the sheets. Then use the display to draw some conclusions about which types of plants are pollinated by wind and which are pollinated by animals.

Most trees are wind-pollinated. Plants with bright, showy, and scented flowers are typically animal pollinated. (You might want to coordinate the choice of plants to avoid overlap of data.)

Additional Lab 11 The Effect of Chemicals on Heart Rate

Problem

How do chemicals affect the heart rate of *Daphnia*?

Introduction

In humans and other vertebrates, blood flows within a closed system of blood vessels. In many invertebrates, blood is not entirely contained within vessels, but also flows freely through body cavities. In both open and closed circulatory systems, one or more hearts pump blood through the body. The rate at which the heart pumps blood can be affected by various stimuli, including chemicals.

In this lab you will work with *Daphnia*. These small, shrimplike animals have an open circulatory system. Because *Daphnia* have a transparent outer skeleton, you can observe their hearts beating under a microscope. You will study the effect of hydrogen peroxide (H_2O_2) on the heart rate of a *Daphnia*.

Skills Focus

Measure, Draw Conclusions, Graph

Materials

- depression slide
- pipette
- *Daphnia*
- cotton ball
- forceps
- coverslip
- dissecting probe
- compound microscope
- timer or clock with second hand
- hydrogen peroxide solution
- graph paper

Safety 🖐 🦺 🧪 ⚗️ 🔌 🧤

Hydrogen peroxide (H_2O_2) solution can be irritating. If the solution gets in your eye, tell your teacher and immediately use the eye wash fountain. Rinse off any solution that spills on your skin or clothing. To avoid harming the *Daphnia,* use only two drops of the hydrogen peroxide solution. Recall the rules for handling a microscope. To avoid electrical shocks, make sure the cords, plugs, and your hands are dry when using the light source. Alert your teacher if you break a glass object. Wash your hands thoroughly with soap and warm water before leaving the lab.

Big Idea

The rate at which the heart beats is affected by stimuli, such as chemicals.

Skills Objectives

Students will be able to
- measure the effect of an environmental factor on heart rate.
- interpret a graph to reveal a trend.

Preparation Time

25 minutes

Class Time

45 minutes

Group Size

Pairs

Materials

Order *Daphnia magna* from a biological supply house. Follow the care instructions that arrive with the culture.

Advance Preparation

Make 500 mL of stock solution, by adding 0.5 mL of 3% hydrogen peroxide to a volumetric flask and adding spring water to volume.

Use the table to prepare a set of solutions with different concentrations. Distribute each solution in a labeled dropper bottle, which can be shared by two groups.

H_2O_2 (mg/L)	Stock solution (mL)	Spring water (mL)
0	0	25
0.5	0.4	24.6
1.0	0.8	24.2
1.5	1.2	23.8
2.0	1.7	23.3
2.5	2.1	22.9
3.0	2.5	22.5

Pre-Lab Questions

1. **Apply Concepts** *Daphnia* are about 2–3 mm long. Why won't you use the high-power objective to observe the *Daphnia*?

   Sample answer: Because *Daphnia* are large enough to be seen with the unaided eye, the field of view would be too narrow under high power.

2. **Design an Experiment** What purpose does Part A of this experiment serve?

   Sample answer: Part A acts as the control for Part B. Without the data in Part A, it would not be possible to tell what effect, if any, hydrogen peroxide has on the heart rate.

3. **Infer** Why might the results of this lab interest a scientist who is studying the effects of chemicals on the human heart?

   Results from this lab may apply to other organisms with hearts, including humans.

Procedure

The response of a *Daphnia* may become erratic and unreliable when the *Daphnia* is kept in a small amount of water for a long time. Try to move calmly, but quickly, through the steps of the procedure. Discuss in advance how to divide up the tasks for each trial.

Part A: Measure the Heart Rate of a *Daphnia*

Teaching Tip
Demonstrate how to use a paper towel to draw a liquid under a coverslip. Students need to keep enough liquid around the *Daphnia* so that it is not stressed.

1. Bring your slide and pipette to the location where the *Daphnia* are stored. Use the pipette to transfer a small drop of liquid containing a *Daphnia* to the well of the slide. **CAUTION:** The drop needs to be small to keep the *Daphnia* from swimming out of the field of view.

2. Carefully carry the slide back to your workstation. Use the forceps to pull a few fibers from the cotton ball and place them on the drop of water. The fibers will slow down the *Daphnia*.

Step 2
Demonstrate how to remove some fibers from a cotton ball. Make sure students use only a few fibers so that the view of the *Daphnia* is not obstructed.

3. Touch one edge of a coverslip to the side of the drop of water and use the probe to help you slowly lower the coverslip.

4. Make sure the low-power objective is clicked into position before you place the slide on the microscope stage.

5. Look through the eyepiece of the microscope. Use Figure 1 to help you locate the heart of the *Daphnia*.

Figure 1 Internal anatomy of a *Daphnia*

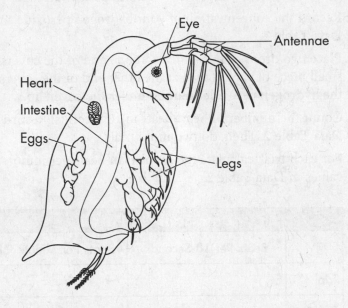

6. Count the number of heart beats in 10 seconds. One partner should do the timing and one should do the counting. Record the result in Data Table 1. Then, do two more trials.

7. For each trial, multiply the number of beats you counted in 10 seconds by 6 to determine the number of beats per minute (BPM). Record these values in Data Table 1.

8. Calculate the average heart rate per minute.

Data Table 1: Part A		
	Beats Per 10 Seconds	**Beats Per Minute (BPM)**
Trial 1		
Trial 2		
Trial 3		
Average heart rate (BPM):		

Disposal
Follow the instructions for disposal of *Daphnia* that arrive with the culture.

Part B: Measure the Effect of Hydrogen Peroxide

To gather a reasonable amount of data in a relatively short period of time, groups will use different concentrations of hydrogen peroxide. When you are done with Part B, you will pool your data.

9. Record the concentration of your hydrogen peroxide solution in Data Table 2.

10. Place two drops of the solution at one end of the coverslip. Hold a small piece of paper towel at the other end of the coverslip to draw the hydrogen peroxide solution under the coverslip.

11. Count the number of heart beats in 10 seconds. Record the result in Data Table 2. Then, do two more trials.

12. For each trial, calculate the number of beats per minute. Record these values in Data Table 2.

Data Table 2: Part B		
	Beats Per 10 Seconds	**Beats Per Minute (BPM)**
Trial 1		
Trial 2		
Trial 3		
Hydrogen peroxide concentration (mg/L):		
Average heart rate (BPM):		

13. Enter the class data in Data Table 3.

Data Table 3: Class Data	
Concentration of H_2O_2 (mg/L)	**Average Heart Rate (BPM)**
0	
0.5	
1.0	
1.5	
2.0	
2.5	
3.0	

Analyze and Conclude

1. Draw Conclusions In general, what effect did adding hydrogen peroxide have on the heart rate of *Daphnia*?

The heart rate of *Daphnia* slowed down with the addition of hydrogen peroxide.

_____

2. Graph Use the data in Data Table 3 to make a graph of heart rate versus hydrogen peroxide concentration. Plot concentration on the *x*-axis and heart rate on the *y*-axis. Ask your teacher whether you should use graph paper, a graphing calculator, or graphing software.

3. Interpret Graphs Describe any trend you see in your graph.

As the concentration of hydrogen peroxide increases, the heart rate decreases,

especially at concentrations above 1.0 mg/L.

_____

4. Classify Stimulants are chemicals that increase the heart rate. Depressants are chemicals that slow down the heart rate. Does hydrogen peroxide act as a stimulant or a depressant in *Daphnia*?

Hydrogen peroxide acts as a depressant.

_____

5. Evaluate Based on your observations, can you predict the effect of hydrogen peroxide on humans? Why or why not?

Sample answer: The results suggest that hydrogen peroxide might slow down the

heart rate in humans. However, humans are not closely related to *Daphnia*. So

reactions that take place in *Daphnia* may not occur in the exact same way in humans.

_____

6. Infer What environmental factors other than the presence of chemicals might affect the heart rate of *Daphnia*?

Sample answer: Factors such as water temperature and dissolved oxygen

concentration might affect the heart rate of *Daphnia*.

_____

Extend Your Inquiry

What effect might caffeine have on the heart rate of *Daphnia*? Form a hypothesis and design an experiment to answer this question. Before you begin, have your teacher approve your plan.

The concentration of caffeine in the stock solution should not exceed 100 mg/L. Caffeine should increase the heart rate in *Daphnia*. Students may know that caffeine acts as a stimulant in humans.

Additional Lab 12 Observing Hydra

Problem

How does a hydra respond to stimuli in its environment?

Introduction

All animals have body systems that allow them to sense and respond to changes in their environment. These systems help them find food, escape from predators, and locate a mate. Most animals have some type of nervous system. In general, certain nerve cells are specialized to sense stimuli and others are specialized to coordinate a response. For instance, sensory nerve cells might detect a temperature drop, and motor neurons may coordinate the animal's move to a warmer area.

Hydras are small aquatic animals that are closely related to jellyfish, coral, and sea anemones. They feed on tiny animals, plants, and microorganisms. In a hydra, the nerve cells form a nerve net, which is much simpler than the complex nervous system of a human. A hydra does have some cells that are specialized for the detection of touch and chemicals.

In this lab, you will observe the anatomy of a hydra, and how the hydra responds when it senses nearby prey.

Skills Focus

Observe, Predict, Infer

Materials

- petri dish
- hydra
- 2 pipettes
- dissecting microscope
- toothpick
- *Daphnia*

Safety 🜂 🜄 🜂 🜂 🜂

Alert your teacher if you break a glass object. Do not touch broken glass. Always treat live organisms with respect. Review the rules for handling a microscope. To avoid electrical shocks, make sure the cords, plugs, and your hands are dry when using the light source. Follow your teacher's instructions for disposal of materials. Wash your hands thoroughly with soap and warm water before leaving the lab.

Big Idea

Animals have cells that sense changes in their environments and help the animal respond to those changes.

Skills Objectives

Students will be able to
- observe a hydra respond to specific stimuli.
- Infer how the hydra might respond to other stimuli in its environment.

Preparation Time

30 minutes

Class Time

Part A: 15 minutes
Part B: 15 minutes

Group Size

Pairs

Materials

Order *Hydra* and *Daphnia magna* from a supply house. Note: Brown *Hydra* tend to be larger and healthier in winter. Follow the care instructions that arrive with the cultures.

Advance Preparation

A *Hydra* culture can undergo a period in which the animals refuse to feed and eventually die. Check to make sure the animals in your culture are still active before doing the lab.

If you place a jar of *Hydra* in a refrigerator for a few days without feeding them, the animals will begin to rise to the surface, which will make them easier for students to collect.

Teaching Tip
If you don't have sufficient dissecting microscopes, you could substitute regular compound microscopes and use watch glasses instead of petri dishes. Students may find it harder to focus on the hydra with this equipment.

Pre-Lab Questions

1. **Explain** How will you move the live organisms from one container to another?

   I will use a pipette to move the organisms.
   _____

2. **Observe** Examine the drawing of the hydra. Describe the shape of its body and its major features.

   Sample answer: The hydra has a long, thin body. On one end are

   tentacles and an opening into the body. At the other end is a foot. Along

   one side is a bud.
   _____

   _____

3. **Predict** How do you think a hydra will respond when a *Daphnia* is placed in its environment?

   Sample answer: The hydra will reach out and grab the *Daphnia* with its

   tentacles and pull it to its mouth.
   _____

Procedure

Part A: Response to Touch

Step 1
Demonstrate how to collect and transfer a single hydra.

Step 2
Remind students that budding is a form of asexual reproduction.

1. Use a pipette to gently transfer a hydra from its culture to your petri dish. If the water that you collect with the hydra doesn't completely cover the hydra, add a little more water from the culture. Set the pipette aside. You will need it again in Step 8.

2. Place the petri dish on the stage of a dissecting microscope. Observe the hydra under low power. Compare what you see to the drawing in Figure 1. **NOTE:** Not all hydras will have a bud.

Figure 1 Anatomy of a hydra

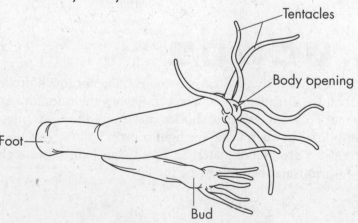

3. Use a toothpick to gently touch the side of the hydra. Record what you observe. **CAUTION:** To avoid injuring the hydra, do not poke it sharply.

   Observation: _____

   _____

4. Hold the toothpick so that it is very near, *but not touching*, one of the hydra's tentacles. Record what you observe.

   Observation: _____

   _____

5. Gently touch one of the hydra's tentacles with the toothpick. Record what you observe.

   Observation: _____

   _____

Part B: Feeding Behavior

6. Use a new pipette to collect a *Daphnia* from its container and transfer it to the water in the petri dish.

7. As you look through the microscope, observe how the hydra responds. Record your observations. **NOTE:** Be patient. The hydra may not react immediately.

   Observations: _____

   _____

   _____

   _____

Step 6
Suggest that students place a small container beneath the tip of the pipette as they carry the *Daphnia* from the culture container to the petri dish.

8. When you are done, use the first pipette to carefully return the hydra to its culture container.

Analyze and Conclude

1. **Observe** How did the hydra respond to being touched with a toothpick?

   The hydra pulled in its tentacles until it looked like a round blob.

   _____

2. **Infer** Which part of the hydra is most sensitive to touch? Use your observations to support your inference.

   Sample answer: The tentacles are the most sensitive to touch because the

   hydra moved its tentacles even when the toothpick was near, but not touching, a

   tentacle.

   _____

3. **Predict** How might a hydra respond when it senses a threat in its natural environment?

Sample answer: If a hydra senses a threat, it might respond by pulling in (or retracting) its tentacles and body.

4. **Infer** What are two possible types of stimuli that might have allowed the hydra to detect the presence of the *Daphnia*?

Sample answer: The *Daphnia* may have caused vibrations in the water that were detected by nerve cells that are sensitive to touch. The *Daphnia* may have released chemicals into the water that were detected by nerve cells that are sensitive to chemicals.

5. **Draw Conclusions** A hydra spends most of its time attached to one spot by its adhesive foot. Explain how an animal that does not move freely is able to be a successful predator.

Sample answer: The hydra is able to sense prey that swim near and extend its long tentacles to capture the prey.

Extend Your Inquiry

View prepared slides of neurons. Draw a sketch of what you see. Then write a paragraph explaining how the structure of these highly specialized cells is adapted to their function.

Students should note that neurons are long cells that have extensions at both of their ends. They may conclude that these extensions help each neuron to communicate with other neurons in a nerve net or in a more complex nervous system.

Additional Lab 13 Reducing Excess Gas

Problem

On which type of food is a gas-reducing digestive aid most effective?

Introduction

Many of the foods that are essential to a healthy diet contain fiber, which is sometimes referred to as roughage. Fiber is made up of complex carbohydrates that your body does not digest. Fiber is generally found in plant products, such as vegetables and grains. It is not a source of energy or of building materials for cells. But it does add bulk to the contents of the digestive system, which helps move the contents through the small and large intestines.

Bacteria that live in the large intestine can digest some of the fiber. These helpful bacteria produce some molecules that you need, such as vitamin K. They also produce gases. Excess gas in the large intestine can cause bloating and discomfort. Some people use a digestive aid that breaks down fiber to help reduce the amount of gas produced. Glucose is one product of this breakdown.

In this lab, you will test the effectiveness of the digestive aid on different types of food. You will test for the presence of glucose before and after the digestive aid is added to samples of food.

Skills Focus

Measure, Compare and Contrast, Draw Conclusions

Materials

- 5 small plastic cups
- glass-marking pencil
- 1-tbsp measuring spoon
- food samples
- digestive aid
- stirring rod
- 11 glucose test strips
- timer or clock with second hand

Safety ⚠

Do not taste any of the food samples used in the lab. Alert your teacher if you have an allergy to any of the foods being tested.

Big Idea
Scientists can use their understanding of digestion to develop products that can minimize digestive problems.

Skills Objectives
Students will be able to
• use an indicator to track the results of a reaction.
• use lab results to draw conclusions about processes that occur in the human body.

Preparation Time
50 minutes

Class Time
25 minutes

Group Size
Small groups

Materials
The digestive aid Beano and glucose test strips are available in pharmacies.

Advance Preparation
The day before the lab, put the dried beans in water to soak overnight and cook some of the broccoli. On the day of the lab, use a food processor to mash or chop the foods. Put each food in a separate labeled container. If you use canned beans, rinse off the liquid in which the beans are stored before mashing them.

Pre-Lab Questions

1. **Review** What class of chemicals are responsible for the digestion of complex carbohydrates and other large molecules?

   Enzymes are responsible for the chemical digestion of complex

   carbohydrates (as well as lipids and proteins).

   _____

2. **Relate Cause and Effect** Why is glucose a useful indicator for the breakdown of fiber?

   When complex carbohydrates are broken down, one of the products

   is glucose.

   _____

3. **Control Variables** What is the purpose of the cup that contains only water?

   Sample answer: Because water will be added to all the cups, it is

   important to know what effect, if any, the digestive aid has on water.

   _____

4. **Infer** Why will the food samples be mashed before you test them?

   Students may say that mashing the food simulates what happens during

   mechanical digestion, or they may know that an increase in surface area

   can speed up a reaction.

Procedure

You will be testing the effect of a digestive aid on raw and cooked broccoli, and on soaked and cooked beans.

1. Label the cups Water, Raw Broccoli, Cooked Broccoli, Soaked Beans, and Cooked Beans.

2. Add one level tablespoon of water to each cup.

3. Add one level tablespoon of each food sample to the appropriate cup. Use the spoon to mix the food with the water. **CAUTION:** Rinse off the measuring spoon between food samples.

4. Use a separate glucose test strip to test for glucose in each cup. In the data table on the next page, record the color of the test strip and the amount of glucose that color corresponds to.

5. Place one drop of the digestive aid on a glucose test strip. Record the results in the table.

6. Add 5 drops of digestive aid to each cup. Use a stirring rod to mix the contents of each cup thoroughly. Rinse the stirring rod between samples.

Step 3
For students whose workstation is not near a sink, supply a large container of water for rinsing the measuring spoon.

7. Let the cups sit for 5 minutes.

8. After five minutes, repeat Step 4. CAUTION: It is important to test all the samples at the same time and to keep the test strips in the mixtures for the same length of time. You will need to work as a team to achieve this goal.

Step 8
Stress the importance of placing and removing the strips at the same time, but defer the explanation until after students answer Analyze and Conclude Question 3.

Data Table: Amount of Glucose					
	Water	Raw Broccoli	Cooked Broccoli	Soaked Beans	Cooked Beans
Before digestive aid is added					
After digestive aid is added					
Digestive Aid:					

Analyze and Conclude

1. **Compare and Contrast** Which food sample produced the most glucose? Which food sample produced the least glucose?

   Sample answer: Soaked beans produced the most glucose. The cooked broccoli produced the least glucose.

2. **Draw Conclusions** What effect does cooking have on the fiber content of food? Use the results of your experiment to support your answer.

   The cooked samples produced less glucose than their uncooked counterparts. Thus, cooking must have broken down some of the fiber, leaving less fiber for the digestive aid to break down.

3. **Control Variables** Why was it important to test all the samples at the same time in Step 8?

   Sample answer: It is important to control the time of the reaction. Otherwise, it would not be clear which variable was affecting the amount of glucose produced.

4. Draw Conclusions How does the digestive aid reduce the amount of gas in the large intestine?

Sample answer: The digestive aid breaks down some of the fiber before it reaches the

bacteria in the large intestine.

_____

5. Infer The digestive aid you used is also available as a tablet. The instructions say to take the tablet just before eating. What is the reason for this instruction?

Sample answer: Taking the tablet at meal time ensures that the enzyme and the food

are in the digestive system at the same time.

_____

6. Perform Error Analysis Explain why this experiment was not a perfect model for what happens when a person uses a digestive aid to reduce gas.

Sample answer: The lab did not reflect the conditions that exist in a human digestive

tract in terms of number of substances present, pH, temperature, and so on.

_____

_____

Extend Your Inquiry

Research the difference between soluble and insoluble fiber, including which type of fiber can cause excess gas.

The fiber that causes gas is soluble fiber. Insoluble fiber passes through the large intestine without being affected by the bacteria.

Additional Lab 14 Modeling Breathing

Problem
How does air move into and out of the lungs?

Introduction
There are times when you might notice your breathing; for example, when running to catch a bus or climbing a steep hill. But most of the time, you probably are not aware of your breathing. While you focus on other things, your nervous system controls the movement of air into and out of your lungs.

When the level of carbon dioxide in your blood rises, sensory neurons send impulses to a breathing center in your brain. The breathing center responds by sending impulses that cause your diaphragm and muscles between your ribs to contract. Your rib cage rises and air rushes into your lungs. When your diaphragm relaxes and your rib cage lowers, air is exhaled from your lungs.

How does the movement of the diaphragm and rib cage cause air to be inhaled or exhaled? In this lab, you will make a working model of human lungs that will help you answer this question.

Skills Focus
Use Models, Form a Hypothesis, Relate Cause and Effect

Materials
- small, clear plastic bottle
- scissors
- small round balloon
- one-hole rubber stopper
- large round balloon

Safety ✂
Use the scissors only as instructed. Do not direct the points of the scissors toward yourself or others. Tell your teacher if you have an allergy to latex.

Big Idea
As the diaphragm and rib cage move, the air pressure in the chest cavity changes. These changes in air pressure cause air to be inhaled or exhaled.

Skills Objectives
Students will be able to
- use a model to determine how air moves into and out of the lungs.
- modify the model to reflect changed conditions.

Preparation Time
25 minutes

Class Time
45 minutes

Group Size
Small groups

Advance Preparation
Ask students to bring in 16-oz or 20-oz bottles to use for the lab. Make sure the bottles are clean before the students use them.
   To save class time and reduce the risk of injury, you could cut off the bottoms of the bottles before class.

Safety
Pair students who have an allergy to latex with students who do not.

Pre-Lab Questions

1. **Use Models** In your model, which balloon will represent the lungs? Which will represent the diaphragm?

   The small balloon will represent the lungs and the large balloon will

   represent the diaphragm.

2. **Use Models** In your model, what does the bottle represent? What does the hole in the rubber stopper represent?

   The bottle represents the chest wall, and the hole represents the air

   passages leading to the lungs.

3. **Predict** What do you think will happen when you pull down on the large balloon?

   Some students may correctly predict that the small balloon will fill with

   air and expand when they pull down on the large balloon.

Procedure

Part A: Model of Healthy Lungs

Use Figure 1 to guide you as you construct your model.

1. Place a clear plastic bottle on its side. Press one point of the scissors through the side of the bottle about 1 cm from the bottom. **CAUTION:** The tough plastic may cause the scissors to slip when you try to puncture the bottle.

2. Using the scissors, cut off the bottom of the bottle. Trim any rough spots from the edge.

3. Stretch the small balloon. Then blow into the balloon until it expands. Release the air. Repeat this action two more times.

4. Pull the opening of the small balloon over the bottom of a one-hole rubber stopper.

Figure 1 Completed Model

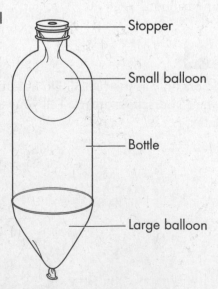

Stopper

Small balloon

Bottle

Large balloon

5. Insert the balloon through the mouth of the bottle. Press the stopper tightly into the bottle so that it holds the lip of the balloon in place.

6. Stretch the large balloon. Then blow into the balloon until it expands. Release the air. Repeat this action two more times.

7. Make a cut across the rounded, closed end of the large balloon about 1 cm from the end. Tie the other end closed.

8. Stretch the large balloon far enough over the cut end of the bottle to keep it from slipping off the bottle.

9. Watch the small balloon as you pull down on the knot of the large balloon. Continue watching the small balloon as you push up on the large balloon. Record your observations.

Observations: Pulling down on the large ballon causes the small balloon to inflate; pushing up causes the small balloon to deflate.

Step 9
Stress that students need to pull gently on the large balloon to avoid pulling it off the bottle.

Part B: Model a Chest Injury

10. **Form a Hypothesis** Suppose the skin and muscles of the chest were punctured. Air would be able to enter the chest cavity through the wound. How would such an injury affect a person's ability to breathe? Record the hypothesis you will test to answer this question.

Hypothesis: *Sample answer:* If the chest wall were punctured, the lungs would not be able to expand.

11. **Design an Experiment** Decide how you can modify your model to represent the situation described in Step 10. Record what you intend to do. Include any necessary safety cautions.

Experimental Design: _____

_____

_____

_____

_____

_____

_____

12. Repeat Step 9 and record your observations.

Observations: The small balloon no longer inflates or deflates as the large balloon is pulled or pushed.

_____

Analyze and Conclude

1. **Observe** In Part A, what happened to the volume of air in the bottle when you pulled down on the large balloon? What happened to the volume when you pushed up on the large balloon?

   The volume increased when the balloon was pulled down and decreased when the balloon was pushed up.

2. **Infer** How did the changes in volume affect the air pressure in the bottle? *Hint:* The relationship between the pressure and volume of a gas is an inverse relationship.

   When the volume increased, the pressure decreased. When the volume decreased, the pressure increased.

3. **Relate Cause and Effect** Explain how the changes in air pressure in the bottle caused the movement of air into and out of the small balloon.

   Decreased air pressure in the bottle allowed air to enter the small balloon through the hole in the stopper. Increased air pressure in the bottle pushed air out of the small balloon.

4. **Use Models** What part of the breathing process were you modeling when you pulled down on the large balloon? What part of the process were you modeling when you pushed up on the large balloon?

   I was modeling the contraction of the diaphragm during inhalation and the relaxation of the diaphragm during exhalation.

5. **Draw Conclusions** Based on your observations in Part B, how does a punctured chest wall affect a person's ability to breathe?

   Sample answer: When the chest wall is punctured, the changes in air pressure required for inhalation and exhalation cannot occur.

Extend Your Inquiry

A person with asthma or emphysema will have trouble breathing. Find out what changes to the respiratory system occur in people who have these conditions. Design a model to demonstrate the effect asthma or emphysema has on a person's ability to breathe.

The model for asthma needs to reflect the narrowing of the passageways leading to the lungs. Students could use clay or another material to narrow the hole in the stopper. The model for emphysema needs to reflect the loss of elasticity in the lungs. Students could replace the small balloon with a small plastic bag, which would be less responsive to changes in pressure. With both models, there should be less inflation or deflation of the "lung" as the "diaphragm" is moved.

Additional Lab 15 Modeling Disease Transmission

Problem
How does an infectious disease spread through a population?

Introduction
Human behavior can play an important role in the spread of infectious diseases. You may inhale pathogens that are released into the air when an infected person coughs or sneezes. You may ingest food that has been contaminated because the cook did not prepare or store the food properly. Or the cook may not have washed his or her hands before preparing the food.

In the early stages of a disease, people may not have any obvious symptoms. Because they don't know that they are infected, they may behave in ways that put others at risk of infection.

In this lab, you will model the situation in which a person is unaware of his or her infection. You will use a simulated exchange of body fluids to track the progression of the disease through the class. Then you will use the data to try to identify the original host.

Skills Focus
Use Models, Analyze Data, Organize Data

Materials
- plastic vial
- simulated body fluid
- microtube
- pipette
- fine-tip permanent marker
- disease indicator solution

Safety 🖐
Wash your hands thoroughly with soap and warm water after completing the activity.

Big Idea
Infectious diseases can be spread through coughing, sneezing, physical contact, exchange of body fluids, contaminated food or water, and infected animals.

Skills Objectives
Students will be able to
- model the transmission of a disease.
- trace the progression of the disease through a population.

Preparation Time
15 minutes

Class Time
Part A: 10 minutes
Part B: 15 minutes

Group Size
Individuals

Advance Preparation
Dissolve half the packet of simulated disease-causing agent in 15 ml of distilled water, and mix well. Pour the sample into one of the vials. Add an equal amount of distilled water to each of the remaining vials. Number the vials and record which vial has the "pathogen."

Dissolve the disease indicator powder in 30 mL of distilled water. Set up the testing station and make a copy of Data Table 2 on the board.

Pre-Lab Questions

1. **Review** How can hand washing help to prevent the transmission of some infectious diseases?

   Sample answer: Hand washing can get rid of pathogens that are

   transferred by body-to-body contact or by contact with objects that an

   infected person has touched.

   _____

2. **Use Models** Briefly describe the method you will use to simulate an exchange of body fluids.

   Working with a partner, I will mix the contents of two vials in one vial.

   Then I will divide the mixed contents evenly between the two vials.

   _____

3. **Control Variables** Why must each person transfer 1 mL of fluid to a microtube before beginning Round 1?

   Sample answer: We will need an uncontaminated sample of each fluid in

   order to confirm the identity of the original host.

   _____

Procedure

Part A: Model the Spread of an Infectious Disease

1. Obtain a vial of simulated body fluid from your teacher. Use a pipette to transfer about 1 mL of the liquid to the microtube. Write your initials on the lid. Set the tube aside until Part B. **NOTE:** Only one of the vials will contain any "pathogens."

2. Find a classmate to be your partner for Round 1. Record this person's name in Data Table 1 on the next page.

3. Carefully pour the contents of one vial into the other vial. Use the pipette to gently stir the mixture. Then use the pipette to transfer liquid into the empty vial. The vials should have about the same volume of liquid when you are done.

4. For Rounds 2 and 3, repeat Steps 2 and 3. Find a different partner for each round.

5. Take your vial to the testing station set up by your teacher. Add 4 drops of the disease indicator solution to your vial. Record whether the liquid remains clear, turns pink, or turns blue.

   Test result: _____

Data Table 1	
Round	Partner's Name
1	
2	
3	

Part B: Trace the Progression of the Disease

If the liquid in your vial turned pink or remained clear, your test was positive for the disease. If the liquid turned blue, your test was negative and you were not infected.

6. Your teacher will provide a data table on the board to record the results from Part A. If your test was positive, write your name in the first column. Also record the names of your partners.

7. Use Data Table 2 to make a copy of the class data. Then place a star next to the name of any partner who tested positive for the disease.

8. As a class, use the data to identify the only two people who could have been the original host for the disease.

Names of possible hosts: _____

_____

9. After the class has reached a consensus, add one drop of the disease indicator solution to your microtube. The sample that tests positive belongs to the original host.

Name of original host: _____

Data Table 2			
Infected People	Partners' Names		
	Round 1	Round 2	Round 3

Analyze and Conclude

1. **Organize Data** Make a flow chart in the space below to show how the disease spread from the original host through the class. Start with the name of the original host.

2. **Calculate** What were the odds that an uninfected person would become infected in Round 1? Explain.

   Sample answer: Assuming a class size of 30, the odds would be 1 in 29. Of the

   29 uninfected people at the beginning of the round, only one could partner

   with the infected person.

3. **Analyze Data** What happened to the odds of becoming infected in later rounds?

   Because the total population remained the same while the number of infected

   people increased, the odds of an uninfected person becoming infected also

   increased.

4. **Use Models** In what ways was this activity a realistic model for the spread of infectious disease through direct contact?

   Sample answer: The model was realistic in that the infection was able to spread

   quickly in a short period of time. It was also realistic because the infected person was

   not aware of the infection.

5. **Infer** When people test positive for a sexually-transmitted infection, why are they encouraged to inform all the people with whom they have had recent sexual contact?

Sample answer: The people with whom they have had contact need to be tested to see if they are infected. If they test positive, they can receive treatment, and they can avoid engaging in behaviors that put other people at risk.

Extend Your Inquiry

How could you modify the design of the activity so that it could serve as a model for the spread of infectious disease through indirect contact? **CAUTION**: Do not do the experiment.

Designs should reflect an understanding of the difference between direct and indirect contact. Example: Put the infected sample in a spray bottle. Place open vials of the uninfected samples at even intervals along a lab bench. Stand at one end of the bench and spray a mist into the air above the table. Allow time for the mist to settle. Test the samples in the vials to see if any became infected.

Quick Lab 2.1 **Model an Ionic Compound**

Problem

How do ionic compounds form?

Introduction

When sodium metal and chlorine gas react, the product is a white solid known as table salt. The chemical name for this familiar compound is sodium chloride (NaCl). The formula indicates that equal numbers of sodium and chlorine atoms react when sodium chloride is produced.

In this lab, you will work with your classmates to build a model of sodium chloride. Refer to the diagrams below of a sodium chloride crystal as you build your model. The diagram on the left provides a clear view of how the ions are arranged. The diagram on the right provides a more realistic model of how closely packed the ions are.

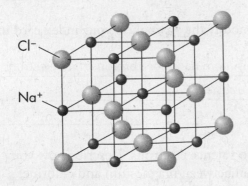
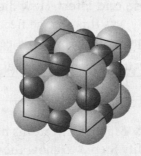

Skills Focus

Use Models, Calculate, Relate Cause and Effect

Materials

- popcorn kernels
- index cards
- permanent markers

Safety

Wash your hands thoroughly with soap and warm water before leaving the lab.

Big Idea
Chemical reactions involve changes in the chemical bonds that join atoms in compounds.

Skills Objectives
Students will be able to
- model the formation of an ionic bond and a crystal of an ionic compound.
- relate the type of bond to a compound's properties.

Preparation Time
10 minutes

Class Time
15 minutes

Group Size
Individuals

Advance Preparation
Make an equal number of sodium and chlorine index cards. Pick a location where students will have enough space to model the crystal.

Procedure

In this lab, you will represent the nucleus of an atom. The popcorn kernels will represent your atom's electrons.

Step 4
Students could stand close together or join hands to represent the bonding in the crystal.

Teaching Tip
Remind students that their model represents a tiny portion of an actual crystal.

1. Your teacher will give you an index card with the symbol Na for sodium or Cl for chlorine.
2. Collect one popcorn kernel for each electron in an atom of your assigned element.
3. Find a partner with whom you can model forming an ionic bond. After you form the bond, use a marker to change the symbol on your card to reflect what happened to your atom as the bond formed.
4. Join with the rest of your classmates to model the arrangement of ions across one plane of a sodium chloride crystal.

Analyze and Conclude

1. **Use Models** How did you model the formation of an ionic bond?

   The person representing the sodium atom gave a kernel to the person representing

   the chlorine atom.

2. **Relate Cause and Effect** How did you modify the symbol on your index card in Step 3? Why was this change necessary?

   I added a charge to the symbol because my atom had more protons than electrons

   (or more electrons than protons) after the transfer.

3. **Use Models** Magnesium atoms have two valence electrons. Describe how you would modify Step 3 to show the reaction between magnesium and chlorine.

   A person representing a magnesium atom would have to bond with two people

   representing chlorine atoms and give one kernel to each person.

4. **Draw Conclusions** What is the main factor that determines the arrangement of ions in an ionic compound? Explain.

   The main factor is the charge on the ions. The ions are arranged so that a given ion

   is surrounded by ions with an opposite charge.

5. **Apply Concepts** Use what you know about ionic bonds to explain why sodium chloride has a melting point of about 800°C.

   Sample answer: Considerable energy is required to break the strong bonds between

   oppositely charged ions in an ionic compound.

Quick Lab 7.2 Making a Model of a Cell

Problem

How can you use models to better understand cell structure?

Introduction

Each part of a plant cell has a specific function, which is often reflected in the size, shape, and location of the part. For example, the nucleus, which controls what happens in a cell, is located in the center of the cell. In this lab, you will work with your classmates to make a model of a plant cell.

Skills Focus

Use Models, Calculate, Compare and Contrast, Infer

Materials

- craft materials
- index cards
- scissors
- tape or glue

Safety ✂

Do not direct the points of the scissors toward yourself or others. Use the scissors only as instructed.

Procedure

Your classroom will represent a plant cell. You will make a model of an organelle or other cell part to place in your classroom "cell."

1. Use the table on page 207 of your textbook to select a part to model. Figure 7–14 on page 206 will give you an idea of the relative sizes of various cell parts and their possible positions in the cell.

2. Use the materials provided to build a three-dimensional model of your chosen cell part. Refer to other drawings in your textbook, such as those in Figures 7–11, 7-12, and 7–13, to make your model as complete and accurate as possible.

3. Label an index card with the name of your cell part, and list its main features and functions. Attach the card to your model.

4. Place your model at an appropriate location in your classroom.

5. As a class, review the completed model. If necessary, relocate some of the cell parts to reflect the spatial and functional relationships between parts of the cell.

Big Idea
The structure of a cell part is adapted to its function.

Skills Objectives
Students will be able to
• make a three-dimensional model of a cell.
• relate the structure of cell parts to their functions.

Preparation Time
20 minutes to gather materials

Class Time
30 minutes

Group Size
Individuals

Advance Preparation
Collect a variety of craft items, such as construction paper, yarn, balloons, and cardboard tubes. Allow students to use other materials as desired.

Teaching Tips
To avoid having many models of one organelle and no models of another, assign groups of students to work on a related set of cell parts, such as the organelles involved in protein production.
   If you want to avoid having to suspend structures in the middle of the classroom, use one inside wall to represent the cell, and have students attach their models to that wall.

Step 2
For organelles such as ribosomes, the drawings in Chapter 7 may not provide enough detail. Use other images to supplement the drawings in the textbook.

Analyze and Conclude

1. **Calculate** A typical plant cell has a width of 50 micrometers (μm), or 5×10^{-5} m. Calculate the scale of your classroom cell model. *Hint:* Divide the width of your classroom by the width of a typical plant cell. Use the same unit for both measurements.

   Sample answer: For a room that is 5 m (5×10^6 μm) wide, the scale would be

   100,000 : 1. _____

   _____

2. **Compare and Contrast** How is your model of a cell part similar to the actual cell part? How is it different?

   The cell parts should be similar in shape and structure to the actual part. They

   should be an appropriate size relative to the overall size of the classroom "cell." The

   models are much larger than the actual parts, are made from different materials,

   and, of course, do not function.

   _____

   _____

3. **Infer** How is the structure of your cell part adapted to its function?

   Sample answers: Membranes have pores that allow materials to move in and out of

   the nucleus and the cell. The nucleus is surrounded by a membrane that protects

   the DNA that is stored in the nucleus. The mazelike passages in the endoplasmic

   reticulum and the Golgi apparatus resemble an assembly line in a factory, and may

   reflect a process with many steps.

4. **Evaluate** If you were starting over, what would you do to improve your model?

   Students may say that they would choose different materials or do more upfront

   planning so that it would be easier to relate one part to another in the overall model.

   _____

Quick Lab 10.1 Modeling the Relationship Between Surface Area and Volume

Problem
How does cell size affect a cell's ability to function?

Introduction
In this lab you will construct a set of paper cubes. The cubes will represent cells at different stages of growth. After you construct your cubes, you will calculate the volume, surface area, and ratio of surface area to volume of each cube.

Skills Focus
Use Models, Calculate, Design an Experiment

Materials
- patterns for 6-cm, 5-cm, 4-cm, and 3-cm cubes
- scissors
- tape or glue

Safety ✂
Do not direct the points of the scissors toward yourself or others. Use the scissors only as instructed.

Procedure
1. Cut out the patterns on pages 295, 297, and 299 and fold them along the dashed lines. Use the tabs to tape or glue the sides together. Do not tape down the top side.

2. Calculate the surface area of each cube. Find the area of one side of the cube and multiply that area by the number of sides. Record your results in the data table on the next page.

3. Calculate the volume of each cube. Multiply width times length times height. Record the results in the data table.

Big Idea
The structure and function of a cell are related.

Skills Objectives
Students will be able to
- make a model of a cell.
- relate the surface area and volume of a cell.

Class Time
25 minutes

Group Size
Individuals

Teaching Tip
To limit the amount of class time required, have each student make one or two cubes of an assigned size. Divide the work so you will have at least eight 3-cm cubes to compare with the 6-cm cube.

Step 2
Remind students that the length, width, and height are equal for a cube.

4. Divide the surface area by the volume to find the ratio of surface area to volume. Record your results in the data table.

Sample Data

Data Table			
Width of Side	Surface Area (cm²)	Volume (cm³)	Ratio of Surface Area to Volume
6 cm	216	216	1 : 1
5 cm	150	125	1.2 : 1
4 cm	96	64	1.5 : 1
3 cm	54	27	2 : 1

5. Use your data to calculate the number of 3-cm cubes that would fit in the same volume as the 6-cm cube. Also calculate the total surface area for the smaller cubes.

Number of 3-cm cubes: _____ 8

Total surface area of smaller cubes: _____ 432 cm²

Analyze and Conclude

1. **Review** Describe the function of a cell membrane and its relationship to what happens inside a cell.

The cell membrane provides the surface across which materials are exchanged

between a cell and its environment.

2. **Draw Conclusions** How did the ratio of surface area to volume change as the size of the cubes decreased?

The ratio of surface area to volume increased.

3. **Relate Cause and Effect** As a cell grows, what happens to the amount of activity in the cell and the need for materials to be exchanged across the cell membrane?

As a cell grows there is more activity in the cell and a greater need for materials to be

exchanged across the cell membrane.

4. **Draw Conclusions** How could the growth of a cell affect its ability to survive?

Sample answer: The rate at which materials are exchanged at the cell membrane does

not keep pace with the increase in cell activity.

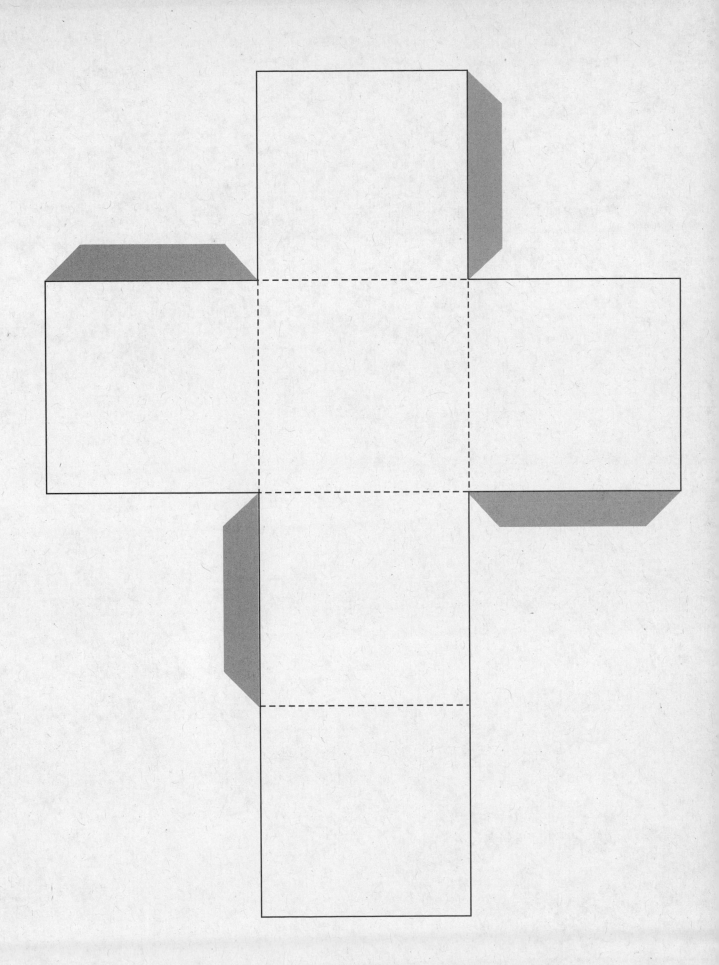

Quick Lab 11.2 **How Are Dimples Inherited?**

Problem
How can you predict the outcome of a genetic cross?

Introduction
Alleles that you inherited from your parents determine whether or not you have dimples. In this lab, you will use digits from telephone numbers and Punnett squares to model the inheritance of dimples.

Skills Focus
Use Models, Analyze Data

Procedure
1. Write down the last four digits of a telephone number. You will use these digits to represent the alleles in a gene. Odd digits will represent the allele for dimples, a dominant trait. Even digits will represent the allele for the recessive trait of no dimples. Count 0 as an even digit.

2. Use the first two digits in your number to represent a father's genotype. Use the symbols *D* and *d* to write his genotype. Refer to the example in Figure 1.

   Father's genotype: *Sample answer: dd* _____

3. Use the last two digits in your number to represent a mother's genotype.

   Mother's genotype: *Sample answer: Dd* _____

Figure 1 Sample of genotype based on four random digits

Father's genotype is *dd* (2 even digits).   Mother's genotype is *Dd* (1 odd digit and 1 even digit).

46 | 38

4. Record the alleles that could be found in all the possible gametes that each parent could produce.

   Father's alleles: *Sample answer: d and d* _____

   Mother's alleles: *Sample answer: D and d* _____

Big Idea
The probability of phenotypes in offspring depends on the genotypes of their parents.

Skills Objectives
Students will be able to
• predict the distribution of phenotypes from a genetic cross.
• relate genotypes to phenotypes.

Class Time
15 minutes

Group Size
Individuals

Teaching Tip
Make sure students know the difference between a genotype and a phenotype. If necessary, review how to calculate a probability.

Step 5
Students will need the results for the three possible crosses (heterozygous, homozygous dominant, and homozygous recessive) before they answer the Analyze and Conclude questions. Record an example of each cross on the board.

5. Use the Punnett square to predict the genotype combinations for a cross between the father and mother. First, enter the data from Step 4. Place the father's possible alleles in the top row and the mother's possible alleles in the left column. Complete the square by combining the genotypes of the gametes.

Sample Data

Father

		d	*d*
	D	*Dd*	*Dd*
Mother	*d*	*dd*	*dd*

6. Determine the percentage of students in your class who inherited alleles for dimples.

_____

Analyze and Conclude

1. **Relate Cause and Effect** What are the possible genotypes for a person with dimples? For a person with no dimples?

   For dimples, the genotypes are *DD* and *Dd*. For no dimples the genotype is *dd*.

   _____

2. **Analyze Data** What is the probability that a child will have dimples when both parents are heterozygous for the gene that determines dimples?

   The probability is 3 out of 4 or 75 percent.

3. **Analyze Data** What is the probability that a child will have dimples when one parent is homozygous for the dimple allele and the other is heterozygous for the gene that determines dimples?

   The probability is 4 out of 4 or 100 percent.

4. **Analyze Data** What is the probability that a child will have dimples when both parents are homozygous for the no dimple allele?

   The probability is 0 out of 4 or 0 percent.

5. **Draw Conclusions** Which type of cross could have produced the percentage of dimples among students in your class?

   Class averages are usually close to the results for two heterozygous parents.

   _____

Quick Lab 15.2 **Inserting Genetic Markers**

Problem
How are restriction enzymes used to recombine DNA?

Introduction
Scientists know how to combine DNA from two or more sources. When the process is done right, a cell will copy a gene that was inserted into its DNA when it copies the full strand of DNA. This technology has been used to turn bacteria into "factories" for human proteins, such as insulin.

Scientists often work with small circular pieces of DNA called plasmids, which are found in bacteria. The human genes are inserted into the plasmids. Genetic markers are also inserted. The markers allow scientists to track whether the recombined DNA was successfully introduced into the bacteria.

Scientists use restriction enzymes to control the location of inserted genes and markers. Bacteria produce restriction enzymes. The enzymes act as a defense against viruses that invade bacteria.

Skills Focus
Interpret Tables, Predict

Procedure
For each restriction enzyme, there is a recognition sequence that determines the location where the enzyme can cut a DNA strand. For example, the enzyme Eco RI can cut a DNA strand between guanine and adenine when the sequence GAATTC appears in the strand. In the table on page 304, an asterisk shows the location of the cut in the recognition sequence for six restriction enzymes.

1. Examine the base sequence below. Use a caret (^) to mark a location in the sequence where the Eco RI enzyme could cut the DNA. Use a vertical line to mark a location where the Taq I enzyme could cut the DNA.

   CTT|CGA TAT CAG ATT TAA ATC GCG TGT GTA CTT ACT
   GGG GAT CGC ATC ACG GTG᠕AAT TCC CCC CTT CTC TAC
   CTC CTT TGA ATT CGA ACT ACA GCG CTT CCC GGG TTT

2. Use a caret to mark two locations where the Hha I enzyme could cut the DNA. *Hint:* Read the sequence forward and backward.

   CTT CGA TAT CAG ATT TAA ATC᠕GCG TGT GTA CTT ACT
   GGG GAT CGC ATC ACG GTG AAT TCC CCC CTT CTC TAC
   CTC CTT TGA ATT CGA ACT ACA GCG᠕CTT CCC GGG TTT

Big Idea — Through recombinant DNA technology, scientists can alter the genetic composition of living organisms.

Skills Objectives — Students will be able to • identify recognition sequences for restriction enzymes in a sequence of bases. • predict the effect of restriction enzymes on a DNA strand.

Class Time — 15 minutes

Group Size — Individuals

Teaching Tip — Some students may ask whether a restriction enzyme can cut DNA within codons as well as between codons. The answer is yes. The enzyme is unaffected by the grouping of bases into three-letter codes.

3. Use a caret to mark the location where both the Sma 1 enzyme and the Hae III enzyme could cut the DNA.

CTT CGA TAT CAG ATT TAA ATC GCG TGT GTA CTT ACT
GGG GAT CGC ATC ACG GTG AAT TCC CCC CTT CTC TAC
CTC CTT TGA ATT CGA ACT ACA GCG CTT CCC^GGG TTT

Examples of Restriction Enzymes		
Enzyme	**Bacterial Source**	**Recognition Sequence**
Eco RI	*Escherichia coli*	G*AATTC
Hae III	*Haemophilus aegyptius*	GG*CC
Hha I	*Haemophilus haemolyticus*	GCG*C
Sma I	*Serratia marcescens*	CCC*GGG
Taq I	*Thermophilus aquaticus*	T*CGA

Analyze and Conclude

1. **Predict** Suppose the recognition sequence for a restriction enzyme appears three times along a DNA strand. What could happen when the enzyme is used to insert a gene into a plasmid?

The gene could be inserted in three locations.

_____

2. **Infer** Which restriction enzyme might give a scientist more control over the location of an inserted gene—Eco RI or Hae III? Why?

Sample answer: Eco RI might give the scientist more control over the location because the recognition sequence is longer and thus likely to appear fewer times in a DNA strand than the sequence for Hae III.

_____

3. **Infer** How could restriction enzymes help bacteria defend against viruses? *Hint:* Viruses contain nucleic acids.

Sample answer: The restriction enzymes could digest or break down nucleic acids in an invading virus.

_____

Quick Lab 20.1 **How Do Viruses Differ in Structure?**

Problem
How can models help you compare the structure of viruses?

Introduction
Viruses share a few characteristics with living organisms. Viruses have a genetic code and can evolve. But viruses cannot do many of the things that living organisms do. For example, viruses must invade the cells of living organisms in order to reproduce. Viruses can be classified by the type of organism they infect, such as plants, animals, or bacteria.

In this lab, you will make models of viruses. You will use the models to look for similarities and differences among viruses.

Skills Focus
Use Models, Measure, Calculate, Compare and Contrast

Materials
- craft materials
- scissors
- tape or glue
- metric ruler

Safety ✂
Do not direct the points of the scissors toward yourself or others. Use the scissors only as instructed.

Procedure
Refer to Figure 20–1 on page 575 of your textbook as you make your models. Record your measurements and the results of your calculations in the data table on the next page.

1. Use the materials provided to make models of the viruses shown in Figure 20–1.

2. Use the labels in Figure 20–1 to label the parts of your models.

3. Measure the length of each model in centimeters. For the influenza virus, use its diameter as its length.

4. Convert the length of each model into nanometers by using the formula 1 cm = 10 million nm.

Big Idea
Viruses have adaptations that increase their ability to successfully invade a host cell.

Skills Objectives
Students will be able to
- make models of viruses.
- use a conversion factor for measurements.
- calculate the scale of their models.

Preparation Time
30 minutes to gather materials

Class Time
25 minutes

Group Size
Pairs

Materials
Possible useful materials other than paper include bubble wrap, pushpins, and pipe cleaners.

Teaching Tip
Before students begin, make sure they know how to use scientific notation and a conversion factor. Also review the concept of scale.

5. Measure the length of each magnified image in Figure 20–1 in centimeters. For the tobacco mosaic virus, measure the vertical rod in the center of the field of view.

6. Divide the length of each magnified image by the magnification to determine the actual length of each virus.

7. Convert the lengths from Step 6 into nanometers.

8. Divide the length of each model by the length of the actual virus to determine how much larger your models are than the viruses they represent.

Sample Data

Data Table			
	T4 Bacteriophage	**Tobacco Mosaic Virus**	**Influenza Virus**
Length of model (cm)			
Length of model (nm)			
Length of virus image (cm)	1.5	0.8	2.4
Actual length of virus (cm)	2.5×10^{-5}	2×10^{-6}	1.1×10^{-4}
Actual length of virus (nm)	250	20	1100
Scale of model to actual virus			

Analyze and Conclude

1. **Compare and Contrast** What do all viruses have in common?

All viruses have a capsid and either DNA or RNA.

2. **Compare and Contrast** What structures are found in only some viruses?

Structures found in only some viruses include a head, tail sheath, tail fibers, and a membrane envelope.

3. **Evaluate** Explain why it can be useful to make a large-scale model of a tiny object.

Sample answer: With a large-scale model, it can be easier to visualize the details of an object's structure or how the parts of the object are related to one another.

Appendix A How to Form a Hypothesis

What is a hypothesis?

A hypothesis is a possible explanation for a set of observations or a possible answer to a scientific question. A hypothesis is designed to be tested in an experiment. Thus, hypotheses are a central part of scientific methodology. Knowing how to form a hypothesis is an important skill.

Many scientific investigations begin with observations. For instance, you may notice that one pond has more algae growing in it than another, or that a bumblebee in a field visits one type of flower more than others. Observations like these often lead to questions such as, "Why does one pond have more algae than another pond? Why do bumblebees seem to prefer one type of flower more than others?" To answer questions like these, you must first make a hypothesis.

Why should you make a hypothesis?

The main purpose of a hypothesis is to set up a statement that can be supported or disproved by evidence. Once you've made a hypothesis, you can design an experiment to help you determine whether it is right or wrong.

Sometimes what you observe and the data you collect will not support your hypothesis. In science, the important thing is not whether a hypothesis is right or wrong. The important thing is what you learn from an experiment. In fact, for scientists, a hypothesis that is wrong can be just as valuable as a hypothesis that is right.

You will need to design a procedure for some experiments. But often you will be asked to do experiments that have been designed for you. A hypothesis is a useful tool even when you are following a predesigned procedure. Making a hypothesis will ensure that you understand the purpose of a lab and why you will be asked to make certain types of observations.

This appendix describes the "full version" of a hypothesis, which tends to be long and full of details. Such detailed statements are essential for a scientist who is doing research. But for most of the labs in this manual, it will be acceptable for you to write shorter hypotheses with fewer details.

How is a hypothesis related to experimental design?

Most experiments test the relationship between two factors. You change the independent variable. Then you observe whether the dependent variable changes in response. A useful hypothesis should state how you think the variables are related. In the full version, you must also state how the relationship will affect the results of the experiment.

The following statement is a fully developed hypothesis. *If the presence of fertilizer is related to increased algal growth, then algae that are provided with fertilizer will exhibit greater growth than algae that are not provided with fertilizer.* Is this hypothesis useful? Yes, because it relates the use of fertilizer to the growth of algae. It also describes what results to expect if the hypothesis is correct.

Practice Identify the variables in this hypothesis. *If the heart rate of* Daphnia *is related to the concentration of salt in their water, then changing the salt concentration of a* Daphnia's *water will cause its heart rate to change.*

Dependent variable: Salt concentration

_____

Independent variable: Heart rate

_____

How can you evaluate a hypothesis?

For a hypothesis to be of value during the experimental design process, it must be possible to test the hypothesis. This rule is true whether the hypothesis is fully developed or a shorter version with fewer details.

A statement like "My cat's favorite food is tuna" may or may not be true, but there is no way to test it. However, it would be possible to test the statement "If a cat prefers tuna to dry cat food, then the cat will eat the tuna first when the two foods are placed side by side."

A hypothesis should also contain language that suggests *how* it can be tested. A useful hypothesis often will take the form of an "if, then" statement. In the first part of the statement, you should summarize the relationship you think might be taking place (*If the presence of fertilizer is related to algal growth in ponds…*). In the second part, you should predict how you think this relationship will affect the results of your experiment (*…then algae that are provided with fertilizer in the laboratory will exhibit greater growth than algae that are not provided with fertilizer*).

Comparison of Hypotheses	
Poor Hypothesis	**Useful Hypothesis**
Salt water will decrease plant growth.	*Full version:* If a high concentration of salt in water causes decreased plant growth, then potted plants that are given salt water will grow more slowly than potted plants that are given tap water. *Shorter version:* Plants that are given salt water will grow more slowly than plants that are given tap water.
The effectiveness of enzymes may be affected by water temperature.	*Full version:* If the effectiveness of enzymes is related to water temperature, then the amount of product from an enzyme-catalyzed reaction will vary at different temperatures. *Shorter version:* The amount of product from an enzyme-catalyzed reaction will vary at different temperatures.
Bumblebees prefer yellow flowers to red flowers.	*Full version:* If bumblebees visit yellow flowers more often than red flowers, then bumblebees that are kept in the laboratory will visit a fake yellow flower more often than a fake red flower. *Shorter version:* When both types of flowers are present, bumblebees will visit fake yellow flowers more often than fake red flowers.

Practice Your Skills

1. Both of these hypotheses are in the form of an "if, then" statement. Which hypothesis is more useful, and why?

   a. If heart rate is related to caffeine intake, then coffee drinkers will have higher heart rates.

   b. If a higher heart rate is related to caffeine intake, then the heart rate of most people will be higher 30 minutes after they drink a cup of coffee.

   Statement B is more useful because it suggests a way to test the relationship

   between heart rate and caffeine intake.

2. Write the missing "if" statement for this "then" statement: …then ants placed halfway between solutions of sugar and an artificial sweetener will move toward both solutions with equal frequency.

   If ants are equally attracted to sugar and artificial sweeteners

Rewrite the hypotheses in Questions 3–5 so that they are more useful for experimental design.

3. Mouthwash A will kill more bacteria in laboratory cultures than Mouthwash B will.

   If Mouthwash A is more effective at killing bacteria than Mouthwash B, then a

   bacterial culture that is treated with Mouthwash A will have fewer live bacteria than

   a culture that is treated with Mouthwash B.

4. Colonies of *E. coli* bacteria will grow faster in culture dishes kept at 35°C than in dishes kept at 25°C.

   If *E. coli* bacteria reproduce faster at 35°C than at 25°C, then colonies in culture

   dishes that are kept at 35°C will grow faster than ones kept at 25°C.

5. Bean plants will grow more slowly when exposed to acid rain.

   If the increased acidity of rainwater is related to slower bean plant growth, then

   bean plants that are provided with water that is more acidic will grow more slowly

   than bean plants that are provided with water that is less acidic.

Appendix B Presenting Data

When you do a lab, you may be asked to record your observations in words or drawings. You may have to make and record measurements. How you organize the data you collect can affect your ability to analyze the data, which is an important part of the experimental process. When you present data in a clear and logical way, you also make it easier for others to interpret and evaluate your results.

Using Data Tables

When scientists do experiments, they typically do many trials using the same procedure. Once the scientists analyze the results, they may adjust the procedure and do more trials. This process can continue for months or years, resulting in a vast amount of data. Data tables are an excellent way to organize large amounts of data.

Example A team of researchers collected venom from ten different species of snakes. They tested the venom to determine how toxic each sample was. They also collected data about people who died after being bitten by each type of snake. Compare the following description of the data they collected with the same data presented in a data table. In which format are the results easier to analyze?

For the southern United States copperhead, the death rate was less than 1 percent. For the western diamondback rattlesnake, the rate was 5–15 percent. The rate was 5–20 percent for the eastern coral snake and the king cobra. For the Indian krait, the rate was 77 percent. For the European viper, the rate was 1–5 percent. The rate was 100 percent for the bushmaster and 10–20 percent for the fer-de-lance. For both the black-necked cobra and the puff adder, the death rate was 11–40 percent.

Death Rates After Snake Bites	
Type of Snake	**Death Rate (%)**
Black-necked cobra	11–40
Bushmaster	Typically 100
Copperhead	Less than 1
Eastern coral snake	5–20
European viper	1–5
Fer-de-lance	10–20
Indian krait	77
King cobra	5–20
Puff adder	11–40
Rattlesnake	5–15

Each column in a data table should have a head that describes the data in the column. In the table about snake bites, the column heads are the independent variable (Type of Snake) and the dependent variable (Death Rate). When the variable is a measurement, the unit of measurement, such as (cm) for length or (g) for mass, is often included with the head.

The rows in a table may be arranged by trial (Trial 1, Trial 2, and so on) or by the days on which measurements are made (Day 1, Day 3, Day 5, and so on). But sometimes the choice is less obvious.

Practice How are the rows ordered in the snake-bite table?

The snakes are listed in alphabetical order.

How might you rearrange the rows to make the data easier to analyze?

Sample answer: I might order the rows from the smallest percentage of deaths to the largest percentage of deaths (or vice versa).

Once you have a completed data table, you can apply another important scientific skill—posing questions. For example, scientists looking at the data on snake bites might wonder about the reliability of the data. They might ask questions such as, "What procedure did the researchers use to gather this data?" "How large were the samples that were used to calculate the percentages?"

Practice Some of the ranges in the snake-bite table are very broad—the 11–40 percent death rate for the puff adder, for example. Perhaps data from different sources were combined. If so, think of a follow-up question that a scientist might want to ask.

Follow-up question: _Sample answer:_ What variables other than the type of snake could affect the death rate from snake bites?

Have you ever jotted down notes while working in the lab and been unable to locate the notes later? Have you found the notes but been unable to figure out what you meant? Making a data table in advance helps ensure that the data you collect will not get lost and that all the data will be recorded.

For some labs in this manual, a data table will be provided for you to fill in. For other labs, you will be asked to construct an appropriate data table. You will need to decide how to best arrange the data in the table. Experiments often require a data table with more than two columns.

Example Students who were studying inherited physical traits collected data on hair color from three different classes.

Class 1
Black: 2
Blond: 3
Brown: 20
Red: 0

Class 2
Black: 0
Blond: 7
Brown: 18
Red: 1

Class 3
Black: 4
Blond: 12
Brown: 15
Red: 0

The hair-color data could be arranged in a table as follows. This arrangement draws attention to differences among the classes.

Distribution of Hair Color by Class			
Hair Color	Class 1	Class 2	Class 3
Black	2	0	4
Blond	3	7	12
Brown	20	18	15
Red	0	1	0

Practice The table could be constructed to focus more on hair color and less on the individual classes. The rearranged data has been entered in the table below. Complete the table by filling in the missing heads.

Hair Color of Students				
	Hair Color			
	Black	Blond	Brown	Red
Class 1	2	3	20	0
Class 2	0	7	18	1
Class 3	4	12	15	0
Total	6	22	53	1

Making a table in advance also gives you a chance to evaluate your experimental design before you begin. While constructing a data table for the study on hair color, you might be prompted to think, "How will I decide whether to classify a color as dark brown or as black?" "Will all the hair colors I observe be natural?" "Will I be able to draw any useful conclusions if I survey only three classes?"

Using Graphs

A graph is a pictorial representation of data. Graphs are used to show a relationship between two or more factors. Plotting the data you collect on a graph may reveal a pattern that isn't obvious when data is organized in a table. Before you plot your data, you will need to decide which type of graph to use.

Line Graphs

A line graph has one or more lines connecting a series of data points. A line graph is often the best choice for showing how an independent variable is related to a dependent variable. With a line graph, you are also able to estimate values for points that lie between or beyond the measured data points.

Example This line graph relates the length of a tortoise shell to the age of a tortoise. One line shows data for a tortoise that was raised in a zoo. The second line shows data collected from wild tortoises of the same species. Having the two lines on one graph makes it easier to compare the effect of a third variable—the conditions under which growth occurred.

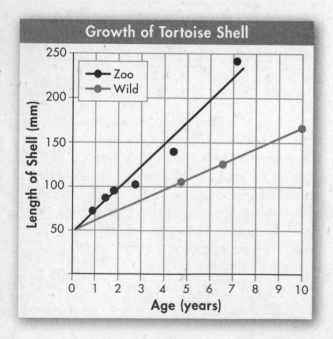

Practice Fish "breathe" by pumping water through their mouths and over their gills, where oxygen is extracted. Use the data in the table to make a graph that relates the temperature of the water to the breathing rate of a fish.

Decide which variable is the independent variable and place it on the horizontal axis, or x-axis. Place the dependent variable on the vertical axis, or y-axis. Label the axes.

Choose a scale for each axis. Consider the range of data and the number of available squares. If your scale unit is too large, your graph will be too small and difficult to read. If your scale unit is too small, some of your data will not fit on the graph. Units that are multiples of 1, 2, 5, and 10 are easiest to work with.

Temperature (°C)	Rate (per minute)
10	15
15	25
18	30
20	38
23	60
25	57
27	25

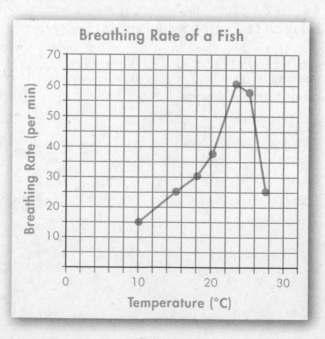

Bar Graphs

You can also use a bar graph to compare data. Like a line graph, a bar graph has an *x*-axis and a *y*-axis. But instead of points, a bar graph uses a series of columns, or bars, to display data. Bar graphs are especially useful when the data is not continuous—when you cannot use the graph to estimate values that were not measured. On many bar graphs, the *x*-axis lists categories rather than a numerical scale.

Example A driver must be alert and able to react quickly to changing road conditions or to the actions of other drivers. The following bar graph shows how alcohol can affect a driver's ability to react. What is the relationship between the blood alcohol concentration and the reaction time?

The graph reveals a direct relationship between

the variables. Reaction time increases as the blood

alcohol concentration increases.

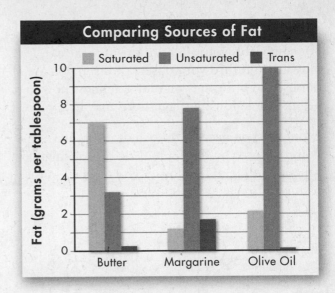

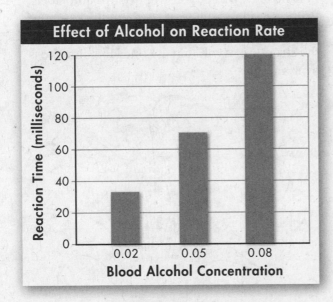

Recall that you can introduce a third variable to a line graph by adding lines. You can do something similar with the bars on a bar graph.

Example The following bar graph compares the fat content of butter, margarine, and olive oil. For each source, the data is divided by type of fat—saturated, unsaturated, and trans fat.

Practice Use the table to make a bar graph showing the percentage of students at each grade who take part in vigorous physical activity. Place the grades on the *x*-axis and the percentage on the *y*-axis. Start your *y*-axis scale just above the jagged line. Use different colored bars for males and females, and add a legend.

Grade	Males	Females
9th	74%	64%
10th	71%	58%
11th	70%	52%
12th	63%	49%

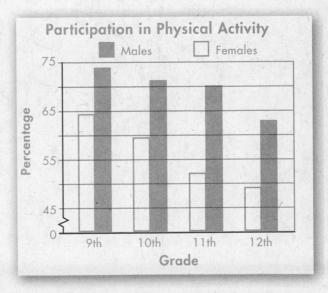

Using Drawings

For some labs, you will be asked to make a drawing to record your observations. If you are not used to drawing, you may not know how to begin. The following suggestions may help.

Example You need to make a drawing of a flower before you dissect it. Start by drawing the general outline of the flower. Use a pencil in case you need to make corrections.

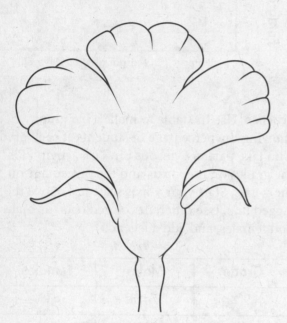

Next, add the different structures. Focus on the general shape and location of each structure.

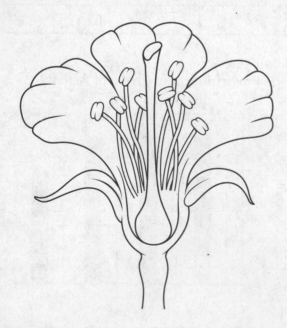

You may choose to use shading to highlight some features of your drawing. The shading in this drawing emphasizes the path that the pollen travels to reach the ovary.

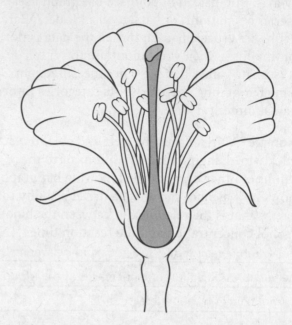

For most drawings, you will need to add labels. Print the labels and position them horizontally. Use a ruler to draw a line between the label and the structure. Avoid having one label line cross over another.

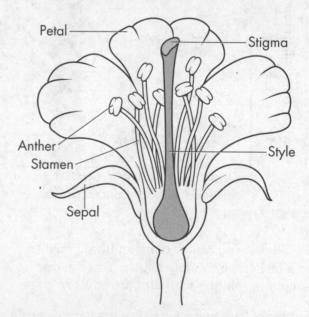

When you draw objects that you view with a microscope, use a circle to represent the field of view. Also include the magnification at which you viewed the object.

Appendix C Measurements and Calculations

The Metric System

The measurement system used by scientists is the International System of Units (SI). Because SI is a metric system, all SI units are related by a power of 10, which makes it easy to convert one SI unit to another. In the lab, you will mainly measure length, mass, volume, and temperature.

Length The SI unit for length is the meter (m). A meter is slightly longer than a yard.

Mass The SI unit for mass is the gram (g). A paper clip has a mass of about one gram.

Volume of a Liquid The SI unit for the volume of a liquid is the liter (L). A liter is slightly more than a quart.

Temperature The SI unit for temperature is degrees Celsius (°C). Water freezes at 0°C and boils at 100°C.

The table lists some SI prefixes. *Larger* and *smaller* refer to what happens when a prefix is placed before a unit. For example, the *c* in the unit cm indicates that a centimeter is 100 times smaller than a meter.

Common SI Prefixes		
Prefix	**Symbol**	**Meaning**
kilo-	k	1000 times larger
hecto-	h	100 times larger
deka-	da	10 times larger
deci-	d	10 times smaller
centi-	c	100 times smaller
milli-	m	1000 times smaller
micro-	μ	1 million times smaller
nano-	n	1000 million times smaller

Accuracy and Precision

Your measurements need to be both accurate and precise. Accuracy refers to how close a measurement is to the actual value. Precision refers to how close a group of measurements are to each other. The level of precision that is possible depends on the measuring instrument. For example, on one ruler, the smallest unit is a centimeter. On a second ruler, the smallest unit is a millimeter. Measurements made with the second ruler will be more precise than those made with the first ruler.

Significant Figures

The number of significant figures you record for a measurement depends on the precision of the measuring instrument. Significant figures are all of the digits that are known in a measurement, plus one added digit, which is an estimate.

Example Look at the measured lengths of the peanut in the drawing. With Ruler A, the length has two significant figures because the estimated digit is the distance between centimeter marks. With Ruler B, the length has three significant figures because the estimated digit is the distance between millimeter marks.

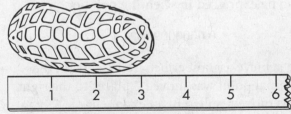

a. Measured length = 3.3 cm

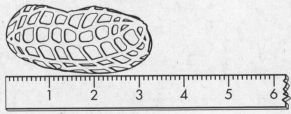

b. Measured length = 3.29 cm

Scientific Notation

Using scientific notation makes it easier to work with numbers that are very large or very small. For example, the diameter of a bacterial cell might be 0.9 micrometers, or 0.0000009 μm. A number with so many zeros is difficult to work with, especially if you need to do a calculation.

Numbers can be expressed as a base and an exponent. The exponent tells you how many times the base is multiplied by itself. The number 15,625, for example, can be expressed as follows:

$$15,625 = 25 \times 25 \times 25 = 25^3$$

In this example, the base is 25 and the exponent is 3. In scientific notation, the base is always the number 10. A number written in scientific notation is expressed as the product of two factors, a number between 1 and 10 and the number 10 with an exponent.

Example The number 51,203 can be expressed in scientific notation as follows:

$$51,203 = 5.1203 \times 10^4$$

To achieve a number between 1 and 10, the decimal point was moved 4 places to the left. This move resulted in an exponent of 4. Note that the first factor includes all the significant digits in the original number.

Example Numbers that are less than 1 can also be expressed in scientific notation.

$$0.0000009 = 9 \times 10^{-7}$$

To achieve a number between 1 and 10, the decimal point was moved 7 places to the right. This move resulted in an exponent of –7.

Calculating Averages

When you do an experiment that includes multiple trials, you will usually be asked to calculate an average. However, an *average* can be calculated in several ways. The method you will use will depend on what you are trying to learn from the data. Scientists often use the term *central tendency* to refer to the "middle," or typical, value in a set of data.

Mean In common usage, the term *average* refers to a numerical average, or *mean*. The mean is the sum of the data divided by the number of items. Consider the following data:

6.2 mL, 8.0 mL, 6.4 mL, 6.2 mL, 6.7 mL

The mean for this data is 6.7 mL. In this case, the mean is probably higher than it should be because of the 8.0 mL data point, which is not typical. The median might be a better choice.

Median The median is the middle number in a set of ordered data. Often the data needs to be ordered before you can determine the mean. For example, 6.2 mL, 8.0 mL, 6.4 mL, 6.2 mL, and 6.7 mL would be reordered as follows:

6.2 mL, 6.2 mL, 6.4 mL, 6.7 mL, 8.0 mL

There are an equal number of data points above the median, which is 6.4 mL. When the number of data points is even, the median is the mean of the two middle points.

Mode The number that appears most often in a set of data is called the mode. In the example above, the mode is 6.2 mL. The mode is useful when you are dealing with categories of data, such as T-shirt sizes. Knowing the mode would help a buyer who is ordering stock for a store.

Practice Your Skills

1. How much smaller is a milliliter than a liter? How much larger is a centimeter than a millimeter? How many grams are in a kilogram?

A milliliter is 1000 times smaller than a liter. A centimeter is 10 times larger than a millimeter. There are 1000 grams in a kilogram.

2. You are using a 25-mL graduated cylinder to measure the volume of a liquid. The smallest marked unit on the cylinder is a milliliter. The volume is more than 10 mL and less than 15 mL. How many significant figures can you report in your answer? Explain.

The answer should have three significant figures, including the estimated distance between one milliliter mark and the next.

3. For adult women, the average number of white blood cells per liter of blood is 5.8 billion. Express this data in scientific notation. *Hint:* You may want to write out the number with all its zeroes first.

5,800,000,000 or 5.8×10^9 white blood cells

4. In a garden, the heights of five sunflowers are 135.0 cm, 162.5 cm, 180.0 cm, 185.0 cm, and 167.5 cm. Calculate the mean and the median for this data.

The mean is 166.0 cm. The median is 167.5 cm.

5. In a second garden, the heights of five sunflowers are 130.0 cm, 162.5 cm, 165.0 cm, 160.0 cm, and 162.5 cm. For this data, would you use the mean or the median, and why?

Sample answer: The mean is 156 cm. The median is 162.5 cm. I would use the median, because the 130.0 cm data point is not typical.

6. What is the mode for the data in Question 5?

The mode is 162.5 cm.

Appendix D Laboratory Techniques

Measuring Volume

The instruments you will use to measure the volume of a liquid are graduated cylinders and pipettes.

Graduated Cylinders

A liquid in a graduated cylinder has a slightly curved surface called a meniscus. To obtain an accurate measurement, read the volume with your eye at the same level as the bottom of the meniscus. To make the meniscus easier to see, place a dark piece of paper behind the cylinder while you make the reading.

Your readings will be more precise if you choose the smallest cylinder that will contain the liquid. Make sure the volume does not exceed the graduated part of the cylinder.

Types of Pipettes

Pipettes are used to transfer a liquid from one container to another or to measure and dispense a specific amount of a liquid. In a few labs, you will use a pipette to move a tiny organism from one container to another. The drawing shows four types of pipettes.

Volumetric Pipettes These pipettes are designed to dispense a specific fixed volume of liquid. They have only one mark. When the pipette is filled to that mark, it will deliver the exact volume etched on the side of the pipette.

Graduated Pipettes These pipettes have a series of marks along the length of the pipette similar to the marks on a graduated cylinder. You take a reading before and after you release liquid from the pipette. The difference between the readings is the volume of the released liquid. A volume measured with a graduated pipette will be less accurate than the same volume measured with a volumetric pipette.

Dropper Pipettes These pipettes have no markings. They are used to transfer liquid from one container to another or to add liquid to a container one drop at a time.

Micropipettes As their name implies, these pipettes are designed to dispense small amounts of a liquid—less than 1 milliliter. Micropipettes are especially useful when a scientist is working with very small samples, such as those used to analyze DNA.

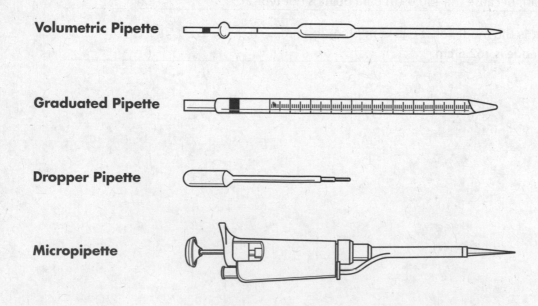

Volumetric Pipette

Graduated Pipette

Dropper Pipette

Micropipette

Using a Volumetric Pipette

Pipettes allow you to draw up and release a liquid in a controlled way. Suction is used to pull the liquid into the pipette. To create the suction with a volumetric pipette, you may use a pipette pump. Or you may use a plain rubber bulb or a bulb with an automatic valve. These instructions are for the bulb without a valve. CAUTION: Never use your mouth to draw a liquid into a pipette.

1. If you are right-handed, hold the pipette in your right hand and the bulb in your left. Do the opposite if you are left-handed.

2. Place the tip of the pipette into the liquid.

3. Compress the bulb, and press the hole in the bulb against the upper end of the pipette. Insert the end of the pipette a tiny bit into the bulb to create the seal. CAUTION: Do not push the pipette too far into the bulb.

4. Slowly release pressure on the bulb so that liquid is drawn into the pipette to a level about 2 cm above the marked line.

5. Remove the bulb and put your index finger over the end of the pipette at the same time.

6. With your index finger pressed firmly against the end of the pipette, remove the pipette from the liquid.

7. Slowly reduce the pressure from your finger to allow some liquid to drain into a waste container. Stop when the bottom of the meniscus is at the marked line.

8. Release the remaining liquid into the receiving container. Wait 20 seconds.

9. Gently touch the pipette tip to the inside of the container. Do not worry about the small amount of liquid that remains in the tip.

Using a Dropper Pipette

The action of a dropper pipette is similar to that of an eye dropper. The bulb is part of the pipette. It is used to draw in and release liquid.

Using a Micropipette

A plunger controls the movement of a liquid into and out of a micropipette.

1. Some micropipettes have a set volume. Others have rings in the center of the pipette to set a volume. Turn the rings clockwise to increase the volume and counterclockwise to decrease the volume. CAUTION: Do not set a volume beyond the marked range of the micropipette.

2. Attach a tip to the end of the pipette.

3. When you push down on the plunger, it will stop at a point that is determined by the set volume. When you push harder, the plunger will stop at a second point, beyond which the plunger cannot go.

4. Push down on the plunger to the first point. Place the tip just below the surface of the liquid. When you slowly release the plunger, liquid will be drawn up.

5. Push the plunger to the second point to release the liquid into a container.

6. Use the tip ejector to remove the tip.

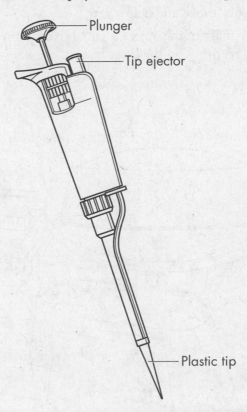

Plunger

Tip ejector

Plastic tip

Measuring Mass

When you determine the mass of an object, you are comparing its mass with a known mass. There are many types of laboratory balances, but triple-beam balances are fairly common.

Using a Triple-Beam Balance

Refer to the drawing as you read these steps.

1. Move all the riders to the left side of their beams.

2. Check to see that the scale is balanced. The pointer should move an equal distance above and below the zero line or come to rest at the zero line. If necessary, use the zero adjustment screw.

3. Place your object on the pan. Slide the riders gently along the beams, one at a time, starting with the largest rider. If a beam is notched, be sure that the rider is in a notch.

4. Moving the riders increases the mass of the beams. When the added masses of the moved riders are equal to the mass of the object, the pointer should come to rest at zero or swing evenly above and below zero.

5. The mass of the object is equal to the sum of the readings on the three beams.

Caring for a Triple-Beam Balance

A balance is a precision instrument that must be handled with care. Follow these rules to keep from damaging your balance.

1. Any object placed on the balance must be dry and at room temperature.

2. Do not place chemicals directly on the pan of a balance. Place liquids in containers. Find the mass of the empty, dry container first. Place solids in a container or on weighing paper. If you use weighing paper, zero the balance with the paper on the pan.

3. If you spill a chemical on or near a balance, notify your teacher and clean up the spill immediately.

4. Never try to measure an object with a mass that is likely to exceed the capacity of the balance.

5. When you are done, return all riders to the zero position, remove your sample, and, if necessary, clean off the pan.

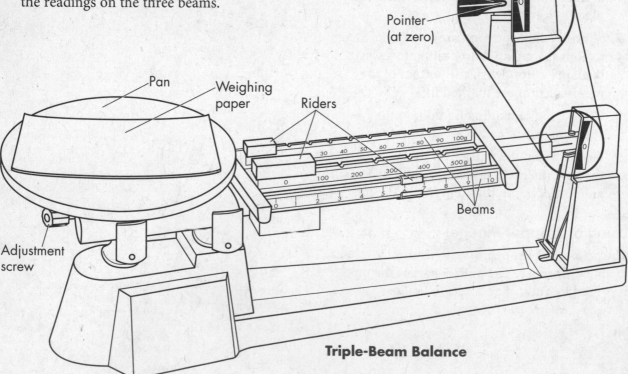

Pointer (at zero)

Pan

Weighing paper

Riders

Beams

Adjustment screw

Triple-Beam Balance

Caring for Your Microscope

The microscope used in most biology classes is a compound microscope with a combination of lenses. The eyepiece lens is located in the top part of the microscope. Other lenses, called objective lenses, are at the bottom of the body tube on the revolving nosepiece. By rotating the nosepiece, you can select an appropriate objective with which to view your specimen.

The magnification for each objective is etched on its side. To determine the total magnification, multiply the power of the objective by the power of the eyepiece lens.

Rules for Using a Microscope

A microscope is a precision instrument that requires careful use. To protect the microscope, follow these rules.

1. Always carry a microscope with two hands. Grasp the arm of the microscope with one hand, and place your other hand under the base. Hold the microscope in an upright position so that the eyepiece cannot fall out.

2. Place the microscope on a flat surface with the arm facing you and the base about 10 cm from the edge.

3. Always start with the low-power objective in position. If necessary, rotate the nosepiece to bring the lens into position. A click will indicate that it is in position.

4. Always view the microscope from the side when you rotate the nosepiece to avoid damaging an objective or a slide.

5. Use the coarse adjustment knob to move the low-power objective as close to the stage as possible without touching the stage. Always view the microscope from the side as you move an objective *toward* the stage.

6. As you view a slide through the eyepiece, turn the coarse adjustment knob to move the low-power objective *away* from the stage until the object comes into focus.

7. To avoid eyestrain, keep both eyes open when you look through the eyepiece.

8. When you view an object with the high-power objective, use the fine adjustment knob to obtain a sharper focus. Never use the coarse adjustment.

9. To avoid scratching the lenses, always use lens paper to clean the lenses. Use a new piece of paper for each lens.

1. **Eyepiece:** Contains a magnifying lens
2. **Arm:** Supports the body tube
3. **Low-power objective:** Provides the least magnification and largest field of view
4. **Stage:** Supports the slide being observed
5. **Opening of the stage:** Permits light to pass up to the eyepiece
6. **Fine adjustment knob:** Moves the body tube slightly to adjust the image
7. **Coarse adjustment knob:** Moves the body tube to focus the image
8. **Base:** Supports the microscope
9. **Illuminator:** Produces light or reflects light up toward the eyepiece
10. **Diaphragm:** Regulates the amount of light passing up toward the eyepiece
11. **Stage clips:** Hold the slide in place
12. **High-power objective:** Provides greater magnification and a smaller field of view
13. **Nosepiece:** Holds the objectives and can be rotated to change the magnification
14. **Body tube:** Maintains the proper distance between the eyepiece and the objectives

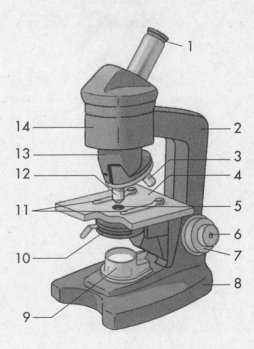

Using a Gas Burner

Many labs use hot plates as a heat source, but some labs still use gas burners. The two most common models are the Bunsen burner and the Tirrell burner. With both models, you can adjust the flame by controlling the amount of air and the amount of gas that mix in the tube.

Both types of burners have a device on the tube (or barrel) to adjust the amount of air. With both types of burners, the amount of gas can be controlled at the main gas valve. With the Tirrell burner, a valve at the base of the burner can also control the flow of gas.

Refer to the drawings of the burners as you read these instructions.

1. Examine your burner to determine which model you have.

2. Connect the burner to the gas outlet with rubber tubing. CAUTION: Do not use a gas burner to heat flammable materials.

3. Close the air vents by rotating the sleeve on the Bunsen burner or adjusting the height of the tube on the Tirrell burner.

4. If you have a Tirrell burner, also close the gas control valve at the base of the burner.

5. Hold a lit match about 2 cm above and just to the right of the tube. CAUTION: Make sure you use a safety match.

6. If you have a Bunsen burner, slowly open the main gas valve. If you have a Tirrell burner, first open the gas supply fully, and then slowly open the gas valve on the tube. CAUTION: If the flame goes out after you light it, reduce the amount of gas.

7. If you have a gas lighter, hold the striker about 2 cm above and just to the right of the tube. With a gas lighter, you must produce the spark as you open the main gas supply on the Bunsen burner or the gas valve on the Tirrell burner.

8. The hottest and most efficient flame is blue and has the distinct regions shown in the drawing. Open the air vents slowly until you have a light-blue, cone-shaped flame.

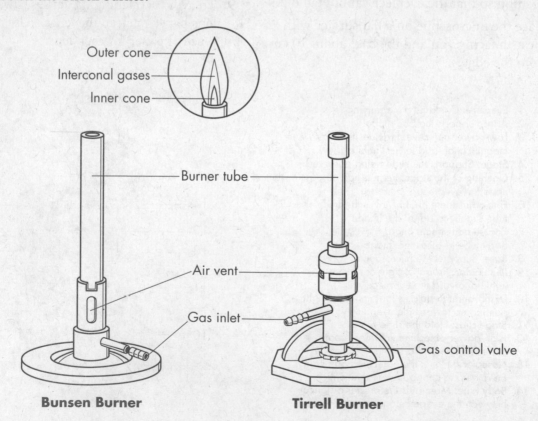

Outer cone

Interconal gases

Inner cone

Burner tube

Air vent

Gas inlet

Gas control valve

Bunsen Burner

Tirrell Burner

Appendix E Science and Technology

Part 1: Technology

What is technology?

Technology is an application of science to meet specific needs. The need may be global, such as an application that will protect crops from insects. The need may be practical, such as an application that cleans clothes or dishes. The need may be personal, such as an application that makes music portable. All technology involves the handling of materials and an understanding of the processes needed to make the best use of different materials. Technology changes the way people live and how they interact with the world.

A technological application is human-made. It does not occur naturally. For example, until the late nineteenth century, a common way to relieve a toothache was to chew on the bark of a willow tree. The bark contains salicin, a naturally occurring substance that relieves headaches and muscle pain. A derivative of salicin, salicylic acid, is the key ingredient in aspirin, which was first sold in 1899. Both satisfy the same need, but only the aspirin is an application of technology. Chewing willow bark is not.

Different areas of science are used in technology. Consider, for example, *biotechnology*, the combination of biology and technology. Pest-resistant crops, artificial insulin to treat diabetes, and enzymes to clean clothes have all come from biotechnology.

How are science and technology related?

Science is the study of the natural world to understand how it functions. Technology is the use of this understanding to make devices that can change how people interact with the natural world. In the example of the aspirin tablet, basic science provided an understanding of the compound salicin and how to isolate it as crystalline salicylic acid. Technology provided the means of making a tablet that is easy to swallow and can be widely available.

Another example of how an advance in science contributes to advances in technology is the discovery that a changing magnetic field can produce an electric field. This knowledge led to the development of the electric motor. Compared to previous ways of harnessing power, such as windmills to grind flour or horses to haul loads, the electric motor is a significant advance in technology.

Just as advances in science contribute to advances in technology, advances in technology contribute to advances in science.

- The microscope is an example of an advance in technology that contributed to advances in science. Microscopes allow us to see beyond the visual range of humans.

- The application of computers and technological processes for copying and manipulating DNA has resulted in a detailed map of the human genome.

How does technology progress?

Two factors drive technological progress: (1) an increase in people's knowledge or understanding of science and (2) the needs people seek to satisfy. With factor 1, the more you know, the more you get to do. With factor 2, the more you do, the more you may want to do even more.

Think about how technology has affected communication in just the last 50 years. The phone your grandparents used when they were your age was much bigger and heavier than a cellphone, and was permanently attached to a wall. There were no cellphones, no texting, no talking while walking around outdoors.

If you needed to call someone and were not at home, you would have to find a pay phone. Pay phones used to be everywhere. They met a common need and were a profitable business. Today, cellphones have made public pay phones practically *obsolete*—they have been replaced by a better, alternative technology.

What is a technological system?

Applications of technology often involve groups of parts that work together as a system. A technological system has an overall *purpose*, or goal, and four basic parts to meet that goal: the *input*, the *process*, the *output*, and *feedback*.

For example, the *purpose*, or goal, of your school's central heating or cooling system is to heat or cool the classrooms. The *input* is the fuel that makes the system work: electricity, natural gas, geothermal heat, oil, or solar panels. The *process* is the sequence of actions that the system undergoes to reach its goal. Here, the process includes distributing hot or cool water or air to your classroom. The *output* is the hot or cool air. The *feedback* is a device, such as a thermostat, that measures temperature and controls when the system turns off and on.

Feedback is the information that a system uses to monitor the input, processes, and output so that it can adjust itself to meet the goal. Because any technological system can fail, system feedback is a necessary element. Feedback lets you know whether the system is functioning as intended.

What are trade-offs?

When designing a technological system, there may be *trade-offs* to consider. A *trade-off* is an exchange in which one benefit is given up in order to obtain another.

Suppose a family is trying to decide on the heating system for a new house. The *input* is the fuel. What trade-offs are involved in choosing the fuel? The local electric plant is coal-fired. The family is concerned about the effect of fossil fuels on the environment. They might trade off, that is give up, a cheaper mechanical system and choose a more expensive system of solar panels.

Consider trade-offs for designing a *process*. Should the family pipe hot water under the floors or along the baseboards for heat? If they decide to run the pipes under the floor, then they are trading off easy access to the plumbing for a better distribution of heat.

After considering all the options, the family will want to avoid making trade-offs that will compromise the system's goal of providing a reliable source of heat.

What are side effects?

Technological systems usually have *side effects*. Side effects are harmful secondary effects that result from some function of the system. For example, medicines often have side effects. Some side effects, such as sleepiness caused by an allergy medication, are minor. Other side effects, such as internal bleeding caused by a painkiller, can be serious.

What is risk-benefit analysis?

In deciding whether to use a particular technology—or how to use it—you must analyze its possible risks and benefits. For example, the drugs used for cancer treatment often cause nausea, fatigue, and hair loss. In such cases, the benefits of such treatment usually outweigh the risks. Risk-benefit analysis can involve a consideration of human values—principles or goals, such as health or personal freedom, that a person or society thinks are important. For example, the use of insecticides to protect crops might be considered too great a risk if it endangers a community's water resources.

How do engineering and technology differ?

Engineering is the use of devices and processes produced by technology to design and manufacture complex systems and structures. Advances in technology lead to advances in engineering. For example, technology helps manufacturers produce a steel I-beam that is strong and carries weight efficiently. Engineering helps designers put together a system of I-beams and other structures to make a bridge or high-rise building. Like technology, engineering involves the application of scientific principles to solve problems. It also relies on math and technical skill.

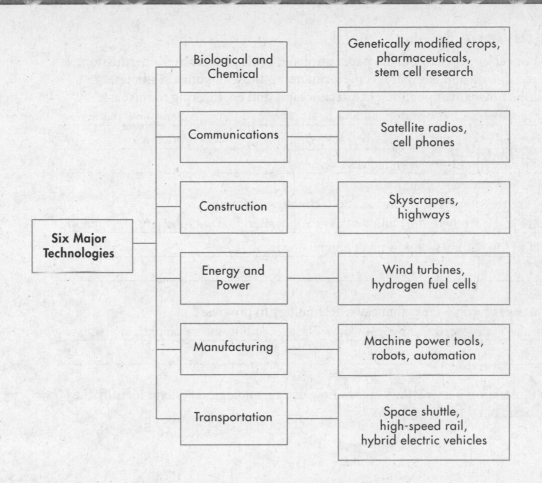

Six Major Technologies		
	Biological and Chemical	Genetically modified crops, pharmaceuticals, stem cell research
	Communications	Satellite radios, cell phones
	Construction	Skyscrapers, highways
	Energy and Power	Wind turbines, hydrogen fuel cells
	Manufacturing	Machine power tools, robots, automation
	Transportation	Space shuttle, high-speed rail, hybrid electric vehicles

Is technology a product or a process?

Technology is not an object. It's not a DVD player or a satellite or a gaming system. Technology is the *process* through which such objects are made. Innovations in technology have advanced human civilization over thousands of years. Technology has led to ways to harness power and store energy. It has led to more fuel-efficient cars and smaller computers. Technology is neither inherently good nor inherently bad.

What are major areas of technology?

The diagram shows six major technologies and a few examples of each. Notice how different areas of technology overlap. For example, advances in several technologies have led to today's faster and more fuel-efficient cars. Advances in energy and power technology have led to better fuel sources. Manufacturing technology is what allows people to make use of lightweight yet strong materials. Transportation technology has improved car design with more efficient engines and streamlined bodies. Construction technology provides the roads and bridges that allow people to travel great distances over rough terrain, rivers, and other obstacles.

What might the future hold?

As society advances, what works today may be obsolete by the next generation. The changes you can expect to see in your lifetime will depend on both technological advances and society's values.

Transportation is a good example. As we learn more about climate change and habitat loss, changes in thinking may affect the way vehicles are designed and how people think about highway systems. Communities might decide to design transportation systems and ways of living that make commuting by car obsolete. Imagine ribbons of highway turned into green spaces that provide bike trails, skateboarding arenas, and pedestrian walk zones.

Practice Your Skills

1. Use a sheet of paper to build a paper airplane. With your teacher's permission, fly the airplane and compare its performance to those of your classmates. Describe how you applied science, technology, and engineering to this task.

   Sample answer: A basic understanding of lift is needed to understand how planes fly. The use of paper and folds to create a device is a form of technology. The specific design of the plane involves engineering.

2. How are the purposes of science and technology different?

   Science is the study of the natural world to understand how it functions. Technology modifies the natural world to meet human needs.

3. What are the two factors that cause technology to progress?

   Technology progresses as people's knowledge (scientific understanding) increases and as new needs arise to be satisfied.

4. The illustration below shows an example of a technological system. Identify the four basic parts of this system.

   The input of this system is the energy produced by pressing against the pedals. The process involves sitting on the bike and pushing the pedals, while steering with the handlebars. The output is forward motion. The feedback monitors speed and balance.

5. Name one way that people traveled long distances in the past that is now obsolete. What are two ways that people travel long distances today? How might people travel long distances in the future?

   Sample answer: Traveling by horseback or on a stagecoach is obsolete. People currently travel long distances by car, airplane, or train. They might use mini-rockets to travel long distances in the future.

Part 2: Evaluate a Design

The goal of technology is meeting a specific need or solving a problem. The best designs are often collaborations in which people from different backgrounds work together to design the best solution or product. A manufacturing company might have a design team with artists, scientists, mathematicians, and engineers. An *engineer* is a person who is trained to use both technology and scientific knowledge to solve practical problems.

How does the design process work?

Product design teams follow a process that has six basic phases.

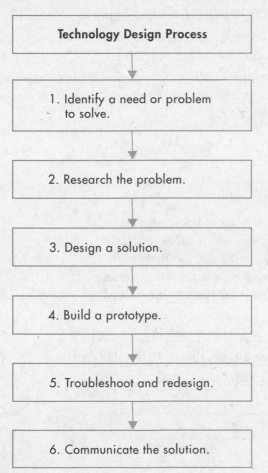

Technology Design Process

1. Identify a need or problem to solve.

2. Research the problem.

3. Design a solution.

4. Build a prototype.

5. Troubleshoot and redesign.

6. Communicate the solution.

An important part of designing a solution through teamwork is *brainstorming*. Brainstorming provides members of the design team the opportunity to freely suggest any creative solution to a problem. The free exchange of ideas can inspire further creativity among the team and lead to the best solution.

How do technology and product design influence one another?

Sometimes product designs push improvements in technology. An inventor may come up with a product idea that requires the development of the manufacturing technology needed to produce the product.

In 1941, George de Mestral, a Swiss engineer, came up with the idea for a product you now know as Velcro. His invention came from a simple observation: While removing the burs attached to his dog's fur, he wondered what it was that made the burs take such a strong hold. He took a closer look at the burs. Under the magnifying glass, he could see that the burs had tiny hooks. From this observation came inspiration.

At the time, the technology needed to manufacture Velcro was not available. It took about 10 years to create a loom that could produce the specialized fabrics with hooks and loops. At first, Velcro was mostly used in highly specialized applications. For example, the aerospace industry of the 1960s used Velcro to enable astronauts to more easily get in and out of their bulky space suits. Today, Velcro is a common substitute for zippers and shoelaces.

Improvements in technology can also push innovation. Lasers are devices that produce beams of light from electromagnetic radiation. The first lasers were of interest mostly to the scientific community, who began studying their properties in the 1960s. Certain types of lasers were used in industrial applications, for example, in welding. Today, a day probably doesn't go by without your using laser technology. Lasers are used to read compact discs and DVDs. They are also used in the optical fibers that supply digital information to your computer.

What are limiting factors in design?

Sometimes, the finished product does not match the original product design. The differences can be due to the *limiting factors* that affect the design. A limiting factor is any characteristic or feature of the finished product that most affects the design. With Velcro, the first limiting factor was technology. There were no technological means available to manufacture the product as designed. Other limiting factors can include cost and materials. In the case of Velcro, the first strips were manufactured using cotton. The cotton was soon replaced by synthetic fibers, which offered greater strength and durability.

Some inventors and design teams conceive of products that cannot be manufactured and sold because the designs are based on an *emerging technology*. Scientists and engineers understand the science, basic principles, and theory behind the product design. However, the design cannot be implemented until the technology is fully developed. One such example is the use of stem cells to reverse paralysis due to spinal cord injuries.

What is a patent?

A *patent* is a legal document issued by the government that gives an inventor legal rights over an invention so that no one can copy it. In the United States, a patent typically lasts for 20 years. George de Mestral was issued a U.S. patent for Velcro in 1955.

How is a product design evaluated?

The evaluation of a design takes into account three basic criteria.

1. Functional requirements: does the product do what it's supposed to do?

2. Constraints: are there any factors that limit the design from functioning as it should?

3. Overall performance: does the product meet all of its design objectives?

A *performance metric* is a quantifiable measure of the product's capacity to meet all of its design specifications.

Practice Your Skills

1. One product that is part of almost every student's life is a backpack. List five qualities you value in a backpack and assign each a relative point value. Indicate if there are any design constraints associated with those qualities. Evaluate your own backpack in terms of functional requirements and design constraints. Rate its overall performance using your scale, indicating how many points it received against the possible total.

   Sample answer: Five functional requirements of a backpack: (1) large carrying

   capacity, design constraint is limit in size: 10 points; (2) adjustable straps: 10 points;

   (3) outside pocket for pens and pencils: 8 points; (4) outside pocket for cellphone:

   2 points; (5) separate carrier for water bottle: 2 points.

   _____

   _____

   _____

2. One recent technological advance in backpack design is the rolling pack. In addition to shoulder straps, a rolling pack has a pair of wheels at its base and a retracting handle so that you can pull the pack. Identify at least two trade-offs with this design.

Sample answer: Because of the frame for the wheels and handle, the pack will be rigid, making it difficult to squeeze into a locker. The frame will reduce the carrying capacity of the pack. The added materials will make the pack heavier and more expensive. The rollers are only useful on flat surfaces and could be difficult to manage on stairs.

3. The data table provides dimensions for two models of backpacks. Determine the carrying capacity, or volume, of each (volume = length × width × depth). Both are sold for the same price. What does this information suggest about a design constraint in the manufacturing process?

Comparison of Backpack Types				
Type of Pack	Length (cm)	Width (cm)	Depth (cm)	Volume (cm)
Shoulder pack	48	35	25	42,000 cm³
Rolling pack	44	24	20	21,120 cm³

The rolling pack has a smaller volume and carrying capacity. The process and materials probably make it more expensive to produce than the traditional backpack.

4. Assume the average textbook is 28.5 cm × 23.0 cm × 4.5 cm. How many textbooks do you typically carry to school each day? Is each pack capable of carrying all your textbooks? Which value determines this?

Because the length and width of each pack is greater than those of a textbook, the critical value is depth. The backpack can hold five textbooks; the rolling pack holds four books.

5. Are you carrying more than the maximum safety load? How do you know?

Student answers should include the method used to determine their answer.

6. Apply a risk-benefit analysis to the following situation. Dylan plans to purchase a shoulder pack or a rolling pack. The mass of a backpack should be no more than 15 percent of a person's body mass. Dylan weighs 115 pounds and typically carries five textbooks each day. Calculate the total mass of Dylan's textbooks, assuming an average mass of 1.65 kg each. Determine Dylan's maximum safe load in kilograms and make a recommendation. *Hint:* To convert weight in pounds to mass in kilograms, multiply the pounds by 0.45 and round up.

Dylan's mass is 52 kg, so the maximum safe load is 7.8 kg. Five books have a total

mass of 8.25 kg. Dylan should not be carrying five books in a backpack. Four books

have a total mass of 6.6 kg, which is within the safe load for Dylan. Given that both

packs can carry four books, Dylan needs to reduce the number of books he carries

and then choose a pack based on personal preference.

7. If you invented a product, would you obtain a patent? Explain the advantages of a patent.

Sample answer: I want the legal protection that a patent provides; I own the

invention and want to control how it's used; I want to make money from my

invention and not let others benefit unfairly from my work.

8. Some biotechnology companies have patented certain gene sequences that may have medical applications. From the point of view of societal values, what might be the problem with allowing such patents?

Sample answer: The disadvantage of such a patent is the company claims ownership

of a "product" that is readily found in nature. It was not "invented" in the normal

sense. The patent might limit others who wish to develop treatments using that

sequence, and 20 years is a long time to wait for the patent to lapse.

Part 3: **Prototypes and Scale Models**

Technology is developed to meet a specific need or solve a particular problem. Once the problem is defined, a team will be chosen to work on the problem. Engineers usually have a central role on the team. Engineers are trained to use both technological and scientific knowledge to solve practical problems.

In the early stages of the design process, the engineers will spend time researching the problem fully. They are likely to spend time reading books and articles to gather background information. They may attend conferences where the latest ideas in their field are discussed. They may also perform experiments related to the technology being designed. The engineers may be working to develop a new product or improve an existing one. Either way, they may want to talk to potential customers to find out what the customers want. This part of the process is called market research.

During the development process, engineers often need to make technical drawings, or blueprints, and build prototypes.

What is a blueprint?

With the results of their research in hand, the design team will identify the materials and processes needed. They will make a sketch of their proposed solution and then make technical drawings. A technical drawing shows the dimensions of the design product and indicates the materials to be used. It contains all the information needed to build the product.

An engineering drawing is often referred to as a *blueprint*. The name comes from a printing process that was once used to produce many copies of a hand-drawn technical drawing. Today, engineers use computers to create technical drawings of their designs. Computers have made the job of creating technical drawings much easier. They enable the design team to view their design in three dimensions and make adjustments.

What is a prototype?

A design team may choose to build a prototype of their product design. A *prototype* is a working model used to test a design. Prototypes are used to test the operation of a product, including how well it works, how long it lasts, and how safe it is to use. Sometimes the prototype is built as a *scale model*. A scale model has the same proportions as the product but is built to a different scale.

Prototype testing allows the design team to identify problems with their design. The process of analyzing a design problem and finding a way to fix it is called *troubleshooting*. Based on the testing, the engineers may need to redesign the product, or some part of it, to address one or more design problems. With the testing done and adjustments made, the design product can then move on to the manufacturing stage.

Practice Your Skills

1. Suppose a wealthy inventor who once went to your school has returned to announce a team competition. She has convinced the principal to make available a little-used alcove outside the main office. The competition is to design an ideal locker, which the inventor will then manufacture. Your team's goal is to design the ideal locker and build a prototype or produce a scale drawing. To begin, you need to do some research, using your own locker. Describe the design features of your locker, including materials.

   Sample answer: My locker is made of metal, painted gray. It is one of a pair that fits

   into a space that is 66 inches high by 12 inches wide by 12 inches deep. Each locker

   is 30 inches high. The two lockers sit on four 6-inch legs. The doors have six air

   vents at the top and bottom. My locker has two hooks inside, one on each side. The

   locker handle is metal and is designed to hold a combination lock.

2. The alcove is located in the main hallway and measures 10 feet high by 6 feet wide by 2 feet deep. There is an electrical outlet located in the floorboards. Consider whether all that space is usable space. Identify one design constraint in making use of that space for student lockers.

   A locker has to be within easy reach, so the lockers will still need to be between

   5 and 6 feet in height.

   _____

3. Work with your team to brainstorm features of your ideal locker. Make a list of your requirements and determine the locker's dimensions. Remember to keep in mind that the locker you design is part of a system of lockers that must fit into the alcove. Consider how many lockers you want to put in that space. Identify the materials you would like to use.

   Students might suggest a much larger locker size, but remind them that the doors

   cannot be so wide when open as to obstruct the area in front. They might design

   lockers with electric outlets for recharging laptops and cellphones. Their designs

   might call for construction with "green" materials.

   _____

   _____

   _____

   _____

4. Build a scale model of your ideal locker or make a scale drawing. Evaluate your ideal locker design. Does it meet all the specified requirements? How does it compare to your current locker?

   Sample answer: Yes. The lockers have more room for all our stuff. The added shelves

   will help to keep everything organized. The color coding scheme will make it easy

   to distinguish one locker from another.